AUSTRALIA
Its Resources and Development

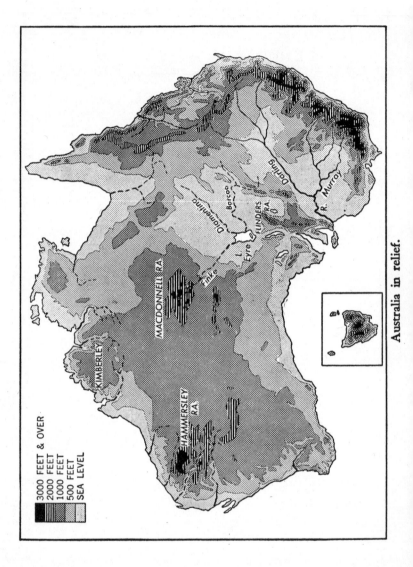

Australia in relief.

AUSTRALIA

Its Resources and Development

Edited by

G. L. WOOD

PROFESSOR OF COMMERCE
UNIVERSITY OF MELBOURNE

With a Foreword by
W. S. ROBINSON

New York
THE MACMILLAN COMPANY
1954

TO THOSE
WHO DEVELOPED AND DEFENDED AUSTRALIA
WITH GRATITUDE AND ADMIRATION

FOREWORD

THIS BOOK has been produced at my request in the hope that it will make more widely known the nature and extent of the resources of Australia, what the splendid achievements of her people have made of them, and what opportunities exist for their further development. It does not profess to be exhaustive, but it does seek to answer many of the more important questions which are being asked about the Commonwealth.

Long association with the practical problems involved in developing Australian production has made me completely confident of the ability of the Australian people to use their resources wisely for the promotion of high levels of well-being at home and abroad. True, these resources are less abundant than those of the so richly endowed United States, upon which, after more than three centuries of development, a population around twenty times that of Australia directly depends. Australia's development is still in its infancy, and her resources in relation to her population compare very favorably with those of other countries. Her pioneers developed them to a level sufficient to provide her people with the necessities and comforts of civilization. This book is therefore my tribute to the achievement of the Australian people in attaining contentment and freedom.

It is also an expression of confidence in the future of Australia. One can measure the resources of a country only by the yardstick of present-day scientific knowledge. But science is not static. From its discoveries Australia has as much—perhaps more—to gain as any other country, and the distinguished and ever-widening activities of the Council for Scientific and Industrial Research show that this is fully recognized in the Commonwealth. Many of her present-day resources would

have gone unlisted in an inventory of fifty years ago. Within
the lifetime of her older citizens, electrical power has transformed her cities and countryside; the internal combustion
engine has revolutionized transport by road and air and multiplied the means of communication; the production and use
of fertilizers has increased the yield wrested from a grudging
soil, and refrigeration and other processes have enabled men to
conserve it; cyanidation has facilitated the recovery of gold;
the flotation process has added immensely to the production
of non-ferrous metals. These and many other discoveries have
multiplied Australia's resources: they will be increased still
further by scientific developments, both predictable and as yet
unforeseen. The progress of the world does not depend upon
what one generation perceives as physical fact, but upon the
facts that hope and vision, nourished by the desire for better
things, disclose. For a creative people, today is tomorrow's
yesterday.

Australia is, indeed, a land of opportunity. The attractive-
ness of some of the more fertile and settled areas of the world
has unhappily been diminished by war, unrest and famine and
their frustrated peoples long for a new life in happier lands
like America and Australia. Even in normal times population
tends to flow where man can find a sufficiency of food and
raw materials for his industry. Australia is a large exporter of
both. Her progress depends in the main upon the speed and
vigour with which she applies her efforts to the conservation of water, prevention of soil erosion, promotion of scientific research, extension of roads, and development of air
transport. Most people are now well aware of the importance
of soil and water conservation, and both government and
private industry have done much to further scientific research.
The pivotal importance of air transport is perhaps less generally recognized. Air transport can reduce the wide gap which
separates Australia from the great world centers of population.
By the expansion of air transport Australia's scattered resources

can be sufficiently concentrated to justify their rapid development, and through air transport she can play her proper part in developing the resources of the neighboring islands, as is essential to her security and economic well-being. The courageous enterprise of an air-minded Australia has been rewarded with notable success. These efforts must be widened and continued.

The various sections of this book have been contributed by Australian authorities on the subjects with which they deal. These writers, and they alone, are responsible for the views they express. Their work has been done under the general editorship of Professor Gordon Wood of the University of Melbourne, to whom my thanks are due. My grateful acknowledgment must also be made to Mr. Randal Heymanson of Australia and New York, with whom I discussed the project from its inception and who gave me invaluable advice and assistance at all its stages. I should also like to express my appreciation of the work of Miss Joyce Wood, who drew the diagrams.

No book, however comprehensive, can give an adequate picture of a country and those who are interested enough to read about Australia should sooner or later visit it. They will not be disappointed. Australia is no longer the Antipodes, lying on the edge of nowhere, but America's partner across the Pacific. To-day one can reach the Commonwealth by air from the United States more swiftly than one could travel between New York and San Francisco a few years ago. It is my hope that this volume will not only make people in the United States curious to see Australia for themselves, but that it will be accepted by them as expressing in some small measure the gratitude of all Australians for help so generously given in time of peril to both our countries.

W. S. ROBINSON

London—New York

CONTENTS

xi

MAPS, DIAGRAMS, AND PLATES

PLATES

Acknowledgment is hereby given to the Australian National Publicity Association for use of Plates 1, 10, 14, 15, 16, 19, and 28; the Australian News and Information Bureau for Plate 2; the Western Australian Tourist Bureau for Plate 9; the Australian National Travel Association for Plates 17 and 20; the W. A. Newspapers Ltd., Perth, W. A., for Plate 18; the Royal Australian Air Force, Pt. Pirie, S. A., for Plate 23; B. Sheppard for Plate 25; and the Allied Works Council for Plate 27.

INTRODUCTION

FOR MANY centuries the centre of gravity of human affairs lay somewhere in Asia. For a relatively short span, under the stimulus of Western science and invention, the centre shifted to Europe. In our day, owing to the political and industrial development of Japan, China, India and Russia, the centre is tending to move back again towards Asia with its teeming millions, and towards the Pacific. For the white race the change may be ominous, and to those outliers of European civilization, Australia and New Zealand, it must mean a great urgent impulse to thought and action. Interposed between Europe and Asia politically and geographically are the Soviet and the United States, vast collections of natural resources controlled by vigorous peoples with widely different traditions; and the possibilities for the whole world are immense.

History is again being shaped by geography under its modern title of economic resources. The war has imposed a new emphasis upon the control of resources. Foodstuffs, raw materials, technical knowledge, manpower, engineering capacity, managerial efficiency, have become the weapons with which wars are waged; and chemists, physicists, metallurgists, economists, are the makers of the new weapons. International power depends upon efficiency in using resources; and tied in with the issue is the question whether Europe can retain the initiative in putting actual and potential resources to productive—or destructive—use. If Asia wrests that initiative from the hands—and brains—of the West, the social progress which is the great achievement of the white peoples will be imperilled, along with the political dominance they attained and the technological leadership which their science conferred.

The high standards of living which the white races enjoy,

and the military power which gave them success in war and trade, depend upon technical efficiency. The war is won, but there is no guarantee that the white races will retain their technical superiority. After incredibly rapid development Japan occupied by violence a vast rich empire from which she ousted European influence for a time. High standards of living, however, may soften the fibre, lower the reproductive rate, and weaken the initiative and energies of the high-standard peoples. It would be stupid to disregard the possibility ,that a modern cycle of rise and decline could repeat the cycles of the past.

If this is to be the trend of world dynamics, and if Western civilization is to be engaged in a long-term struggle for survival against Asia, the people of Australia and New Zealand, remote from Europe but cheek by jowl with Asia, must be vitally concerned. Australians and New Zealanders, set on the very frontiers of the Orient, are acutely aware that their territories may become a spillway for Asia's ever-multiplying millions. They cannot ignore the disproportion, both in numbers and in rate of increase, between the white and yellow peoples in the Pacific area. They are also more immediately concerned about the great industrial strides Japan and India have made in recent years. By 1950 China and India will probably contain 900 million people. Japan proper will probably contain 80 million people, but her rate of increase must be slowed down if the depletion of her industrial economy continues. India yearly adds an increment to its population equal to Australia's total. The net reproduction rate in Japan (1.571 for 1930) is much higher than in Australia (.956 for 1930), and the rate for the United States (.961 for 1935) is not much better than that for Australia.

Although the Japanese cycle has been shattered it is well to review her past achievements. Even before the war Japan was already a major manufacturing nation. Between 1933 and 1940 she had achieved a most impressive diversification of her industries, an increase of 100 per cent in her industrial output, and a stronger strategic position with respect to certain essential materials and manufactures. Largely owing to a thorough system of state control of commerce, Japan achieved a great increase in her foreign trade as well as a favourable balance of payments, and an expansion of production which attained full employment without resort to foreign loans. Her recovery from the depression after 1930 was more rapid and impressive even than that of Australia.

The total effect of Japan's expansion was to change the situation not only in the Pacific Basin, but for the world as a whole. The people of Australia have become abruptly aware of Asia, and of the thousand million Asiatics with whose future their own is inescapably linked. That realization is not yet fully shared by the peoples of Britain and the eastern United States. To them the Western Pacific has been a backwater of the world for generations, while the economics and politics of Europe have absorbed their thought and energies. Australia's focus, on the other hand, is the Far East, or rather for her the Near North. Here is "an Asia everywhere awakened and awakening"; and a new approach to international problems has become inescapable.

Except in Japan, the impact of modern industry has only begun to change the basic pattern of Asia. After the war change may be rapid, but now the masses of Asia live on the very edge of starvation. The low productivity of labour, the continuous rise in numbers, and the spread of ideas will produce great pressures for change, threaten the existence of the young democracies of the South Seas. The necessity for new views upon the significance of Asia, and for policies based on the facts of these conditions needs little emphasis.

Metamorphosis is always the real result of war. New economic and political patterns are shaping. The development of Australia will be largely conditioned by her physical resources and her political and social evolution on the one hand, and by world changes on the other. Australia's advance from a collection of farming colonies to an industrial Commonwealth in a century and a half is surpassed in tempo only by Japan's march from a hermit kingdom to a Great Power in less than half that time. In 1877, more than two decades after the Australian colonies had been granted self-government, and at the moment when the United States was emerging from the "terrible ten years" of reconstruction following the Civil War, the Shogun and the feudal system he represented fell; and Japan committed herself to policies which arose from Admiral Perry's visit and led to her tragic mistake of Pearl Harbor.

Into such a short time have the events which have brought about the metamorphosis of the Pacific been telescoped. During that time the whole world economy has been undergoing rapid changes; and, because of developments in transport accelerated by war, distance measured in time has abruptly contracted. The journey from London to Melbourne by sailing ship, which took over ninety days a century ago, was shortened by fast steamship to thirty days; but, by air, the journey now takes three days, and by 1950 will take less. Measured by travelling time, the vast Pacific is already a mere sea, and formerly remote countries have become next-door neighbours. While it has hastened commercial travel and communication, this breathless contraction of time and distance has intensified every problem of defence. International privacy is a thing of the past. For the objectives of war or peace we are already living in a new world, and speed in adapting ourselves to the new order of speed is one of the tests of fitness to survive.

This climax of change in the world at large has been matched by change within Australia. Social, economic, and political evolution has been hastened by depression and war. Into a decade has been packed a cycle of change. Over the whole range of industry in Australia—on farms, in factories and elsewhere—advances have been made which amount to a remarkable improvement in the use of resources of all kinds. Successful application of scientific knowledge has been matched by more efficient organization and management. In rural production, and within the limits imposed by climate, surface, and soils, output has been continuously enlarged and the yield per unit steadily raised. The use of modern machinery, better understanding and care of the soils, the breeding of animal and vegetable types suitable to the conditions of the continent, and the extension of technical knowledge have made it possible to take more from the land, but the problem of maintaining fertility is troublesome. Total production and quality of crops such as wheat and fruit have risen steadily, whilst animal husbandry—the art of breeding and feeding— has increased the average weight of fleece, and the yield of milk per cow. These results have, admittedly, not been achieved without mistakes which have led to large losses. The necessity for water conservation, the deficiencies of the soils, the prevalence of pests, the vagaries of the climate and the menace of erosion had to be learned by sad experience. Scientific surveys, the study of marketing, improvements in transport, provision of rural credit, and education and guidance of the settler have raised rural industries to a new level of efficiency. But already the need for adaptation and change is looming for farmers and pastoralists.

The advance in manufacturing has been even more striking. The world depression of the years after 1930 was responsible for policies of self-sufficiency in all countries. Australia, in common with other countries, was forced to adopt defensive economic and monetary policies. An old-style investment recovery enabled Australia to emerge from the depression more rapidly than most countries. The war, and the peculiar position Australia occupied as the industrial base for Allied operations in the South-west Pacific and South-east Asia, stimulated a further expansion of manufacturing of a different type. Heavy and precision industries came into being, and Australia became a highly industrialized country. Measured by the amount of machinery per worker, the total output, the capital employed or the wages paid, new heights were reached; but what proportion of these new developments can survive after the war is, of course, uncertain; but a further wide expansion of industrial activity may confidently be expected.

These, then, are the complexities of the democracies of the South Seas; and the members of those democracies wish both the facts of their resources and the direction of their policies to be understood and endorsed by the people of Britain and the United States. The co-operation of specialists in many branches of science has made this study possible, and it represents the physical and economic framework within which these British dominions are working out their social and political destiny.

Chapter I

THE AUSTRALIAN ACHIEVEMENT

BY G. L. WOOD

Professor of Commerce, University of Melbourne

THE FACT

UNTIL 1900 Australia was a group of self-governing colonies with no common bond except ancestry and allegiance to the British crown, and no common interests save those which geography and trade imposed upon them. By the act of federation the six colonies formally became a union; but, despite the written constitution, much of the looseness of the old connection persisted. Only as the parts were welded on the anvil of world events was a true federation gradually wrought and a national temper given to the new Commonwealth.

With the act of federation, a new phase of pioneering with new frontiers and new problems came into being. The new century ushered in a new era in politics and economics, and a new tempo in world affairs to which only the Renaissance, the Reformation, and the Industrial Revolution can be compared. Into this stream of accelerating change the new Commonwealth was drawn almost at its inception. Into less than five decades the young nation has been compelled to compress its political growing pains, its adolescent industrial fevers, and its adult adjustments to the international system. All the world was amazed by the Japanese transformation after 1853. The transformation of Australia has been little less remarkable; but its very smoothness, and the absence of violent internal conflict during the transition, have disguised the fundamental nature of the metamorphosis. With a truly national sense the

7

Australians have taken the occasion as it came by to further their conception of democracy as a society free to determine its way of life and to co-operate with other democracies.

The development of the federation has meant forty years of political adaptation to modern conditions, and of experiment in social and industrial relations. These formative years have been marked by brisk battles of principle in a long campaign from which the social and institutional pattern of a new nation painfully emerged. It was little less than a triumph for gradualism and tolerance that often looked like apathy and political unsophistication. Experiments which were decried and ridiculed in older countries as being extreme and unpractical have come to be accepted in the countries of the critics as sound measures of liberal progressivism. Tribunals for fixing wages; arbitration as a method for settling industrial disputes; free and compulsory education; old-age, widows' and invalid pensions; child endowment; compulsory voting; national control of monetary policy; each has been a battleground, each has been a test of the willingness of a people to surrender individual rights for the common good, each has squarely matched a new security with a new responsibility. In their political life the Australians have made many mistakes; but never one that meant a repudiation of democratic ideals.

These, however, were but the pathology of political controversy, the epidemics necessary to develop immunities. They might still have left a narrow nationalism sheltering behind imperial protection, had it not been for the influence of world revolution which both destroyed and saved. The greatest economic depression of history, coming between two world wars within a span of twenty years, might easily have thrown an untried polity into chaos. Like some great metallurgical process these happenings did little but fuse and refine, consolidate and toughen the structure of the Commonwealth. From a population of 5,000,000 the despatch of 330,000 troops overseas; the loss of 60,000 by death, casualties by wounds and sickness totalling 260,000; and the expenditure of £600,000,-000 in the war of 1914–18 might have excused unwillingness on the part of a young nation to accept unlimited responsibilities in war for the second time in a generation. Its readiness to take up the burden and make the sacrifice in 1939, the unhesitating despatch of its trained soldiers and invaluable equipment to distant theatres of war, the military value of their work on land, on sea, and in the air call for no eulogy or forensic. This was but the classic pattern of the defence of freedom by freemen; the pattern that is the special possession of no one nation, but is the final proof of achievement for all.

In the Second World War the Australian achievement is no less distinguished. Seven men out of every ten between the ages of eighteen and thirty-five have served in the fighting forces. Nearly 50,000 women served with the auxiliary services, and 80,000 are employed in heavy industry—a field in which practically no women were engaged before the war. In addition, 40,000 women are employed in full-time work on the land. Over 200,000 more women are working in occupations essential to war than in 1939. In all, the total number of people employed in industry and the services has risen by 600,000 during the war.

From a total population of 7,000,000 people, 900,000 men have been enlisted. Australian troops have served in theatres as widely separated as Great Britain, North Africa, Greece, Crete, Syria, India, Malaya, East Indies, the South-west Pacific generally, and Australia. Up to June, 1945, casualties totalled 87,000—killed 19,000; missing 6,000; prisoners of war 25,000; wounded 37,000. The Australian people have paid the full price of war in those lives which are most precious to a young underdeveloped country.

The financial cost of the war to Australia by June, 1945, was about £2,100,000,000, or an average of about £300 per head of population. War expenditure rose from £55,000,000 from a national income of £860,000,000, or about 6.5 per cent

in 1940, to £560,000,000 from a national income of £1,200,-
000,000, or about 46 per cent in 1944. Taxation rose from
£137,000,000 before the war to £350,000,000 for the financial
year 1943–44. Personal income tax is at least as heavy on low
and middle incomes as in any English-speaking country. On
high incomes and companies it is appreciably heavier. Reciprocal aid in the form of material supplies to American
Forces in the South-west Pacific amounted to about £240
millions in December 1944, compared with £280 millions
from the United States to Australia. In addition a large amount
of reciprocal aid in the form of supplies and services to British
and Dutch forces cannot at present be evaluated.

THE CLAIM

The consequences of Captain Cook in the Pacific were
scarcely less significant than those of Columbus in the Atlantic.
One hundred and fifty years ago Australia was still an unknown wilderness sparsely inhabited by tribes of Stone Age
men. While Napoleon Bonaparte was making his bid for
world power, the English were making half-hearted attempts
to commence settlements in the great southland to which
they laid claim as a result of Cook's discoveries in 1770. The
land which might have become New Holland, and just missed
being Terre Napoléon, became a series of British settlements
—primitive, almost forgotten colonies, strung round a coastal
fringe separated by mountains from the hot plains of the
interior. While the people of the Thirteen Colonies were cele-
brating their hard-won independence and constituting themselves the Republic of the United States, a few shiploads of
people were commencing one of the strangest and most un-
promising migrations in the world's history. These early
settlers found a wilderness; but they founded unknowingly
another New England. They left economic depression and
social inequity in their homeland, to face privations as stern

and conditions as relentless as those braved by the Pilgrim Fathers. They left familiar famine in the Old World to begin afresh in a strange and, for long, niggardly New World. They came as exiles and found, at long last, freedom and opportunity for courage and enterprise.

THE FOUNDERS

The entrance of Europeans upon this prehistoric stage had all the elements of drama. Australia was the complete *terra incognita;* climate, soils, vegetation, animals, and men were all horridly strange to the immigrants. Their first response was to try to carry on the ways of living and working appropriate for England, only to find they were unsuitable for the antipodes. Only after decades were new responses, essays in adaptation, tried; and from that moment a pattern of Australian life began to take shape.

Isolation was almost complete. The first colony was, for long months, a settlement of forgotten men. The situation and character of the country had, indeed, combined to make Australia a hermit continent; the long sea voyage from Europe, and the forbidding appearance of the land, maintained that character for long after Sydney was founded. The Saharan greeting of the west coast to the Dutch navigators and to Dampier was only a few degrees more hostile than that of the east coast. That section of the Great Divide known as the Blue Mountains made of the first settlement a mere beachhead on a barren sandstone coast.

No sketch of these first years of gruelling effort to establish a permanent settlement would be complete without mention of the sterling work of the early governors. Phillip, continually worried by short supplies and the threat of famine to the infant colony, but never losing faith in his "vision splendid" of a new Britain of the south; Macquarie, immersed in the administration problems consequent upon the extension of settlement; and other governors in lesser degree showed leadership, courage, and administrative skill of the highest order. Around them, more or less sympathetic to the governor's aims, a succession of public servants helped to consolidate the occupation and plan the work involved in the extension of settlement. Their tasks were not easy, the facilities available to them pitiably defective, their permanent equipment inadequate for the development of the new land; but slowly they won out of the difficulties which faced them on every side. Looking at the Australian cities or countryside today, few would find it possible to reconstruct the land as it was in 1800, or recreate the epic ventures which were the forerunners of today's attainment. It was only yesterday, but what striving and reward are crowded into the interval! It would be difficult to deny that a few generations of hardy people have done more than well in bringing to its present development a land relatively poor in resources, and seriously handicapped by isolation and the consequent heavy cost of transport.

LEARNING THE ROPES

Within a decade the little settlement was already reaching out to the hinterland. All the painful steps of sustained exploration, carried out mostly on foot, in small parties, and through difficult country completely lacking in food and often lacking water as well, had to be made. There was little of the glamour about exploration in Australia that has come to be associated with the early explorations of Africa or America; but the feats of endurance of Eyre, Sturt, Forrest, or Leichardt rival those of Livingstone or Mungo Park in Africa, or of Hudson or La Salle in North America. Along the coasts, too, far to the north and south and west, went the early navigators on their adventures. The voyages of Bass and Flinders were no less daring and successful than those of Vancouver in the North Pacific, nor that of Sturt along the Murray any less notable than those of the Canadian voyagers along the Great Lakes and inland rivers.

With each probing of the interior came increased knowledge of the possibilities and limitations of the country. Hard on the heels of the explorers, wherever good land and more especially good water was found, came the pioneers—the advance guard pitting their skill and endurance against the tough eucalypt forests or the mallee scrub, driving their flocks and herds out into the hot steppes, tirelessly advancing their crops to the margins of safe farming and beyond, and wagering their wealth, their health, and often their lives in the gamble against recurrent drought. These settlers were the *conquistadores* in a new setting, the shock troops of a new occupation, the splendid infantry of Australian settlement. Their lone patrols were the boundary riders, their cossacks of the hot steppes and savannahs the cattle drovers. For them is no monument, save in the living verse of Adam Lindsay Gordon or Banjo Paterson.

In many ways Australia is the Cinderella of the continents —the youngest in point of European contact and settlement, the most isolated by geography, the most refractory in natural resources, the least attractive judged by resemblance to many countries of Europe or North America. The conditions of early settlement were not such as to endear the new homeland to immigrants, or to provide the human basis upon which a promising extension of European civilization might be built. It would, indeed, in 1800 A.D. have been hard to imagine a less congenial nursery, or a less suitable field for the transplanting of English life and ideas.

It would be easy to be misled by comparisons of the deeds and character of the Australians and the British in their respective homelands. In doing so we lose sight of the time-distance factor. The crowded millions of Britain live in one climate and one environment, however we may emphasize the distinctions between Land's End and John o' Groat's. In Australia a people numbering one-sixth of the population of the United Kingdom have an area twenty-five times as large as Britain to administer and develop, in which every variety of climate from Cornwall to the Congo is represented, where over much of the area there is persistent deficiency of water, and where, in consequence, dense forest is confined to a relatively small part of the continent.

Yet, in face of the initial handicaps and despite early pessimism in "the Mother Country," the Australian people can show a century and a half of development perhaps more rapid and no less soundly based than that of many more favoured countries. The change from a few primitive colonies in the wilderness to an ordered and efficient society will come out well from any impartial appraisement. Australia's development will compare favourably with that made over a much longer time in the United States, Canada, or South Africa. Within a century and a half there stands on those early and seemingly insecure foundations a new Commonwealth, complete with all the equipment and trappings of a modern industrial state. The stone which the builders had almost rejected has become the keystone of European civilization in the South Seas.

THE PATTERN OF SETTLEMENT

The years between the beginning and the end of the century were taken up by the slow process of learning the possibilities and the pitfalls of land use that was characteristic of a similar stage in the United States and Canada. The "squatter," learning in the hard school of experience the conditions which promoted or retarded the health of his flocks, gradually acquired skills and techniques which were of great value even though they were purely empirical. The impact of drought, the constant menace of bush-fire, the endemic plague of parasites, all had to be combated with knowledge gained only from failure and loss. Nevertheless, the broad experience gained by adapting animals and methods of grazing to local conditions provided the basis for the scientific research of later years.

The Industrial Revolution found the English textile trade short of wool; the experiments of Macarthur of Camden in early New South Wales, and the spread of 100,000,000 merinos over the Australian pastures gave the complete answer. The long epic of wool contrasts vividly with the "gold episodes," when thousands of adventurers from overseas competed with Australians for a fortune. By 1860 the known alluvial deposits were almost worked out. A large proportion of the "diggers" were forced to turn to the land, and the exploitation of the wheat belt began in earnest. The story of mechanized farming, superphosphates, and William Farrer begins. By 1890 the limits of cultivation and sheep pastures were known, and the pattern of the rural economy laid down.

The wheat farmer passed through severe trials. Learning early that the wetter coastal fringe did not favour wheat, he struck out into the drier lands across the mountains, and gradually pushed his frontier back towards the desert margins. Erratic rainfall and recurrent drought challenged old agricultural practices, and the farmer evolved the methods of clearing and "dry farming" which made a precarious existence possible even in arid districts, but at the cost of great effort and endurance. Moreover, the exhaustion of these light soils called for remedial measures, and fertilisers became a prerequisite of successful farming. But always and everywhere the unpredictable variation of climatic conditions from year to year, and fluctuations in the price of wheat continued to test his skill, intelligence, and stamina. Then came great hope when William Farrer, by his experiments in wheat breeding, changed the future of farming in the grain-growing areas.

In the forest country, too, the dairy farmer was engaged in establishing his herds upon the grasses which the heavier rainfall made possible. Clearing the forest, fighting the summer peril of bush-fires, and combating stock diseases called for great ingenuity and persistence. Here, too, lack of transport and the difficulties of marketing retarded the industry. Science could perhaps do less in these early stages than could co-operation among producers; but, as the conditions became less strenuous and the importance of yield per cow was insistent, the dairy farmer turned to the study of genetics and nutrition. There was no easy road to success—dogged courage, unlimited patience, and almost superhuman resilience were the requirements for the successful farmer in many parts of the continent. Not for them the test tubes, the soil profiles, and the demonstration plots of their more sophisticated successors. Not for them the power tractors, and the muscle-replacing machinery of a later day. Not for them the motor trucks and all the ease of a spare-parts system. They made their place with horse and buggy or bullock dray. They stood to the plough, or rode tirelessly over the countryside tending their flocks and herds. There are few names mentioned in the despatches of this long hard campaign; but those who served the country well are legion.

In 1842 discoveries of copper had been made at Kapunda, and two decades later at Wallaroo and Moonta in South Australia. More important still, the first artesian bore had been put down at Killara on the inland plains. By 1890 deposits of copper, gold, tin, silver, lead and zinc had been discovered; and Mt. Bischoff (1871), Broken Hill (1883), Mt. Zeehan (1885), Mt. Lyell (1886), became household words. The great gold discoveries at Mount Morgan in Queensland (1882), and at Kalgoorlie and Coolgardie in Western Australia (1890) followed.

In the years between 1880 and 1900 great primary development and tremendous mining expansion was accompanied by feverish provision of transport by sea and land. By sea-route and railway Australia was rapidly knit into the structure of world trade. Primary industry could be expanded and intensified only if markets could be found for the increased output. Moreover, the improvement of transport, especially in refrigeration, greatly enlarged the volume and variety of products which could now be delivered to those markets. So Australia moved inevitably into those economic rivalries with other primary producing countries which sharpen the problems of comparative costs and of world prices. The urge for efficiency came from the overseas' consumer, whose tastes and desires were the sole criterion to be satisfied; and ways and means of pleasing the eye and the palate of unseen customers 12,000 miles away had to be studied. The pioneering period in the orthodox sense was over; and the day of science in rural industry was dawning.

SCIENCE AND THE NEW FRONTIER

By the end of the century it was felt by many that the old "hit-or-miss" methods of development were too costly. After the war of 1914-18 the attempt to settle returned soldiers on the land was only a partial success, and much criticism and investigation followed. It was shown that extensive methods of cultivation amounted to "soil-mining," that over-grazing despoiled the pastures and lowered their carrying capacity; and that, if rural areas were to sustain more people, soil fertility must be not merely maintained but increased. This was all the more imperative in a country where, over large areas, rainfall was unreliable and profitable land-use so chancy. It all emphasized the vital need for conserving water, for scientific study of the soils and for arresting widespread erosion. The frontiers had changed. It was no longer wise to push agriculture further into the erratic rain belts, or to march further into the desert margins in the hope that profits could be made from ephemeral pastures. The problem was how to use the proven areas more efficiently.

At this point experiment became the method of advance.

Rural surveys, experiment stations, breeding and feeding studies were the new method of attack. Soils and seasons were reduced to statistics; the climatologist, the geographer, and the agronomist were enlisted in the drive for more efficient use of land. From Goyder, painfully sketching in 1860 the limits of agriculture in South Australia by observation in the field, to Griffith Taylor, plotting the physical controls of fertility over the whole continent, there is a long line of devoted research and a campaign of displacing guesswork by scientific study. Much of the work was built upon or associated with the knowledge compounded of the experience of pastoralists and farmers.

In 1926 the Australian government created the Council for Scientific and Industrial Research, and modern research methods were enlisted for a concerted attack upon the problems of primary production. This development had been hastened by mechanised farming and the menace of wool substitutes, and the achievement is already great. Among its successes are the complete destruction of prickly pear which had rendered useless thousands of square miles of fertile territory; and the restoration of blighted areas by the demonstration that small mineral deficiencies in the soils were to blame. Hundreds of problems affecting the rural industries are now under continuous investigation, and many are yielding to the continuous pressure for discovery of remedies.

In the development of mineral resources the mining engineer and research worker have had to face peculiar problems; and they have made brilliant contributions to world knowledge and mining practice. Improvements in the mining and treatment of ores have marked the history of such famous mines as Broken Hill (silver-lead-zinc), Mt. Lyell (copper), Mt. Bischoff (tin), and the Kalgoorlie group (gold). The Broken Hill group alone has yielded minerals valued at about £180,-000,000; and in its development standards of efficiency unsurpassed anywhere in the world have been attained. The work of Australians specially distinguished in the treatment of refractory ores is known throughout the mining world.

AUSTRALIA'S CONTRIBUTION TO SCIENCE

It would be wrong to suppose that the brains and energy of the Australians have been devoted entirely to the material problems of development. They have been equally concerned with the making of new knowledge and the transmission of old knowledge, believing that, in a changing world, an uninformed and unsophisticated democracy cannot endure. Pride of British attainments in the arts and sciences was the spur which raised the clear spirit of this young community to study and research, in order that something should be added to world knowledge. Australian names are familiar to the workers in almost every field of science. Admittedly the names are relatively few, but the population is still relatively small, and the scientific history of Australia spans as yet scarcely more than half a century.

To the names of many workers connected with the application of scientific research to practical problems of development, those of many others who were devoted to learning for its own sake should be added. From their labours the whole world has benefited. Many physicists and chemists now living have done work of first-class importance in atomic physics, in thermodynamics, and heat. In mathematics and engineering, in the inventions of peace and of war, Australian names take a high place. They and their successors will come to post-war difficulties with knowledge and understanding; and Australia will not fail to make a worthy contribution to the reconstruction of a disordered world.

Chapter II

CLIMATE AND THE PEOPLING OF AUSTRALIA

BY PATRICIA MCBRIDE

Lecturer in Economic Geography, University of Melbourne

DEFICIENT and uncertain rainfall has severely limited the areas of the continent which can be closely settled. One acre out of every three is desert with no known possibility of permanent use or settlement; an even larger area cannot support more than a sparse population dependent on the pastoral industry. Close settlement, therefore, will be confined to the higher rainfall areas in the east, south and southwest of the continent. Lacking some miracle, three-quarters of Australia is destined to remain desolate or sparsely inhabited. The pattern of population distribution imposed by rainfall is accentuated by the location of minerals within the Commonwealth. All Australia's important deposits of coal, the basic energy resource of modern industrial civilization, lie within the well-watered regions of the east and south. Any development of hydro-electric power, too, will occur along the slopes of the Eastern Highlands and in Tasmania.

In the minds of people of Great Britain and the United States, Australia is associated with droughts. From time to time great losses of sheep or cattle in the dry hinterland or the scorching of wheat crops become headline news. The variability of Australian rainfall is, not unjustly, notorious. Droughts are a problem not only of the drier inland areas, but also at times and to a lesser degree of the coastal districts. Even in most of the wetter districts the probable deficit or excess compared with the average is greater than in most parts of

Europe. (See Fig. IV.) For instance, at Townsville, Queensland, where the average annual rainfall is 47 inches, from 1933 to 1937 the yearly totals were 49, 39, 11, 63 and 24 inches. Every Australian farmer and grazier must gamble on the rainfall; in some areas the odds are longer than in others, but the risk is always present. Each of the capital cities, situated on the

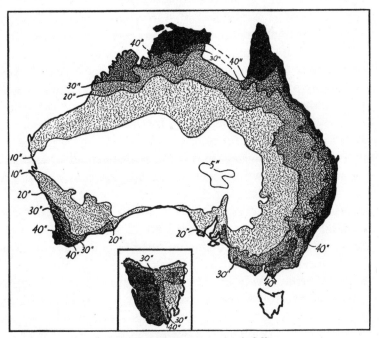

Fig. I. Average annual rainfall.

coast in all cases, has from time to time suffered from water shortage. Many inland cities live always under the threat of water scarcity.

THE MYTH OF THE "VAST OPEN SPACES"

Australians have been accused of preventing other people from occupying areas they themselves are unwilling to develop. Writers have declared that Australia, with about the same area as the United States, should support 120 million people; others have suggested that a continent three-quarters the size of Europe should be able to support at least 200 millions. Such area comparisons are worthless. Australians themselves are concerned about their inability to develop and people these huge areas. The "open spaces" have been wrongly invested with a mystical sort of "Go west young man" appeal. Wrong ideas of "unbounded possibilities" greatly hinder a scientific appreciation of the problem of rapidly enlarging the population. The war has strengthened the view that if Australia is to play a vigorous role in international affairs a larger population is essential. In these circumstances, factors which continue to restrict population growth in Australia should be stated in the plainest terms.

The basic obstacles to closer settlement of Australia's "sparselands" have not been the immigration laws, the alleged laziness of Australians, or the fears of organized labour. Criticisms of suppositious policies of closing the hinterland and tropical north against migrants have clouded the real issues. It is equally untrue to blame an imaginary disappearance of the pioneer spirit for the failure to populate "empty Australia." In the dry interior, pastoralists have for forty years "held on" in areas carrying one sheep to fifteen acres, and subject at intervals to severe droughts sometimes lasting for several years. "The development of the Australian tropics has been no spasmodic or haphazard experimentation, but a determined struggle by strong and resourceful people against almost superhuman odds in which the fetish of a high standard of living has played no part. Neither have the records of previous failures deterred our adventurous people from trying and trying again." [1]

Three-quarters of Australia, in the face of sustained efforts

[1] W. Wynne Williams, "The Settlement of the Australian Tropics," *Economic Record*, Vol. XI, No. 20, p. 33.

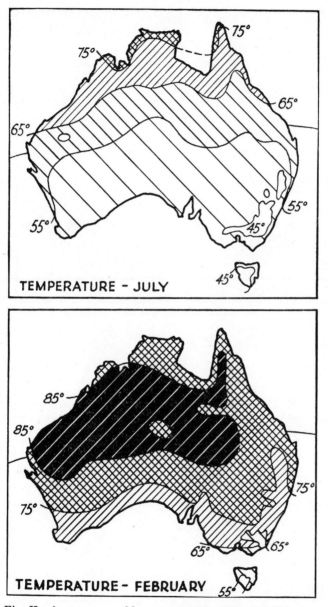

TEMPERATURE - JULY

TEMPERATURE - FEBRUARY

Fig. II. Average monthly temperature: July and February.

23

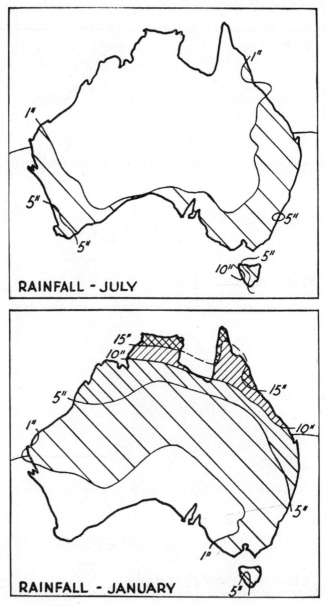

Fig. III. Average monthly rainfall: July and January.

to develop it more intensively, is sparsely settled simply because the climate does not permit crop farming. The rainfall is not only inadequate but "chancy," and is concentrated in a short season. The mean annual rainfall map (see Fig. I) shows that a vast area, 37 per cent of Australia, has an annual rainfall of less than ten inches, and only 15 per cent has a rainfall greater than thirty inches. By way of contrast 60 per cent of the area of the United States receives more than twenty inches of rain a year. The inexorable fact is that Australia is an extremely dry continent, much of it too dry for agriculture in any form. Figures I to IV show that rainfall

(a) is concentrated in the north into the five months of the hot season (November–April);
(b) is concentrated in the south into the late autumn-winter-spring months (May–October);
(c) has no regular season and is both scanty and erratic in the centre;
(d) occurs at all seasons in the east, but long dry spells are not uncommon.

Over the great bulk of Australia there is either a permanent or a seasonal drought, during which plants will not grow. (See Fig. V.) Low rainfall, not low temperature, is the limiting factor for plant growth. Very little of Australia, rugged highland useless for crops, has temperatures low enough to prevent plant growth even in winter.

CLIMATE AND THE CONTROL OF SETTLEMENT

The real control, however, is neither the quantum nor the season rainfall, but the amount remaining in the soil and available for plant growth. The most important factor which determines this is the rate of evaporation, the evaporation factor also greatly affects the amount of moisture which the plant transpires and must replace from the soil through its roots.

Annual rainfall of twenty inches, which supports crops in the south, will not suffice in the hot north.

Investigators at the Waite Institute, Adelaide, found that the common pasture grasses and cultivated plants would grow only when the rainfall (P) was more than one-third of the calculated evaporation (E) from a free water surface. The

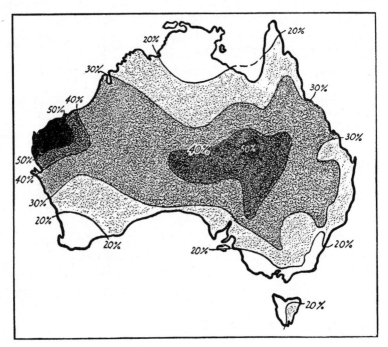

Fig. IV.   Rainfall variability.

formula is generally expressed thus, $P/E > \frac{1}{3}$; and has great significance for determining the agricultural or pastoral possibilities of any area, and the number of months during which the ordinary economic plants will grow, provided other conditions, e.g., temperature and soil, are satisfactory. Since all the important crops have a growing period of five months or more, the formula can be used to map the areas which have a growing period as long as this and are thus *climatically* suited for agriculture. This has been done in Fig. V. It shows that only one-quarter of the continent has a growing period of five or more months, i.e., enough for routine farming of any crop. Moreover, these are the areas in which agricultural develop-

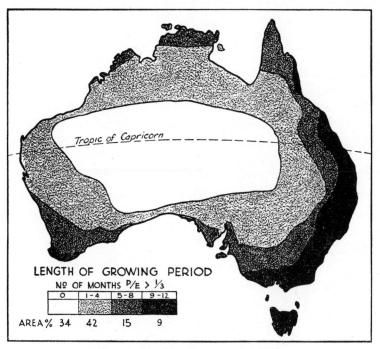

Fig. V. Length of growing period.

ment has taken place in the past and in which we can expect closer settlement through the development of agriculture in the future.

THE AUSTRALIAN DESERT IS NO MYTH

Areas in which there is no month in the year during which ordinary plants will grow constitute deserts. Here the vegetation has adapted itself to make the best use of the brief periods when soil moisture is sufficient, and to withstand the long drought periods. Approximately a third of the continent, i.e., over one million square miles, must be classified as desert. The facts admit no argument. The vegetation consists of a mixture of drought-resistant shrubs and trees (mulga, myall, salt-bush, and bluebush) and ephemerals which flash through the vegetative and reproductive stages after each heavy fall of rain. As Griffith Taylor puts it, "The arid lands of Australia have, in fact, much the same character as the Sahara, except for the absence of moving dunes." Fixed dunes, however, do occur in the northern and southern parts of the Western Desert; and much of the centre is covered with rock debris and gravels. Such a situation would be less difficult if large streams maintained a constant flow of water from their catchments. No permanent rivers, however, exist in Central Australia, despite the extensive drainage system of Lake Eyre which makes such a splendid and misleading appearance in most atlases. It is usually years between the times when floodwaters reach the great "lake," which is normally a salt-encrusted flat.

Of this enormous desert area 600,000 square miles, or no less than 23 per cent of the continent, is unusable and uninhabitable. This area includes the so-called Western Desert, and, to the east of the Macdonnell Ranges, the Arunta Desert also. The remainder of the area supports grazing of the most sparse type—mainly for cattle and not sheep. It will be long before these "sparse-lands" support a population of even one person per square mile.[2] They have been occupied by graziers for half a century; and, judging by the stability of the numbers of stock carried, it would appear that they have long ago reached saturation point. During this time the population has not increased; and in parts has even declined. (See Fig. VI.)

The existence of an Australian desert is not a mere myth

[2] T. Griffith Taylor, "Australia; a Study of Warm Environments and Their Effect on British Settlement" (Methuen, 1940), p. 441.

but a fact to be acknowledged and taken into account in plans for the future development of this area. It is admitted that the Sahara is a desert, unsuited for any but the sparsest of settlement; and it has to be admitted that, for the same reason, one-third of Australia has remained, and will remain, almost unpeopled.

MORE "VAST OPEN SPACES"

Surrounding the desert region is an even larger area in which the growing period is from one to four months. Under these conditions many plants suitable for fodder will thrive. This area (42 per cent of the whole continent) is the great pastoral "outback," providing fair to good grazing for beef cattle in the north, and for sheep in the south. The length of the growing season, and, therefore, the stocking capacity per square mile diminishes as the true desert is approached. During the dry season the stock exist on the dried grasses, supplemented by the perennial vegetation. In a succession of drought years, and particularly along the desert edge, the perennial vegetation may be so "eaten out" that it is unable to recover. In this belt wind erosion is troublesome. The availability of artesian water has been an enormous boon to graziers in this region, enabling them to provide permanent water for their stock in a land where streams are few and far between.

In the Tropical North the summer rainfall promotes the growth of lank grass, sometimes several feet in height. This lank growth, combined with high temperature and humidity, make the area unsuitable for the grazing of sheep, the fleece being light and poor in quality. The area is, therefore, predominantly a beef-cattle region. Distance from permanent water is another test of the capacity of an area to sustain sheep or cattle.

The extension of sheep raising into the Tropical North cannot be regarded as a means of substantially increasing the density of settlement.[3] Neither can any great extension of cattle grazing into lands at present unused be expected. The better grazing country has long been occupied; and the problem is now one of achieving greater efficiency in the use of land already occupied. These improvements, which involve an increased capital outlay, await the development of markets. Moreover, even if greater exploitation of these pastoral lands is possible, the population will continue to be relatively sparse. The extensive natural grasslands of central Queensland, which are the most important pastoral regions of tropical Australia, at present support a sheep population of only one to every three acres, and a human population of one person per square mile. Griffith Taylor suggests that this, in time, may rise to three persons per square mile. Some of the huge stations (ranches) on marginal land have cattle densities of ten per square mile. In the Northern Territory, Bovril Australian Estates Ltd. runs 177,000 cattle on two stations aggregating 12,000 square miles (larger than Belgium!). Eleven stations operated by Northern Agency Ltd. (Vestey's) carry 152,000 cattle on 24,000 square miles. Even on the Barkly Tableland, the stock density is seven head (horses and cattle) per square mile.[4]

On the pastoral lands of the south the possibilities are greater. This region has long been settled, and its problems and limitations are better known. The winter growing-period of from one to four months is insufficient for agriculture. The grazing of sheep, not cattle, is therefore the main industry in this area, which is the important merino-breeding region of the continent. The stocking capacity varies enormously, increasing from an average of about one sheep to fifteen acres, to one sheep to three acres as the zone with a growing period of five months is approached.

[3] Wadham and Wood, "Land Utilization in Australia" (Melbourne University Press, 1939), pp. 110–111.
[4] Payne-Fletcher Commission. Report on Northern Territory (October, 1937).

Plate 1. Sydney, business section and Harbour Bridge.

Plate 2. Aerial view of Melbourne.

Plate 3. The desert margin—bluebush-saltbush association, 8-inch rainfall, South Australia.

Plate 4. The steppe lands—bluebush-saltbush association in good season, 8-inch rainfall, South Australia.

Plate 5. Mulga scrub with ephemeral herbage in good season, 12-inch rainfall, south-west Queensland.

Plate 6. Upland pastures of the South-East. Danthonia grassland, winter rain zone.

Wool growing has been pushed as far as possible into the drier regions. In fact, along the desert margins the sheep population has never regained the figures which it reached in 1890, largely because the carrying capacity has been reduced by over-grazing and soil erosion. Instead of further advance into the desert, a retreat is apparently taking place. Hence, any increase in population in this area, as in the Tropical North, must come from a more efficient use of land which has already been occupied for half a century or more. Since this will require a capital outlay which would not be warranted on areas with a low carrying capacity, such improvements could be expected only along the wetter edge of the pastoral belt. The considerations involved and the extent to which they are likely to be successful will be investigated more closely in a later chapter.

DROUGHTS MUST BE EXPECTED

The general conclusion reached is that the growing period over three-quarters of Australia—2 ¼ million square miles—is not long enough for commercial agriculture. Of this 2 ¼ million square miles, 600,000 cannot be used for any primary industry, another 500,000 square miles provide only very light grazing, and the remainder offers fair to good grazing for sheep or beef cattle. A further bar to development in these areas is the risk of drought. The map (see Fig. IV) gives a measure of the relative reliability of rainfall. The areas in which the drought risk is at its greatest are the central area of Western Australia, and the south-west corner of Queensland. Areas totalling more than half the continent have a variability greater than 30 per cent; these regions are, in general, those in which the rainfall is lowest and the growing period is shortest. In the unoccupied area the variation in the yearly fall has no economic significance; in the pastoral zone it causes wide fluctuations from year to year in the capacity of the land to maintain animals. (See Fig. V.) Drought years, moreover, tend to occur in cycles. Thus, in the State of Queensland alone, it is estimated that owing to droughts from 1926–1932, there was a loss of over 11 million sheep. This high variability of rainfall makes larger holdings necessary. The properties must be big enough to make it possible for the land-holder to recoup in good years his losses during the bad years.

CAN WATER BE BROUGHT TO "THE VAST OPEN SPACES"?

The climatic conditions of the dry interior thus constitute a challenge which many Australians have shown themselves only too ready to accept. Many schemes for providing certain areas with the water they lack have been suggested. One scheme is to flood Lake Eyre Basin, which is below sea-level, by means of a channel cut from the sea at Port Augusta. J. W. Gregory investigated this proposal over forty years ago and concluded that (since the sea water would be useless for irrigation) "the most that could be safely expected would be an improvement of the geographical conditions for some miles around the lake, obtained at a price which might pay if the land were stocked with the sheep that grew a golden fleece." [5] Extended use of artesian water has also been suggested both as a possible means of irrigation for agriculture, and for in-creasing the stocking capacity of the land. Fortunately, much of this area is underlain by artesian water (see Fig. XX), but this source of water is already being severely exploited, the estimated flow for the entire Commonwealth being about 350 million gallons daily. The Great Artesian Basin, covering an area of 600,000 square miles, is, perhaps, the largest artesian basin in the world, but it appears to be already fully utilized. The areas in which the number of artesian bores for watering stock can be increased are limited. Apart from any other con-

[5] "The Dead Heart of Australia" (London, John Murray, 1906), Ch. XVIII, p. 352.

sideration, the high mineral content of the water makes it generally unusable for irrigating crops because the soil would rapidly become "salted" and intolerable to plants.

Irrigation from streams has been widely advocated as the method of developing Australia's dry lands. The only important irrigation zone in the whole of that area with a growing period of less than five months lies along the River Murray in the neighbourhood of Mildura and Renmark. Here, land which before the coming of irrigation was used for sheep pasture is now the most important centre in the Commonwealth for the production of dried and citrus fruits. However, a major extension of the area under irrigation seems unlikely even though more is still possible in the way of water conservation. The Darling, the most westerly tributary of the Murray, frequently ceases to flow in the dry season. The water courses leading into Lake Eyre are normally dry and no practicable system of dams could maintain a permanent flow. In the tropical part of the pastoral belt the water courses are flooded after the monsoonal rains of the summer, but are dry in the cooler months. Owing to the great loss by evaporation, the maintenance of a permanent flow would involve the construction of extremely large dams to impound the summer fall; although in the Ord River Valley, North-west Australia, this would be possible.

Another scheme has recently been advocated by (the late) Dr. J. J. C. Bradfield, an eminent Australian engineer.[6] He proposed to capture the waters of some Queensland streams flowing into the Pacific and to return them through the ranges by tunnels or open channels into the beds of inland rivers. Unfortunately, even if such a project could be carried out, the area affected would be but a tiny proportion of the dry hinterland.

[6] J. J. C. Bradfield, "Restoring Australia's Parched Lands," *Australian Quarterly*, Vol. XIV, No. 2, June, 1942.

The conclusion is that only the remaining 25 per cent of Australia is climatically suitable for agriculture. It is only in this section that land-use can be further intensified and population increased. The section with a five to eight months' growing period constitutes a zone of seasonal agriculture, predominantly wheat-cropping; along the eastern and southern coasts, where the growing period is even longer, such crops as potatoes and fruit are grown and dairying is carried on.

WHERE THE AUSTRALIANS OF THE FUTURE WILL LIVE

All of this small portion of the continent is, however, not suited for development. The great bulk of the highlands is associated with the higher rainfall regions of the east and south. Nearly half of the well-watered littoral of New South Wales, i.e., 23,000 square miles, is practically empty, in spite of excellent rainfall and temperature conditions. For the same reason 11,000 square miles of Victoria, an eighth of the State, is unoccupied, and half of Tasmania is too rugged for use. Apart from barren uplands, poor soils inhibit development in some areas, as for instance in Northern Australia where laterite (iron-stone) and stony soils are widespread. In the temperate south very little land suitable for development is still in the possession of the Crown, and this is mostly inferior or inaccessible country. The "good" land has long been occupied. Although crop acreages expand and contract in response to market conditions, the climatic limits of the zones of different primary industries are already well defined. All that now remains at this stage is to sketch briefly the typical uses to which this good land is put.

Wheat in Australia is a winter-spring crop. The areas of cultivation are, therefore, confined to the south and east, where the rain falls in these seasons. In the south the average summer is almost rainless. In New South Wales an overlap of the winter-rain of the south and the summer-rain of the north occurs. Parts of both the south and east are, therefore, suited for the production of wheat. Further north, the winter months are dry and wheat-growing gives place to other activities. (See Fig. III.) The inland boundary of the wheat belt has already been pushed into territory where the growing period is barely sufficient and the rainfall variability makes production hazardous. For this and other reasons the Federal and State Governments are co-operating in "reconstruction" of these areas by changing wheat farms over to sheep or to sheep and wheat.[7]

For grazing of *dairy cattle*, a growing season of at least nine months is required. Hence this industry is concentrated on the coastal plains of the south and east, and on a few irrigation areas. Dairy cattle are most numerous in the Northern Rivers District of New South Wales, the southern sector of coastal Queensland, the Western and Gippsland districts of Victoria, and on the irrigated lands along the Murray.

Cultivation of *sugar-cane* is limited by the water and temperature requirements of the plant to coastal Queensland. Without irrigation, a minimum annual rainfall of 60 inches is necessary, but much of the Australian crop is grown on irrigated land with a mean annual rainfall of 40 inches or more.

The zones suitable for the production of *other crops*, such as oats, barley, maize, potatoes and flax, are now well defined. In general, any increase in the numbers of people engaged in primary industry in the south and east will take place not so much by the development of unoccupied land, as by substituting more intensive crops and types of farming on land already in use, and increasing the efficiency of the rural industries already established.

In this process, the extended use of irrigation will play some part. The great irrigation schemes already established are associated with the River Murray and its tributaries (see Fig. XIX); but the area which could be irrigated can be developed

[7] Wheat Industry Assistance Act 1938. *Vide infra*, chap. IX.

only slowly. Coastal rivers may, in time, be harnessed for irrigation (and power) as has been done in Queensland.

THE POSSIBILITIES FOR AGRICULTURE IN TROPICAL AUSTRALIA

Nearly 40 per cent of Australia lies within the tropics. This area of more than one million square miles contained in 1935 a population of 193,000, and about 185,000 of these people lived along the "Sugar Coast." The 790,000 square miles in the tropical portions of Northern Territory and Western Australia support over 8,000 people, an average of nearly 100 square miles per person. This meagre population represents the results of the efforts to develop the north during three-quarters of a century. Yet optimists still point to "plenty of good land in the north," a region sufficiently remote and unknown for it to be invested with mythical fertility and fabulous possibilities. What follows is an attempt to summarise what is known (and, more importantly, what is not known) concerning the possibilities for closer settlement, based on agricultural development in the Tropical North, exclusive of the coast of Queensland.

In the first place, the area of tropical Australia which has a growing period sufficient for crops is restricted to the coastal sections of the Kimberleys, the northern part of Arnhem Land, and Cape York Peninsula. Recent work has suggested that because of the tropical conditions another formula should be used,[8] and this gives a slightly larger area with a growing period of five or more months. Prescott claims that, for successful cropping, there should be not merely a growing period of five months or more, but also that one of these months should be very wet, so that the crop can grow actively.[9] When

[8] E. Lawrence, "Climatic Regions of Tropical Australia," *Australian Geographer*, Vol. IV, No. 1, March, 1941.

[9] "The Climate of Tropical Australia in Relation to Possible Agricultural Settlement." Trans. Roy. Soc. S. A. Vol. 62, Part II, 1938.

this condition is applied the area which is climatically suited to agriculture is even more restricted.

The second question concerns the type of crops which can be grown. Comparison with Nigeria, the area most nearly identical in climate with the northern littoral of Australia, indicates that specially adapted crops such as peanuts and millets might be grown. Already peanut growing has been successful, for instance, in the valley of the Daly River, the plants growing during the wet season and requiring little attention. The industry is, however, generously subsidized. Although the area where climate would make agriculture possible is still undefined, much land in that area is characterized by poor soils; much of the surface is stony; and on wide expanses of range country soils are very thin or even absent. It seems certain that, in the absence of irrigation, the agriculture of Northern Australia would be seasonal in character and localised on alluvial valley soils.

There remains the vexed question of the extent to which white settlement is discouraged by the effects of climate upon health. The areas in which agricultural development is possible are those in which the relative humidity is highest and discomfort greatest. Nevertheless, coastal Queensland constitutes the largest and most successful experiment in settling whites in the tropics to be found in the world. Fortunately, the Australian tropics are remarkably free from the worst tropical diseases. After an exhaustive survey, Dr. Grenfell Price concluded that "a century of experiment has proved that white males can survive in these wet-dry (monsoonal) or arid tropics and maintain fair standards of living in the face of isolation and other difficulties provided they abstain from alcoholic excess and engage in hard manual work. The position is more doubtful as regards women and children, but undoubtedly some individuals maintain excellent health and high energy. In the arid and monsoonal regions it may be possible in future to preselect such individuals by scientific research." [10] The training of Australians and Americans for campaigning in Northern Australia, New Guinea, and other tropical islands has yielded much useful knowledge. On the other hand, history and science have clearly shown that a climate resembling that of Northern Australia presents the greatest obstacle to close settlement by any people, white or coloured, which seeks a reasonable standard of life. In these circumstances, a scientific assessment of the climatic difficulties of Northern Australia will be useful. The northern lands should be treated as pastoral and mining areas, and misdirected experiments that may handicap the development of the more hopeful parts of the Commonwealth should be discouraged.

[10] A. Grenfell Price, "White Settlers in the Tropics" (*Am. Geog. Soc.*, 1939), p. 121.

Chapter III

THE AUSTRALIAN POPULATION PROBLEM

BY W. D. FORSYTH

Formerly Research Fellow, University of Melbourne

AUSTRALIA's position will not be understood unless it is realized that the Australian population is no longer at the adolescent stage in which a wide variety of possibilities exists, but has reached maturity, has chosen the permanent elements and forms of community, and is ready for stable, conscious development of existing potentialities. The future of Australian population will be determined, short of *force majeure*, principally by internal forces and needs. Out of various elements sharing distinctively Australian experiences there has been created a unified and self-conscious national community, which is clearly bent on developing in accordance with its established character. That Australia should have reached maturity while numbers are still small does not alter the fact, for there are many small but mature nations, and the smallness of the Australian population appears inconsistent with maturity only against the unusually spacious territorial background.

This is not to say that there can be no great growth of numbers in future and no enriching ethnic and cultural infusions. But it does mean that growth and enrichment coming from outside will be governed by the community's capacity to absorb them without violent changes in its make-up and habits. The growth of Australian civilization will come about by digestion, as it were, rather than by agglomeration.

Australians have never been blind to the risks of their experiment in nation-building. The community is based on

Western standards maintained largely by economic and cultural integration with Atlantic countries; but it lies far outside the Atlantic area and alongside vastly bigger communities which on the whole have not so far adopted, or remotely approached, living standards in the United States or Australia. The contrast between Western and Eastern modes of life is focussed most sharply on Australia, both because Australia carries Atlantic characteristics deep into the Eastern region

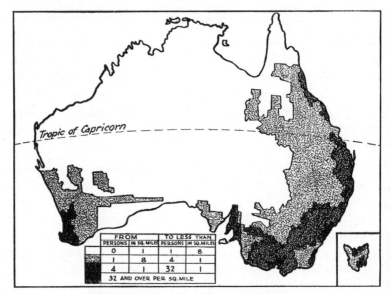

FROM		TO LESS THAN	
PERSONS	IN SQ. MILES	PERSONS	IN SQ.MILES
0		1	8
1	8	4	1
4	1	32	1
32 AND OVER PER SQ.MILE			

Fig. VI. Distribution of population.

and because its apparently great resources are utilized directly by so small a fraction of humanity. In the nature of things, Australia's position must be one of fundamental insecurity while this contrast exists, and Australia has need of sympathetic understanding on the part of other countries in its attempt to construct a civilization. For this it is necessary, as thinking Australians realize, for Australia to demonstrate to the world energy and practical achievement in the development of its resources, in providing a good living for a proportion of the human race commensurate with the economic capacity of the continent, and in developing national strength to the point at which Australia will not be a liability in the field of international security and political stability.

The population, approximately 7,350,000 in March, 1944, is about the size of that of Portugal, Greece, or Peru. It is important to realize that it is no longer substantially a population of immigrants. The proportion born in Australia has risen steadily; at the last census (1933) 86 per cent of the people had been born in the Commonwealth. Not since 1860 has immigration contributed half the increase in any decade. A predominantly indigenous population has thus long been established.

The people derive chiefly from the English, Scots, and Irish, in that order, but there have been minor infusions from other European sources for a century past, and the people are certainly not now "98 per cent British" as could formerly be claimed. The population is nevertheless homogeneous to a high degree, predominantly British and almost wholly European; Asiatic elements are insignificant. The principal Asiatic group. the Chinese, declined from 29,627 in 1901 to 10,846 in 1933. Restrictions against the entry of Asiatics began long before the separate States federated to form the Commonwealth of Australia. After federation, when immigration became subject to Commonwealth legislation, the Immigration Restriction Act of 1901 imposed a dictation test by which, in excluding immigrants, overt reference to colour was deliberately avoided.

Exclusion has in fact been largely based on non-racial considerations. The real demand of Australian immigration policy has been that the immigrant should be a person readily capable of assimilation into the economic and social systems. In the first place, exclusion has not been applied solely to Asiatics—the flow of immigrants from some European countries has long been controlled, and during and since the depression of the early 1930's non-British immigrants have been refused entry unless in possession of sufficient money and other guarantees for their support for a reasonable period after landing in the country.

On the other hand, the exclusion of Asiatics has never been absolute. Facilities have been granted for the entry of bona fide merchants who proposed, and were in a position to promote, trade between Australia and their respective home countries, and they were allowed to bring their wives and minor children with them. Firms with a reasonable turnover in Australia have been permitted to introduce assistants. Business men wishing to revisit their homelands in Asia could arrange for the temporary admission of substitutes to take their places while they were away. Facilities were also afforded for students and tourists, and for the wives and children of Asiatic residents, to reside in or visit Australia.

Asiatics of these types have fitted into Australian ways without friction, and representative Chinese, for example, not only admit that the Australian people have a right to determine the composition of the population by applying social and economic criteria of selection, but themselves argue the undesirability of admitting people of types unlikely to understand and adopt Australian ways in economic and social life.

The universal currency of the term "White Australia," however, has associated Australian immigration policy with racial rather than social considerations. Notwithstanding the disproportionate amount of publicity "White Australia" has always had, it should not be overlooked that several other countries of overseas European settlement are equally if not more exclusive; there are in fact, if not in name, "White Canada," "White New Zealand," and "White America" policies.

The population is not exceptional in being very unevenly distributed, and its density is the lowest among all the continents, largely because natural resources are poor by comparison. It is meaningless to compare Australia's density of two persons to the square mile with Italy's 339, or forty-three for the United States. A fairer comparison would be with Canada, which has a similarly high proportion of economically valueless lands. The distribution within Australia, the bulk of the population living on the coastal margins in the east, south-east and southwest, reflects as in any other country (notably again Canada) the distribution of resources. Victoria, comparatively rich in resources relatively to area, has a density of 21.8; Western Australia, in which the greater part of the rainfall and other resources necessary to support human life is restricted to the southwest corner of the State, has a density of 0.48 to the square mile.

A century of experience has proved that the greater part of the surface of the continent is too dry or too rugged to support significant numbers of people. The opportunities for future settlement lie in the fertile portions of the eastern, south-eastern and south-western margins. But these lands are already occupied and in use, and their capacity to support many more people depends on whether the relation of price to cost of production will make more intensive cultivation worth while. There are virtually no empty spaces left, in the sense of lands not in use which could be taken up by new settlers and would yield them a living. "Closer settlement" on the better lands already settled is the only means by which any large increase in the agricultural population can come about. But this depends on the demand for agricultural produce, which in recent times has not encouraged new settlement—there were fewer men on the land in Australia in 1935 than there had been in 1913, although production was much greater.

In all States a large part of the population is found in the capital cities. More than half of the people of Victoria and New South Wales dwell within the respective metropolitan areas. Together with the other principal industrial centre,

Newcastle, these areas contain two-fifths of the entire population of the Commonwealth. But this high degree of urbanization is not peculiar to Australia. It has been due, as in Canada and Argentina, partly to the special conditions of a "new" country. Rapid expansion of extensive agricultural and pastoral industries producing largely for export involved equally rapid development of commercial, financial, and communications systems which were quite naturally centralized at the most convenient entrepôts. Partly also, urbanization in Australia has been due to factors incidental to industrial development in whatever country it occurs. The pace of urbanization has increased in recent decades; during the 1920's Australian city populations grew twice as fast as the rural population. The industrial boom which followed the depression of the early 1930's and the intense activity of wartime have further stimulated this process. Steps have recently been taken to bring about some decentralization of industry. Nevertheless, after the war Australians will probably be more than ever before a city-dwelling people. This tendency is world-wide and is due to the growing productivity of scientific and mechanized agriculture, coupled with the increasing capacity of secondary and tertiary industries to provide economic opportunity for massive urban populations. Consequently the main migrations of today are towards thickly populated areas and not into the "open spaces."

Until recent years the growth of population in Australia was very rapid. It is remarkable that the idea should ever have gained currency that Australian population growth was slow. Over the forty years, 1881–1921, Australia's rate of growth was second, among all countries of the world, only to that of New Zealand. The average annual rate was 2.2 per cent. Since 1930, however, growth has been very slow. This decline has been due to the practical cessation of immigration and a falling birth rate. Like Canada, New Zealand, and other countries, Australia found that it was not so easy to absorb new population in the changed conditions following the last war as it had been before, and all countries of immigration, not excepting the United States and Brazil, not only ceased to take migrants during the depression but had an actual loss of people by migration for longer or shorter periods during the 30's. During 1930–32, Australia lost 21,000 people by net emigration, 17,000 of them British. The depression, however, only exhibited in a specially pointed way a general long-term decline in absorptive capacity. It is more than half a century since Australia experienced over any five-year period an average annual immigration amounting to more than one per cent of the population. In other overseas countries the declining importance of migration has also been apparent. By the 1930's these countries had obtained their basic equipment of capital and man-power, and the major opportunities of pastoral, agricultural, and mineral exploitation had been taken up. In Australia, for example, the total number of sheep grew by more than 100 million in the fifty years to 1891, but has increased by less than 20 million in the succeeding fifty-odd years; wheat cultivation had for the most part reached the climatic limits of safe cultivation as early as the 90's; and until the present war the value of mineral production had not risen above the level reached in 1900.

The rate of immigration has naturally fallen as the more lavish opportunities have been annexed. It is true that the rate showed a tendency to rise after the last war. This was because Australia, like other Dominions, attempted by means of the Empire Settlement scheme (1922) to force immigration. But the effort was costly and the results disappointing. The policy of extending land settlement ran counter to the main stream of world economic conditions. The number of settlers permanently established through group settlement schemes in Western Australia and Victoria was only a fraction of that aimed at, and costs were prohibitive. Overseas borrowing for these and other schemes, designed to afford a basis for immigration, weakened Australia's financial position and thus increased the severity of the subsequent depression, but brought in only half the people it had been hoped to attract.

The decline of migration would not have affected the rate of growth of population seriously if natural increase had remained high. As total numbers grew the same rate of natural increase would have given an increasing annual addition. At the rate obtaining about 1910, the population of 1940 would have had a natural increase of 120,000 instead of the actual figure of less than 60,000. But natural increase and migration have both fallen away. The decline of fertility not only has reduced the annual increment, it has also affected capacity for future growth. The proportion of children under fifteen has decreased from nearly 40 per cent in the 80's to less than thirty per cent today, a trend obviously adverse to future reproduction. The net reproduction rate shows the extent to which the female part of the population is replacing itself, i.e., the capacity of the population to reproduce itself at current birth and death rates. In Australia the rate fell steadily for a long period, until in the 30's it was below unity, which means that at the birth and death rates of those years the population was no longer providing for replacement. The rate has since returned to slightly above unity, but a continuance at this level means bare replacement, not future growth. Without an improvement of the birth rate (for the age composition of the population is now such that the death rate is unlikely to be reduced much further, and may even rise) [1] the Australian population

---

[1] The great increases among European populations in the past century were due to reduction of mortality, which expanded capacity for growth by saving a rising proportion of female lives at all ages. The margin now left for improvement, however, is small in many countries, including Australia. By 1933, 94 per cent of females born in Australia were reaching age fifteen, and 84 per cent age fifty. Of the thirty-five years of reproductive age, Australian women were on the average living through over thirty. No very great addition to reproductive capacity could be expected from further saving of female lives. The infantile mortality rate in Australia is among the lowest in the world. From about 1910 to 1939 it was reduced from 74 to 34 per thousand—in the latter year the rate for the United States was 48.

would reach a maximum of around 8 million well before the end of the present century and would then cease to grow, and even with a very substantial immigration averaging 40,000 a year (a larger and steadier influx than we have ever maintained over any long period in the past) numbers would still reach a maximum and cease to grow before the end of the present century.

There has been a marked rise in the birth rate during the present war, but this is largely if not wholly attributable to a sudden increase in the number of marriages, which cannot be permanently maintained.[2] It would be unsafe to conclude from this wartime experience that fertility in Australia is permanently on the up-grade.

The peopling of Australia therefore demands energetic measures to encourage elements of population growth, migration, and natural increase. This has been recognized by the present Government. In the Budget speech on 29th September, 1943, the Commonwealth Treasurer said: "Among the lessons this war has brought home to all Australians is the urgent need to increase the population. For Australia's future defence and to safeguard her position as a Pacific power a much larger population is needed. A larger home market would benefit both our primary and secondary industries and encourage the development of those new types of production which go to make up a high standard of living. Our aim must be to ensure social and economic conditions which will foster a vigorous growth from our own stock and, supplementing this domestic growth, will encourage an inflow of suitable migrants."

This recognition of the necessity to foster internal reproduction as well as immigration is important. An unprecedented

---

[2] The number of marriages averaged 60,000 during 1935–39; it has risen to 77,000 in 1940, 75,000 in 1941, and 86,000 in 1942. But this cannot last, since the average number of female births during 1920–30 was only 62,000 and it is mainly from the survivors of this quota of females that the brides of the coming ten to twenty years must be chosen.

volume of immigration would be needed if internal growth fell away still further. To maintain an increase of 120,000 a year, which would approximately double the present population by the end of the century, immigration would have to average 60,000 a year if natural increase kept up to the same figure, more if natural increase declined. With all the effort and expense it involved, the Empire Settlement policy of the pre-depression period enabled Australia to absorb only 30,000 migrants a year. Twice this number of immigrants would be required over the coming sixty years to double the population, and the attempt would fail unless internal growth were restored. The task is certainly a formidable one.

On the other hand, the Empire Settlement policy with its emphasis on land settlement was at a disadvantage in that it was working against the economic stream, and, moreover, the source of migrants on which it concentrated was a contracting one owing to the decline of British population growth. In addition, the period was one of growing autarchy. In future, world conditions may be more favourable, industrial rather than agricultural expansion may be attempted, and non-British sources of population seriously exploited. The most important condition of future absorptive capacity in Australia is the success of attempts to promote a high level of economic activity throughout the world. International arrangements regarding commercial policy, full employment, currency, and exchange, and development in backward areas, will, if successful in promoting economic activity and avoiding autarchy and restrictive policies, make it easier for Australia to maintain a high rate of increase.

The theoretical economic capacity of a country to absorb immigrants, however, is not the sole determinant. In practice, psychological, cultural, and political factors cannot be excluded from consideration. An economy does not exist apart from the community; it is a complex organism, the various processes and structures of which are interdependent. The

Australian economy and the standard of living of the population are bound up with a democratic political apparatus, the satisfactory functioning of which demands a comparatively high degree of political aptitude and intelligence, and a set of co-operative habits which are the product of the community's history. Too big an intrusion of people of a lower standard of political education, or with habits and attitudes incompatible with democratic government, would hamper the working of this system. Moderate numbers, especially of selected types, can be habituated to and absorbed into the Australian politico-economic complex, but to admit large masses in a short period would be to court a breakdown. Cruder methods would necessarily be introduced if the newcomers were to share in political life; if they were not, the system would nevertheless inevitably change for the worse as a result of the division of the community into a politically privileged section on the one hand, and a section without responsibility on the other. In either case political and social poisons would be generated which would debilitate every aspect of Australian life—not least the economic aspect. The foundations of the politico-social structure which makes possible the high productivity of Australian labour, and the consequent high standard of living, would be undermined. In the end this would benefit neither the immigrants nor the outside world, and it would ruin the Commonwealth. This is not an argument against immigration, but it is a most serious argument against either indiscriminate (i.e., non-selective) or over-rapid immigration.

These dangers are not apparent to most Australians because we have had little experience of them. Our past immigrants were on the whole of highly assimilable type, coming chiefly from the parent stock in the British Isles and almost wholly from the cultural cradle, north-western Europe. But they are real dangers for the future, because population growth among the peoples of Britain and north-western Europe has dropped below the level at which any great sustained emigration is likely, and the potential sources are clearly the peoples of southern and eastern Europe—and Asia—whose political, cultural, and social characteristics are very different from those of Australia.

All this is not to say that Australian migration policy must remain as it has been. The Australian public is becoming increasingly aware and articulate concerning migration. It is realised—

   (i) that migrants must be encouraged;
  (ii) that Britain and north-western Europe cannot be expected to provide sufficient numbers over a long period; and
 (iii) that therefore suitable southern and eastern Europeans should be welcomed and positive measures devised to promote their easier assimilation.

There is also more recognition of the acuteness of population problems in some parts of Asia. In regard to what action might be taken, however, there is as yet little clarity in the minds of the public generally. There are advocates of views ranging from complete exclusion to the adoption of a quota system which would be a sign of the social but non-racial basis of Australian policy. But it would be misleading to give any impression except that Australian opinion is overwhelmingly in favour of the maintenance of the essentials of the present policy. Some Australians would like to see an attack on the root problem, Asiatic poverty. Migration merely spreads and does not solve Asia's problem. So long as Asiatic resources remain underdeveloped, and Asiatic population growth unrestricted, there will be redundant labour and abject poverty in Asia. A migration that would change Australia beyond recognition would make no appreciable difference to the Asiatics living at home. Every step which could be taken to raise the standard of living of the Asiatic peoples would tend to reduce the pressure for emigration. The task is too great for any one country; Australia therefore has a vital interest in international action for the development of welfare in Asia. Concerted international action is needed to foster industrial development and the restriction of population growth in Asia. The problem merges here into the wider questions of the promotion of understanding and collaboration between Eastern and Western peoples. Racial distrust and antagonism are more likely to disappear if there grows up a network of international co-operation covering a wide range of practical problems, especially those of economic development in the Pacific area.

Chapter IV

THE SOILS OF AUSTRALIA

BY G. W. LEEPER

Senior Lecturer in Agricultural Chemistry, University of Melbourne

Soil fertility is obviously an important factor in determining the production of wealth from the land. Soils, however, are much less important than climate, especially in Australia, where the threat of drought is so perpetual. To take one instance, the so-called Barkly Tableland of 30,000 square miles in the Northern Territory has a high proportion of good soil; but the annual rainfall there is too scanty for any but large pastoral holdings to succeed, and irrigation of this "tableland" is not possible. Any review of the soils of Australia, therefore, must be confined to the relatively small area which has a favourable climate for agriculture, and to the far smaller area which can be irrigated.

In approaching this subject we should first deal with the notion that virgin soils are necessarily good. No doubt the wealth of the prairies in North America seems to support this belief, but it is false none the less. Natural grassland may or may not be fertile. Natural forest also may or may not be fertile—in some places a temporary fertility may follow the burning of a great forest, but this may last only a few years. We must, therefore, dismiss any preconceived ideas about the soils of Australia.

Australia affords a good illustration of a significant relation between soil and climate, which was discovered first in Russia and later in other continental masses. This may be expressed in the principle that the heavier the rainfall the lower the

reserves of plant nutrients in the soil. These reserves are gradually lost in underground drainage or in the rivers, and what
the scientist terms a "leached" soil is left. The best natural
soil is thus to be expected in rather dry climates; and this
includes, of course, climates that are precarious for agriculture. Two of the largest areas of good soil in Australia—the

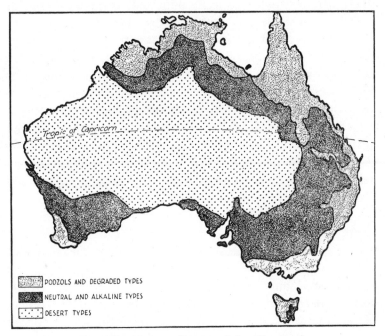

Fig. VII. Major soil zones (after Prescott).

Darling Downs of Queensland and the Wimmera region of
Victoria—are on the dry, inland side of the Dividing Range.
The climate of some of the Darling Downs is risky for agriculture, but that of the Wimmera is reliable. The map of Australia (see Fig. VII) shows the leached soils lying in a zone
roughly parallel to the coast, the unleached and better soils
further inland from this zone, and the desert types—which we
need not consider—still further inland.

This is, of course, a highly generalized picture, from which important details, some favourable and some unfavourable, have purposely been omitted. The crescent-shaped coastal strip of poorer soils includes a great deal of mountainous country which is too rugged for agriculture. Some of this country is vitally important as an area of water catchment; and much of it is also basically important as the main area for producing commercial timber. This rugged country may amount to as much as one-fifth of that part of Australia which has a nine-month season free from drought. It includes not only the Australian Alps, which extend from Mt. Kosciusko in New South Wales through much of the north-east of Victoria, but also many barren tablelands in New South Wales. The south and south-west of Tasmania are particularly rocky and inhospitable. On the other hand, in the same coastal strip small areas of rich soil occur, which are naturally densely settled. These show up in striking contrast to the surrounding areas.

Alluvial river flats mark high levels of fertility along the coast from Melbourne to Cairns. A few isolated patches of volcanic ash, again of small total area, occur in the south-east between Mount Gambier and Melbourne. Deep red soils on plateaus are highly prized from Burnie in Tasmania to Atherton in Queensland—largely for their combination of excellent physical nature and high rainfall. But the main picture for the well-watered coastal country is one of rather poor soils, commonly with an accumulation of heavy clay in the subsoil. Much of this is still under poor scrub or eucalypt forest.

IMPROVEMENT OF POOR SOILS

Low natural fertility, however, can often be remedied if the climate makes it worth while. In Southern Australia there are large areas where good pasture has been established on poor country. Superphosphate is first added to overcome the general deficiency in calcium and phosphorus, and subterranean clover is then sown. This plant is of Mediterraneon origin and has revolutionized agriculture in parts of Australia which receive good winter rains. Given superphosphate, subterranean clover will usually thrive and gradually improve the soil, until land that was once too poor to rear sheep is capable of supporting fat lambs or dairy cows. Even so, superphosphate must continue to be added for many decades. The natural poverty is most acute in Western Australia, where the southwestern corner is one of the most remarkable areas of poor soils in the temperate zones of the world. Both here and in South Australia are large areas for which not only superphosphate but also a light dressing of a copper salt is necessary for the health both of plants and of animals. It is not hard to imagine the low status of any human population which had attempted to live off such country a hundred or more years ago, before the modern knowledge of the effect of fertilizers on plants had been developed.

There are, however, fairly definite limits to the use of superphosphate in building up fertility. The sandstone country which extends from Sydney to Newcastle and inland is both rugged and extremely poor; even its very favourable position close to great centres of population has not led to its use for agriculture. The difficult soils formed on the lava-flows north and west of Melbourne can be worked and improved; but a considerable part of the district, while fairly flat, is too rocky for agriculture.

BETTER (UNLEACHED) SOILS OF DRIER CLIMATES

The belt of better soils ranges from areas of sufficient rainfall nearer the coast—including the pick of the wheat belt—to country which is purely pastoral or which, though dry, can be irrigated. The one general deficiency is phosphorus, though this is not serious in subtropical Queensland and northern

New South Wales. Apart from this, the soils in this drier belt may be described by the Australian expression "f.a.q." (fair average quality). The main exception to this statement is Western Australia, where huge areas to the east of the present wheat belt are hopelessly salty, and where the fair soils of the wheat belt itself are mingled in a complex way with extraordinarily poor sands and gravels, so that wheat farms must cover larger areas than in the eastern States.

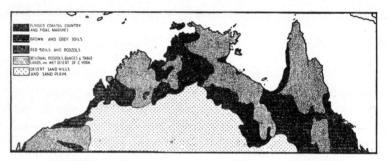

Fig. VIII. Soils of northern Australia (after Prescott).

TROPICAL AUSTRALIA

We know much less of the soils and resources of the northern half of Australia than of the southern half, but it is safe to say that the general story is one of poverty. The wet tropical regions of the world are generally poor. This statement surprises those who hear it for the first time, since the wealth of Java and the luxuriant growth of tropical jungles are common knowledge. Australia, however, contains only a minute area of tropical jungle. Java's cover of volcanic dust, which is so young that the wet climate has not yet impoverished it, is not repeated in the geologically old areas of Northern Australia. Natural erosion is also very important in monsoonal climates, where torrential rain follows a long season of heat and drought. Thus, hills are often devoid of soil, while the river flats are rich. Bare "range" country makes up a large proportion of the total area; and with it we may group the "wet desert" country, in which ironstone covers much of the surface. As in temperate Australia, the better soils lie well away from the coast; in tropical Australia, however, the rich belts lie too far south for sufficient rain to reach them and justify agriculture. These areas are used only for grazing beef cattle. The most interesting soils are the "coastal swamps" at the mouth of some of the larger rivers such as the Daly, Adelaide, and Roper. If these swamps could be drained and the land irrigated, about 3,000 square miles or more might be used for tropical agriculture. If the far north has any agricultural future it is confined to these relatively small areas.

The coastal strip of tropical Queensland, which alone has a rainfall sufficient for tropical agriculture without irrigation, contains the only substantial areas of original dense forest. These lie in the hilly and mountainous country near Cairns and Cooktown. The soils of this whole coastal strip are mostly on the poor side, as one would expect from the heavy rainfall. The naturally good soils have been used intensively; but some of the poorer land still requires scientific experiment before it can be developed.

SOIL EROSION

Australians had been slowly recognizing the seriousness of soil erosion during the few years just before 1939. The position can be summarized under three headings.

(1) Wind erosion has transformed some of the dry inland country into sand dunes and bare clay-pans. This effect is spectacular, but is unimportant because the country is too drought-stricken ever to support more than a very small animal or human population.

(2) Some of the drier wheat-growing country has also suffered from wind-blowing. It is difficult to say how serious and permanent the damage is. The widespread

dust-storms during bad droughts, as in 1944–45, create a popular impression of disaster; yet the main and best established areas have suffered little.

(3) Much more serious is the damage done by run-off in the areas of good rainfall. This is worst where wet spells alternate with drought, and is particularly bad in New South Wales, where wheat is grown on sloping land and summer thunderstorms falling on loose cultivated soil tear away the richest surface layer and carve the country up with steep gullies. Some millions of acres of fairly good land have lost much of their productive value in this way. A similar story can be told of grazing country. Wherever annual droughts are severe, the stock eat the land bare of cover, and heavy rainstorms can then do great damage. Optimistic overstocking and rabbits have both played their part in soil deterioration. Undoubtedly the loss of soil in these districts can be checked; but, meanwhile, much of the very moderate natural wealth of the land is being lost.

DETAILED SURVEYS

Australia has no detailed system of soil survey to be compared with that of the United States. The only region that has been thoroughly mapped is the irrigated land of the Murray and tributaries. Besides this, other areas have been mapped for special purposes—for example, Kangaroo Island, where peculiar problems of soil deficiencies had to be solved. Scientific knowledge of the soils of tropical Australia is much less detailed than that of the south.

Chapter V

PASTURE AND FODDER RESOURCES

BY J. GRIFFITHS DAVIES

Principal Agrostologist

and

C. S. CHRISTIAN

Senior Agrostologist, Division of Plant Industry (C.S.I.R.), Canberra, A.C.T.

THE greater part of Australia lies in the summer-rain zone, mainly monsoonal in type, but the greatest concentration both of population and of livestock is found in the winter-rain areas of the south-east and south-west. On the basis of carrying capacity Australia falls into

(a) a great desert (two-fifths of the total area) which does not and is not likely to carry any stock;

(b) an area of poor pastures carrying sheep or cattle according to the character of the pasture; and

(c) a smaller area carrying a relatively high animal population of varying density.

THE LOW PRODUCTION AREAS

The desert area needs no discussion. The second area, two-fifths of the whole continent, is a wide arc west, north, and east of the desert. Rainfall varies from ten inches a year in the south to as high as forty inches in the northern coastal areas; but here, high evaporation, high winds and the concentration of rainfall in the hot season make for a very low carrying capacity. In this large belt of savannah or open grassland, rainfall is most unreliable; and severe droughts extend sometimes through two, three or more years. At all times, however, the main preoccupation of the pastoralist is water supply for the stock.

The southern or winter-rain portion of this arc carries low-growing vegetation on which mainly sheep are grazed; but in the north the summer rains produce a tall bulky growth which is more suitable for cattle. The carrying capacity is so low that ten acres are required in the southern part of this belt to carry a single merino sheep, and over forty acres of land in the northern part to maintain one head of cattle. As a result the holdings, generally known as "stations," are of great size. In the saltbush sections of South Australia 100 square miles is not enough to enable adequate pasture reserves to be maintained against drought, and to permit the necessary "resting" of land between grazings. In the north cattle stations may be as large as 5,000 to 10,000 square miles. Pastures of such low-carrying capacity demand large areas for efficient operation, and it is this aspect of land holding in Australia which is most misunderstood outside Australia.

Since rainfall is the crucial factor limiting the size of flocks or herds, little or no control can be exercised over the pastures, and so far as science can predict no increase in the number of animals carried can be expected. On the contrary, the tendency is for the animal-land ratio to fall as a result of deterioration of the plant cover owing to over-grazing during droughts and to the wind erosion following the denudation of the surface. Recovery of the "eaten-out" areas is slow; and the outstanding problem of these areas is to prevent exploitative grazing.

The vegetation types on these low-capacity areas vary widely, and are botanically of great interest. A rough classification would divide the whole belt into three regions according to the main type of plant available for stock feed. These are:

1. Saltbush-Bluebush Steppe Lands

In the south, extending from Western Australia around the head of the Great Australian Bight and across South Australia into Victoria and New South Wales, is a belt of "saltbush-bluebush" country (Pl. 3 and 4), comparable in some respects to the sagebrush of the United States. The stock feed mostly on the ephemeral herbage, but in droughts the animals have to fall back on the unattractive but life-sustaining leaves and twigs of the perennial saltbush and bluebush shrubs.

2. Mulga Scrub Lands

North of the saltbush country, in the south-west of Queensland, and in Western Australia from the gold fields around Kalgoorlie to the Murchison, Gascoyne, and Ashburton districts in the extreme north-west, are extensive areas characterised by a low-growing acacia scrub, the mulga (*Acacia aneura*), with ground pasture of low shrubs, grasses and ephemeral herbage (Pl. 5). Drought food reserves are provided by the shrubs and fodder trees, the branches of which are lopped so that the animals can get access to them on the ground.

3. Sub-tropical Grassland

Around the north coast, from Broome to Townsville, is an area of semi-tropical grassland and open forest or savannah, which includes the north-west of Western Australia, the Northern Territory, the Cape York Peninsula of Queensland. This is cattle country, the animals depending largely upon the tall summer-growing grasses of poor value for both summer and winter feed, though certain trees provide "top feed." Throughout this area the low soil fertility and the short growing season resulting from the erratic monsoonal nature of the rainfall prevent any increase above the present rate of stocking.

HIGHER PRODUCTION AREAS

The remaining fifth of the continent, i.e., about 600,000 square miles, which includes all of the rough unproductive country of the east coast highland system known as the Great Divide and of Tasmania, contains most of the highly developed agricultural and pastoral areas. This is the part of Australia, and the only part, for which an increase in animal population can be seriously considered.

This area comprises the south-west corner of the continent from Albany to Geraldton, the eastern coast from Spencer's Gulf in South Australia to Cooktown in Queensland, and the highlands and inland slopes of the Great Divide. The inland boundary of this zone is practically determined by the ten-inch isohyet, except in the Gulf country of north Queensland, where monsoonal rains and impermanence of stock water cause a divergence. In discussing the pasture resources of these higher production areas, the winter-rainfall zone of the south and the summer-rainfall zone of the north will be considered separately.

1. *The Winter-Rainfall Zone*

This zone includes south-eastern New South Wales, most of Victoria and Tasmania, parts of South Australia, and the south-west of Western Australia. The major pasture types are the *Danthonia* grasslands and the pastures on the cleared forest areas (Pl. 6).

(a) *Danthonia Grasslands.* The most important type in this zone is the short grass association which can occur anywhere in the south-east from the ten-inch isohyet to the coast, but which is found at its best development between fifteen and twenty-five inches of rainfall. In Tasmania it is found in the eastern and central districts where twenty to thirty inches of rainfall are usual. This association probably supports more sheep than any other pasture type in Australia. It most commonly occurs as savannah or savannah woodland, but in Western Victoria it is found as treeless grassland. It may also become established in higher rainfall areas after the forest has been cleared, but there the more common practice is to establish mixtures of introduced pasture legumes and grasses.

Like most of the native vegetation, the *Danthonia* grassland is poor in herbaceous legumes, which are so important in maintaining the fertility of the soil and the feeding value of pastures. However, this association has been invaded by numerous annual exotic clovers and medics of Mediterranean origin, and these now form an important element of the pastures. These small but valuable plants have a short growing season, but are heavy seeders. Seeds of the medics and of subterranean clover are produced in pods or "burrs," which are highly nutritious. The dried burrs remain on the ground as a reserve food supply throughout the dry summers and are readily eaten by the sheep. Some of the medic burrs cling to the wool and shorn fleece, and have to be eliminated by carbonization before the wool can be processed, but this disadvantage does not seriously detract from their value in the pastures.

In the *Danthonia* association there occur many other perennial and annual grasses and herbage plants which contribute to the food supply according to the locality and season. One of the most interesting is the Kangaroo grass (*Themeda australis*), practically identical with the Rooi grass of the South African veldt. *Danthonia* and *Stipa* (spear-grass) will stand heavy grazing by sheep, but the Kangaroo grass quickly disappears. It was much more plentiful in earlier times, when native marsupials were the only grazing animals. The average stock-carrying capacity of *Danthonia* grassland is about a sheep to the acre but may be more or less according to the rainfall.

(b) *Pastures of Cleared Forests.* In the higher rainfall areas agriculture follows the clearing of the eucalypt forests. These areas all receive more than twenty inches of rain a year, but mostly between thirty and forty-five inches; and they have a much longer growing season and a more reliable rainfall than the sheep country. Dairying is the main industry, and the herds are maintained out of doors throughout the year. The industry is based on introduced pasture plants of the temperate grasslands of Europe, supplemented by fodder crops such as lucerne (alfalfa), winter cereals and maize. There is a noticeable absence of the use of root crops.

2. The Summer-Rainfall Zone

The major portions of this zone lie in central and south-eastern Queensland, continuing into the northern half of New South Wales. There are several distinct regions, but all have in common the characteristic rapid growth following summer rains, and an equally characteristic deterioration in feeding quality once the plants have reached maturity.

(a) *Inland Pastures of the South*. North of the inland *Danthonia* short-grass pastures of the winter rainfall zone, there is an extension of somewhat similar pastures differing mainly in the occurrence of numerous other species, of which many are summer-growing.[1] Exotic annual legumes have become very useful. The mixture of summer- and winter-growing species in this area provides continuous grazing which is reflected in the stock-carrying capacity.

(b) *The Mitchell Grass Pastures*. The Mitchell grass pastures of western Queensland and parts of New South Wales are distinctly Australian in character. They occur discontinuously from near the Gulf of Carpentaria, south-easterly to Charleville, and again from Cunnamulla to the Darling

---

[1] Red grass (*Bothriochloa ambigua*), Wire grasses (*Aristida* spp.), Tussock grass (*Poa* spp.), and Windmill grass (*Chloris* spp.) are the main secondary grasses on the New England plateau. In the drier western section of New South Wales, Queensland Blue grass (*Dicanthium sericeum*), Kangaroo grass, Australian Millet (*Panicum decompositum*), Umbrella grass (*Digitaria divaricatissima*), Early Spring grass (*Eriochloa* spp.) Sugar Grass (*Eulalia fulva*), Warrego Summer grass (*Paspalidium jubiflorum*), and the Love grasses (*Eragrostis* spp.) all occur commonly.

Downs. They are also found in parts of western New South Wales, in Western Australia in the South Kimberley district, and on the Barkly Tableland in the Northern Territory.

The Mitchell grasses [2] are the most characteristic species in this association, but numerous other species [3] occur quite commonly. Like the Mitchell grass these form perennial tussocks in a very open stand, the bare spaces between them being occupied by a large variety of annual herbage after suitable rains.

The average annual rainfall in the Mitchell grass area varies from ten inches to twenty-five inches, but it is extremely erratic both in amount and in distribution. For example, at Roma in Queensland, the annual rainfall has varied from nine and one-half inches to sixty inches in a period of forty years. The time of year at which the rains occur determines the nature of the ephemeral herbage; and this country can offer totally different pictures in different years according to the nature of the rainfall. This variability makes it difficult to regulate the number of animals grazed, and the grazier has to expect, from time to time, severe droughts and floods. The summer ephemerals [4] contribute three-fourths of the comparatively low yield of ten to twenty hundredweight per acre of dry fodder produced in the best seasons. As the rains normally occur over relatively short periods, the bulk of the feed is produced in a few weeks of rapid growth. In the absence of further rains this growth matures and persists as valuable standing hay which will maintain the stock throughout the winter. Light following rains may destroy the hay, but when good rains occur in late summer or autumn an abundant growth of winter herbage plants [5] occurs.

[2] *Astrebla* spp., four species.
[3] Such as Queensland Blue grass (*Dicanthium sericeum*), Brown Top, and Never Fail (*Eragrostis* sp.).
[4] Mostly annual grasses such as Flinders grass (*Iseilema* spp.), and Button grass (*Dactyloctenium radulans*).
[5] Such as *Plantago, Daucus, Erodium* and the annual medics.

The drier Mitchell grass areas in the west and south of Queensland and in New South Wales are used almost entirely for the production of wool. The rate of stocking varies from one sheep to two acres to one sheep to ten acres. To the north and north-east, either sheep and cattle or cattle alone may be run. One interesting feature of the Mitchell grass areas is the occurrence of a wide variety of native fodder trees such as the myall, belah, boonery, mulga, wilga, budda, which are a valuable source of feed in drought periods.

(c) *Coastal Pastures*. The eastern coast of Australia, from south of Sydney to the far north of Queensland, is an area of high rainfall (25 to 140 inches per annum) in which islands of fertile soils occur within larger areas of very low fertility. The latter are covered with a mixed eucalypt forest and rarely repay the costs of clearing, but are used for cattle at a low rate of stocking. The areas of better soils are used for dairying and mixed farming, and, in parts of Queensland, for sugar production. In the south, the pastures consist mainly of introduced plants.[6] In North Queensland, tropical grasses [7] are the main sown species. The pastures of the Atherton Tableland in North Queensland are similar to those of the southern and central sections of the East Coast.

The use of fodder crops such as maize, sorghums, Sudan grass for soiling or silage, lucerne for hay or pasturage, and cowpeas, is an essential part of farm economy in this area. Dairy cattle are the main stock carried on the coastal pastures, but in recent years there has been an increase in the number of beef stock fattened, particularly in the north.

(d) *Sub-coastal Pastures*. Between the coastal pastures and the inland pastures of southern and central Queensland, and skirting the Darling Downs of southern Queensland, is the sub-coastal belt with a rainfall of twenty-five to forty inches per

[6] *Paspalum dilatatum*, the Dallis grass of the United States, and white clover (*T. repens*).

[7] Such as Para grass (*Brachiaria mutica*), Molasses grass (*Melinis minutiflora*) and Guinea grass (*Panicum maximum*).

annum. This area contains poorer soils covered with open eucalypt forest [8] interspersed with well-defined patches of better soils covered with dense scrub. These scrubs are of two kinds; the softwood forests, similar to rain forest and acacia scrub, the main species being the Brigalow (*Acacia harpophylla*) from which this type of scrub receives its name. In the Brigalow scrubs few grasses are found until the scrub is cleared, when a variety of grasses collectively known as Brigalow grasses, with *Paspalidium* as the major genus, establish on the bare land.

The better soils are used for dairying and mixed farming, or for cattle fattening (Pl. 12). The scrub is rung and later burnt. It is then ploughed, if it is to be used for cropping, but the most common practice is to sow down Rhodes grass (*Chloris gayana*) on the ashes. In the southern Brigalow areas burning early after ringing leads to extensive suckering and re-establishment of the Brigalow. There the practice is to refrain from burning and to allow the native grasses to establish. Such land is used for sheep.

Much of this country was, until recently, covered with the introduced prickly pear (*Opuntia* spp.) to the extent of 60,-000,000 acres, half of which was popularly described as so dense that "a dog could not bark in it." It is only within the last twenty years that this pest, which had reduced the value of the land to practically nothing, has been successfully eradicated, mainly by its introduced natural insect enemies *Cactoblastis cactorum* and the cochineal insects.

The open forest country (Pl. 8) is used mainly for cattle, often in conjunction with the intermixed areas of scrub-land sown to Rhodes grass. Rhodes grass does not persist so well on forest soils as on the scrub soils and is less often sown on them. The better forest soils may be cultivated and used for mixed farming and dairying. The cotton-growing section of

[8] In the forest country the main grasses are Forest Blue (*Bothriochloa intermedia*) and Pitted Blue (*B. decipiens*).

Queensland is in this area, and the alternation of cotton growing with Rhodes grass for dairying is a recommended practice.

Dairying may be practised on Rhodes grass pastures alone; but the most successful procedure where the topography permits is to use them in conjunction with fodder crops such as maize, sorghum, winter cereals in the south, lucerne, and cowpeas. Sorghums for grain have become of increasing importance in recent years. Rhodes grass pastures may persist for twenty to thirty years, but most of them are now showing signs of deterioration. This is no doubt due in part to the almost complete absence of legumes and to the frequent burning of the grass which is necessary to remove the accumulated debris. Fodder legumes in rotation with Rhodes grass are likely to play an important part in the future.

New Rhodes grass pastures will fatten one cattle beast to two acres; but the rate of stocking is reduced to one beast to four acres or more in older pastures. As Rhodes grass pastures are used in conjunction with forest country, the average rate of stocking for this zone is much lower. The forest country alone carries one beast to ten to thirty acres.

(e) *The Darling Downs.* The Darling Downs is an undulating plateau of fertile soil extending south and west of Toowoomba in Queensland. It has an average rainfall of twenty-five to thirty inches per annum. Native pastures consist mainly of the Blue grasses, which are summer growing, but there is a mixture of the southern winter-growing species. The pastures yield heavily in summer, but their quality is poor and they require supplementing with fodder crops in winter. Annual medics have become established in this area and provide valuable feed in seasons when good autumn rains fall.

The area is devoted to wheat and barley growing, mixed farming and dairying, the larger properties specializing in cattle fattening. Sheep fattening and a small amount of fat lamb production is carried on in conjunction with wheat growing; but the area is generally better suited to dairying which is based on the use of summer fodder crops and winter cereals.

Constant cultivation has brought about a loss of fertility and soil structure even of these very rich black soils; and it is probable that sown pastures will play an important role in stabilizing agriculture in the future.

(f) *Spear Grass Pastures.* Between Rockhampton and Ayr, and extending inland, and in some areas south of this zone, there occur the spear grass pastures of Queensland.[9] The pastures are of poor quality, excepting in the young stages; and are frequently burnt to remove the matured growth. This is cattle country only and has a low rate of stocking—about one beast to twenty to forty acres—and there is yet no known way of improving its productivity.

(g) *The Gulf Country.* Along the courses of the rivers flowing into the Gulf of Carpentaria is an area of tall grass country which is used for cattle. The rainfall varies from twenty to forty-five inches. The grasses consist of spear grass, annual sorghums, and other tall species, all summer growing. It also needs from twenty to forty acres to maintain a beast.

IRRIGATED PASTURES

The chief irrigation areas in Australia occur in the Murray River system, with the greatest development at present in Victoria. An extension on the Murrumbidgee in New South Wales is in progress. South Australia has scattered areas along the Murray; and Victoria, New South Wales, South Australia, Western Australia and Queensland have a number of smaller schemes. Most of them were intended for the production of fruits and crops; but there are now about 380,000 acres of irri-

[9] These consist of open ironbark forests on the ridges with black spear grass (*Heteropogon contortus*) as the characteristic pasture species. In the valleys the ironbarks give way to other species of eucalypts, and pitted blue grass takes the place of the spear grass.

gated land in Victoria used for pasture and fodder crops, mainly lucerne. In New South Wales 144,000 acres are irrigated for dairying and fat lamb production; and further use of irrigated land for pasture is likely to be made in the future. Water supplies, however, are far too limited for any large expansion of irrigation, though there exist huge tracts of land which could be so used.

THE IMPROVEMENT OF PASTURES

The improvement of pastures requires capital for seeding, fertilising, fencing and the provision of stock water. It is economic only where the potential carrying capacity of the land is high enough to cover this expenditure. In Australia it is feasible only in areas of higher and reliable rainfall, or where irrigation is possible. Judged by annual rainfall, the area on which pasture improvement would be practicable is probably not much more than half a million square miles, say one-sixth of the total area of Australia.

Much research into methods of pasture improvement has been conducted in Australia, but most of this has been concentrated in the southern winter-rainfall areas. Pasture improvement requires the establishment of suitable species, the addition of the appropriate fertilisers where soils are deficient, and the development of efficient methods of managing the established pasture.

1. *Winter-Rainfall Pastures*

For the winter-rainfall pasture areas suitable species are now available. A satisfactory pasture mixture consists of a perennial grass to provide stability, and a legume to raise the feeding value of the pasturage and to improve or maintain soil fertility. Where rainfall is liberal, the recognized pasture species of the cool temperate climates of Europe have proved satisfactory.

For areas with lower rainfall and a shorter growing season, subterranean clover is the common legume, with *Phalaris tuberosa* as the perennial grass.[10] (Pl. 11.) Subterranean clover is the most important pasture legume Australia possesses at present. It is a self-regenerating annual species of which a large number of naturally occurring strains exist. By a suitable selection of these, it has been possible to extend its use to areas with as little as 17½ inches of rain a year, and with an effective rainfall season as short as five to six months. It is adapted to more acid soils than most legumes, and for this reason is of particular value on the large areas of podsolised soils of low fertility.[11] A somewhat comparable group of winter-growing legumes are the annual medics.[12] These are of particular value in wheat areas where they are common constituents of the pasture "phase" of wheat land cultivation.

One characteristic of the southern pasture areas is the almost universal response which is obtained from the use of superphosphate. Top-dressing with this fertiliser is a necessary preliminary, and adjunct, to the establishment and maintenance of subterranean clover and other legumes. Before the war, more than four million acres of Australian pasture lands were top-dressed with artificial fertilisers, most of which would include superphosphate.

Apart from phosphate, other deficiencies occur in soils of these areas. Nitrogen is usually short, but this is overcome by the satisfactory establishment of legumes. Small applications of potash have been found necessary in parts of Victoria,

---

[10] Perennial ryegrass (*Lolium perenne*) and White clover (*Trifolium repens*), with Cocksfoot (*Dactylis glomerata*) and Red clover (*Trifolium pratense*) as alternative or additional species in more favourable locations, are widely grown in the southern States. Strawberry clover (*Trifolium fragiferum*) also has a limited use on wet or irrigated lands.

[11] Subterranean clover is adapted to large areas in Victoria, New South Wales, South Australia, Tasmania and Western Australia, but its use does not extend to the summer rainfall areas.

[12] *M. denticulata* and its varieties; *Medicago minima, M. laciniata, M. tribuloides*, and related species.

and in some soils of New South Wales and Victoria lime also is used in connection with superphosphate. Deficiencies in minor elements such as copper, cobalt, zinc and molybdenum occur in several areas, particularly on the coast of Western Australia and South Australia; and, unless these elements are supplied, the growth of the pastures and crops is reduced and certain pathological conditions in the stock result. Copper deficiency is now regarded as the cause of "steely" wool produced in parts of Victoria and South Australia, while copper and cobalt are associated in producing the "coast disease" in South Australia. Molybdenum deficiency has now been detected as the cause of poor growth of Subterranean clover in some lateritic soils of Tasmania and South Australia, and of borderline growth of lucerne near Canberra.

With suitable pasture species available for most of the winter-rainfall areas, backed by an increasing knowledge of soil requirements, the remaining problems are mainly those associated with efficient management of the pastures. There is scope for further improvement in methods both of grazing management and of fodder conservation.

2. *Summer-Rainfall Pastures*

Pasture improvement has not reached the same stage of development in the summer-rainfall areas as it has in the southern part of Australia. For example, in 1938–39, Queensland had only half the area of sown grasses of Victoria, although the latter State has an estimated grass area suitable for pasture improvement of only twenty-five to thirty per cent of that of Queensland.

Whereas in the winter-rainfall areas of Australia the pasture species already well known in other parts of the world are established successfully, new species and new methods must be sought for the summer-rainfall areas. The very low fertility of many of the soils associated with heavy summer-rainfall conditions has presented an additional problem.

The chief defect of the summer-rainfall pastures is the absence of pasture legumes. White clover is used extensively along the coastal belt, especially towards the south. Its use does not extend far to the north in Queensland, nor away from the coast, although it does appear on the nearby highlands of southern Queensland, and the Atherton Tableland in the north. *Paspalum dilatatum* is the perennial grass used in conjunction with White clover, and both species have become naturalized. (Pl. 12.)

In the southern inland portions of the summer-rainfall areas where the pastures inter-grade with those of the south, the annual medics are important components of the winter herbage of the black and grey soils of New South Wales and southern Queensland, but they are of very limited value north of this.

Lucerne is used to some extent at low rates of seeding in the north-west of New South Wales, and it promises to have a definite but limited value in southern Queensland and on the highlands. Certain legumes of tropical origin have shown promise on the far northern coast of Queensland, but the extent of their use and application has yet to be determined. There is no legume of importance comparable to those that are available for winter-rainfall pastures. This has hampered the development of pasture improvement more than any other factor. There are undoubtedly numerous soil problems also, but the most obvious one is that of nitrogen deficiency, which can be overcome on large areas only by the use of a satisfactory legume.

There are several introduced perennial grasses which are of importance in the summer-rainfall areas. Apart from *Paspalum* on the coast, Rhodes grass is widely planted in the subcoastal belt south of Rockhampton. It is sown without an accompanying legume on scrub soils following ringing, and burning of the scrub timber. On these particular soils it persists well for many years, but sooner or later shows signs of lowered soil fertility. When planted on the nearby forest soils of lower initial soil fertility the grass lasts for a few years only.[13]

Very little is known at present regarding the soil problems associated with the summer-rainfall pastures or of the best systems of pasture management. In the absence of stable and balanced pasture mixtures for the summer-rainfall areas, it is not surprising that there is little information available regarding improved methods of pasture management and utilization. Pastoralists have developed methods to suit their varied conditions, but these are frequently determined by problems associated with large holdings or inadequate stock water supplies, as well as by deficiencies in the pastures themselves.

FODDER RESOURCES

The major fodder resources of Australia are crops grown for hay, green forage, or silage, cereal grains and the by-products of other primary industries such as molasses from cane sugar, beet pulp, linseed meal, cottonseed meal, etc.

The conservation of hay and fodder is restricted to the better rainfall areas. In good seasons the pastoral areas often produce comparatively high yields of herbage, but the uncertainty of its production, together with other practical difficulties, has not encouraged its conservation on a large scale, and drought feeding depends upon the use of concentrated foods, such as lucerne, hay, grains, and protein concentrates, produced in better rainfall areas. Of a total area of about three million acres sown for fodder crops, more than eighty per cent is for wheat or oaten hay. Another two million acres is sown for green forage.

Very little cereal or pasture hay is produced in the true

[13] On the tropical coast of northern Queensland, Para grass (*Brachiaria mutica*), Molasses grass (*Melinis minutiflora*), and Guinea grass (*Panicum maximum*) are the major grasses sown.

summer-rainfall zone; their place is taken by crops for green forage, and to a lesser extent, by summer-growing hay crops such as lucerne and Sudan grass. Green forage becomes of increasing importance because summer rains often make conditions unsuitable for hay making, and the winter cereal crops do not grow so satisfactorily.

The major summer-growing green forage crops are maize, sorghums (Pl. 13), Sudan grass, and lucerne. Maize is grown on fertile soils along most of the coastal belt of Queensland and New South Wales, and in the sub-coastal areas of southern Queensland. It extends inland in parts of New South Wales, and it is also grown to a lesser extent in Gippsland in Victoria. Very little is grown in South Australia, Western Australia or Tasmania.

Sorghums are more confined to the north than maize. Lucerne is used extensively for green forage in New South Wales and Queensland. Field peas in winter-rainfall areas, and cowpeas in summer-rainfall areas are the other major legume crops used for green forage. Soybeans have been tried in a number of localities but with very little success, and they are yet of no great importance in any part of the Commonwealth.

Chapter VI

THE DEVELOPMENT AND PRESENT LIMITA-
TIONS OF THE AUSTRALIAN SHEEP
INDUSTRY

BY HEDLEY R. MARSTON

*Chief of Division of Biochemistry and General Nutrition, Council for
Scientific and Industrial Research*

THE GROWTH and development of the pastoral industry and the
present limitations of wool production are of primary importance in a study of Australian development. While it would
be a risky or even careless enterprise to speculate as to how far
artificial fibres may shift wool from its pride of place in the
textile industry, the competition by wool substitutes, and so
the immediate future of the wool-producing industry, seems
to bear rather heavily on the cost of production of wool. This,
in turn, depends not a little on the natural limitations imposed
by the environment in which the flocks are grazed. In the brief
treatment which follows, an attempt is made to inform the
reader of the development of the Australian merino and the
fine wool producing industry, of existing disabilities, and of
the ways in which pastoralists are dealing with them.

THE EVOLUTION OF THE AUSTRALIAN MERINO

The Australian merino originated, as its name implies, from
the great Spanish merino flocks.[1] These small, loose-skinned

[1] The Negrettis, the Escurials, the Muros Aquierres, the Montarcos, the
Infantados, and the Paulars were the main cabañas controlled by the
Council of the Mesta during the period when Spain monopolized fine wool
production.

76

animals, densely covered with short, very fine wool, were stabilized in their individual flocks by inbreeding, and all were accustomed to the good living of an easy nomadic existence provided by their migration each year between the Castilian Highlands and the fields of Estramadura.

Until the end of the eighteenth century Spain held a close monopoly of fine wool production: export of breeding stock was punishable by death. The seal was broken in 1765 when the King of Spain presented a small flock of Escurials to his cousin, the Elector of Hanover. In the next twenty years Louis XVI, under similar circumstances, had established a flock at Rambouillet, George III had imported Negrettis to Windsor, and a few Escurials had found their way via Holland to the Cape. Within forty years the Mesta cabañas were finally disrupted. During the Peninsular War the sheep that escaped capture by Napoleon's army were confiscated, sold and dispersed. The King of England received 4,000 Paulars; many others from the famous flocks were taken to America, and from them the Vermont strain developed.

The quality and quantity of Spanish fine wool declined precipitately and the English looms were supplied from Germany, where the original Escurials, fortified with Negretti and Infantado blood, laid the foundation of the Saxon and Silesian strains and, under the new conditions, produced finer, better spinning wool than that of their Spanish forbears.

The original Australian merino types were evolved from the scattered Mesta flocks. In the first years of settlement of New South Wales a few intractable Irish, and coarse, hairy, Indian sheep, which had been introduced for rations, came into the possession of Captain MacArthur. He put an Irish ran with some Bengal ewes and "had the satisfaction to see the lambs . . . bear a mingled fleece of hair and wool." This experiment produced the first Australian studmaster. His impetuous imagination was stimulated to envisage a fine wool-producing industry: little labour was required, and it provided an opportunity for the colony "to pay its ransome and win its way to freedom." He set about it with unrestrained vigour and in 1797 procured the sheep he wanted—a few Escurials from Colonel Gordon's flock in South Africa, and these he supplemented later with ewes and rams, mainly Paulars, from the Royal Stud at Kew (England).

In a few years MacArthur's "abstruse speculations" had borne fruit: the first shipment of wool from the colony was adjudged by English buyers as "equal to the best Saxon," and the industry was launched. Exploration told of boundless grasslands beyond the mountain passes, and on these abundant pastures the industry gained momentum. Settlement spread rapidly "undirected by the fostering care of Government," much to the distress of the Colonial Office. But wool brought prosperity and population; Bradford and the new colony flourished together.

Breeding fine-woolled sheep became a consuming passion. The best merino strains obtainable were imported and infused with that of the original colonial merinos, and from this mixture a variety of types was evolved. In an attempt to increase density of fleece the wrinkled Vermonts were introduced and, with them, characteristics which studmasters since have been at pains to eliminate.

Attracted by the siren call "better land further out" the pastoralists invaded the semi-arid regions. Here the small-framed, fine-wooled merinos did less well. They had neither the constitution to range far from water, nor the ability to deal with the harsher fodder: something more substantial was needed for this environment. The second stage of the evolution of the modern Australian merino was thus initiated. Stimulated by the obvious want, studmasters crossed the fine merino with the stronger Leicester and Lincoln breeds, and from the new assemblage of genes, large-framed, plain-bodied Australian merinos were selected. Although potentially strong-woolled, the new types proved capable of producing under parsimonious feeding conditions a bulky and profitable fleece of medium fine wool.

The result of this intermingling of delicate Spanish weft with the vigorous British yeoman warp has led to the displacement of the pure merino blood in many areas. Attention which previously had been focussed on fineness of fleece,

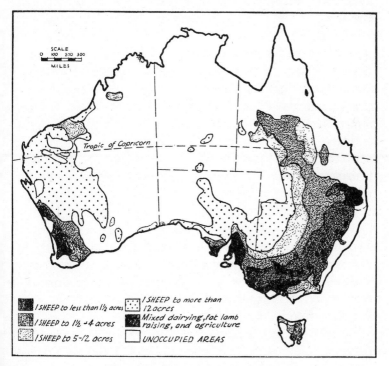

Fig. IX. Distribution of sheep.

shifted to strength of constitution and the value of individual fleece production. Australian merino types now extend from the ultra fine, practically pure Spanish blood, as represented by the Tasmanian and Victorian varieties, to the large-framed, strong-woolled animals as represented by the Peppin and South Australian types. All find their special uses in the vast diversity of grazing country of Australia, and provide a splendid flexible wool-producing stock.

LIMITATIONS IMPOSED BY DROUGHT

The rate of expansion of the pastoral industry reached its peak in the nineties of the last century. A period of good seasons and profitable returns had bred over-confidence, and exuberance carried development beyond the inexorable limits imposed by the natural environment. Water reserves were no longer sufficient to provide for rainless periods of any considerable duration, and cataclysm supervened with the widespread droughts at the close of the century. Sheep numbers were reduced by fifty-odd million to half of the 1891 peak, and there were lean times for all in Australia. The pastoralists henceforth hurried more slowly. Chastened by the dread hand of drought, they built more dams and tapped more frequently the artesian supply. Fodder and not drinking water then became the primary limiting factor, and droughts subsequently took a lesser toll. But thirty years elapsed before the 106 million peak of 1891 was reached again, and, with another ten years of cautious expansion, the sheep population increased to 120 millions, which apparently is about the limit of the sheep-carrying capacity of the natural pastures of the Australian Continent.

The efficient utilization of the vast grassland areas which suffer periodic spells of drought is a major problem. Concentrated fodder suitable for supporting the flocks when the pastures are completely eaten out may be produced in quantity in the coastal areas of high and secure rainfall, and may be stored until required. The costs of the foodstuffs and their transport over the vast distances involved, however, render drought feeding for any considerable period a doubtful venture, and for most part the only sheep that are hand-fed during drought are the valuable breeding stock. The losses supervening on

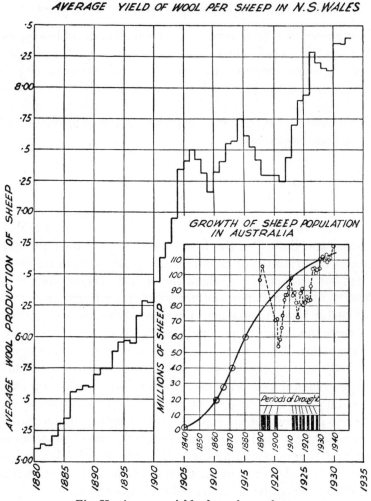

Fig. X. Average yield of wool per sheep.

The main figure indicates the increase of annual average wool production per sheep since 1880. Data provided in *Dalgety's Annual Wool Review, 1935–1936* have been computed in 5-year moving averages which tend to smooth out fluctuations due to seasonal influence. Since the beginning of the century the steady increase in individual fleece weights is due entirely to the improvement of the wool-producing capacity of the Australian Merino. During the major part of the period the nutritional level of the natural pastures has tended to decline rather than improve. The inset shows the growth of the sheep population in Australia. The trend takes the usual sigmoid form of the growth of populations. The broken line shows the fluctuation of the sheep population over the past 50 years due to drought. The periods of widespread drought from 1890 to 1930 are blocked in along the time ordinate.

drought when spread over more favoured years add between ten and fifteen per cent to the overall costs of wool production. Scientific research has indicated the minimum rations necessary to maintain sheep for indefinite periods, and a scheme of fodder production for drought relief which is commensurate with the economic importance of the industry awaits large-scale organization.

LIMITATIONS IMPOSED BY THE NUTRITIONAL ENVIRONMENT

The sheep carrying capacity of the natural grazing lands of Australia is limited in the first instance by the quantity and seasonal distribution of rainfall. In the greater part of the two-thirds of the continent where the annual average rainfall is less than twenty inches, and not all of that effective, the land is suitable only for grazing. There wool production remains supreme, and the sheep population is likely to decline only where the rabbit cannot be controlled effectively. The main bulk of the clip is produced, however, on more favoured country, and here the carrying capacity is being steadily increased as soil fertility is built up by phosphatic manurial dressings and the sowing down of appropriate pasture species. Under such circumstances wool enters more directly into competition with other agricultural products. The size of individual holdings tends to decrease, and settlement becomes closer with the establishment of the many-legged economy of mixed farming. In the drier areas subdivision of the vast holdings, as a rule, has not proved successful. Attempts to settle individual families on sections of 50,000 acres of the saltbush have resulted not infrequently in the selectors retiring after a few years in a cloud of dust, themselves ruined along with the country they sought to conquer.

Nutritional problems associated with wool production resolve into two general classes, those concerned with the supply of materials for conversion to wool fleece, and those concerned with materials essential for maintenance of the health of the sheep. The marked influence which the different available fodders are capable of exerting on the type and amount of fleece produced by sheep of identical breeding when depastured on the variety of terrain and subjected to the wide range of climatic conditions of the Australian Continent, is mainly attributable to the capacity of different pastures to provide the raw materials for conversion to wool. The wool-producing propensity of the modern merino has outpaced the capacity of most natural pastures, which would more than have fulfilled the modest nutritional requirements of its primitive forbears. Sheep and wool statistics are eloquent of the great improvement brought about by selection and management of the flocks. The steady increase of the average wool production of the Australian merino is a measure primarily of its efficiency, and not by any means of its total capacity for wool production. Material increase of individual fleece weights may be expected to continue together with increase in sheep numbers, as modern methods of pasture improvement are applied more extensively.

Since the earliest settlement, sheep depastured continuously on the calcareous dunes which constitute much of the coastal areas of Southern Australia were known to decline after a few months and die if left there, notwithstanding the plentiful pastures. The discovery that a minute quantity of soluble salts of the heavy metal, cobalt, would dramatically restore the health of sheep affected by a sojourn on these deficient tracts has opened a new chapter in the development of southern Australia. Very widely dispersed areas, well favoured with rainfall, have been recognized to be limited in their productivity by deficiencies of cobalt, copper, and zinc within the soils. When relatively small quantities of the missing minor elements are added to superphosphate and applied as manurial dressings, this poor country will produce excellent pastures

WOOL VALUE FLUCTUATION

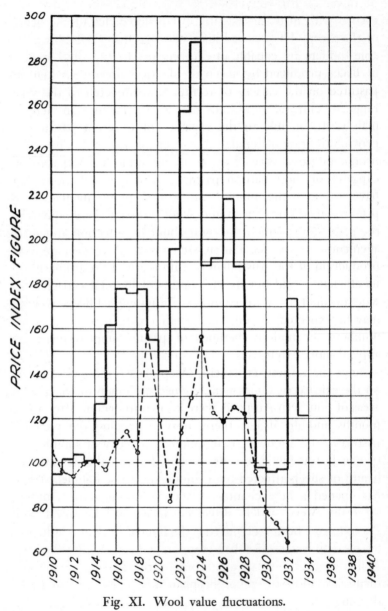

Fig. XI. Wool value fluctuations.

and support healthy flocks and herds. The provision of cobalt and copper to the flocks allows the conduct of profitable sheep farming in areas where previously sheep would all die of deficiency disease within a year, and on the very much more extensive copper-deficient areas periodic treatment of the flocks with this element has resulted in extraordinary improvement in the quality and quantity of the wool produced. A new era of agricultural development in southern Australia has come into being.

Increase in the carrying capacity of the extensive grasslands of the sub-tropical summer-rainfall areas awaits the development of a technique of pasture improvement. In some areas the plant associations which provided splendid pasturage have reverted through injudicious stocking to more primitive and less nutritious types. There can be no reasonable doubt, however, that production from these areas may in future be increased when scientific research devotes itself more vigorously to the agricultural problems of subtropical and semi-arid regions.

The nutritional environment of the natural pastures of Australia, which limits the sheep-grazing capacity to approximately 120 millions, is being improved materially, and with this improvement sheep numbers and individual wool production may confidently be expected to increase.

Fig. XI. Wool value fluctuations.

The fluctuating price levels of Merino wool during the war and post-war period are shown in the figures. This has been drawn up from data presented in *Bulletin 29, Comm. Cur. Census and Statistics,* the average price for the quinquennium 1909–1913 = 100 being used as the basis for comparison. The broken line indicates the relationship between Merino wool price index and the general commodity price index (Sauerbeck). The points are computed by dividing the mean quarterly London market price of Merino wool (Botany 66's clean scoured basis) by the Sauerbeck index and reducing to the base 1909–1913 = 100. The data are from *Wool Survey, Statistical and Intelligence Branch of E.M.B., 1932.* The ratio of the wool price level to the price level of other commodities as indicated by this index was remarkably constant during the decennial interval prior to 1914. The wide oscillations since 1918 have been, to an important extent, the result of the fluctuations in money values. Wool is particularly prone to price fluctuations owing to the relative inelasticity of supply.

LIMITATIONS IMPOSED BY PESTS AND HAZARDS

The predatory dingo, the bane of the squatters' flocks, has been driven back to the dead heart of the Continent. Shut off from the main grazing areas by dog-proof fences and with a high price on its head, the only large Australian carnivore has been controlled by heroic measures and no longer despoils the flocks.

The apparently innocent European rabbit, introduced and jealously guarded by the early settlers, found the Australian environment to its liking and multiplied to plague dimensions. In the more closely settled areas, netting boundary fences, control measures, and unremitting vigilance now restrain its destructiveness. Even here the control has been, and still is, a costly and anxious business. In the less productive semi-arid regions, however, the procedures adopted with success elsewhere are not feasible, and there, when fodder no longer limits its fecundity, the rabbit, with its short gestation and capacity for multiple births, takes an overwhelming toll of the new vegetation that follows the infrequent effective rains. The delicately poised balance of nature, already rendered unstable by the introduction of the sheep, is upset; the soil surface, denuded of permanent vegetation, is beginning to drift, and tragedy is "surely descending on that unhappy and much abused land." The tendency towards injudicious stocking may be disciplined, but at this juncture hopes of controlling the rabbit in the sparsely populated inland are not bright. One might be more sanguine had the large-scale tests with *Myxomatosis cuniculi* proved more encouraging. This extraordinarily infectious virus disease, harmless to all other animals but capable of maintaining its fatal virulence for the rabbit, apparently will not effectively limit the numbers when liberated in the warrens of arid Australia; and this in spite of the fact that the stickfast flea which infests the rabbits is an efficient vector. The failure of what is seemingly an ideal epizootic has grave implications for the future of the inland grazing resources.

The ubiquitous sheep blowfly is perhaps the most obviously troublesome and costly pest of the pastoral industry. It accounts for huge losses of stock, and a great deal of labour is required to combat the results of its activity. As attempts to limit the fly population by means of appropriate parasites have not been successful, other less direct measures are being exploited. The recognition that conformation of the breech causes soiling of the wool and so renders the merino prone to attack by the fly, has led to the adoption of operative means to overcome the anatomical disabilities introduced unwittingly along with other more desirable characteristics. The act of healing after removal of crescent-shaped flaps of skin from either side of the breech enlarges, by stretching, the hairless area; and when its stern is tidied up in this way the merino is less attractive to the fly and, if struck, the breech region no longer provides a good medium for the development of the maggot. A simple and effective palliative is thus available while selective breeding is evolving a more desirable conformation.

Internal parasites, especially the varieties of blood-sucking worms which infest and irritate the mucous membrane of the alimentary canal, impose a serious limitation on wool production in the more densely populated grazing areas. Various methods of control have mitigated the serious loss of efficiency from this cause. The recent discovery of the extraordinary general effectiveness of phenothiazine when administered as a vermifuge, promises results as important in this field as those exerted by the sulphanilamide drugs in the province of zymotic disease. Similarly, the diseases which infect sheep are now better understood and, for the most part, efficient means of control have been discovered.

In all, the serious limitations imposed by pests, parasites, and disease are becoming of less consequence as, one by one, they are being controlled effectively by the application of knowledge provided by scientific research.

In 1926 the Commonwealth Government established the Council for Scientific and Industrial Research, whose basic task is to conduct scientific research. The organization devoted its attention first to agricultural and pastoral problems and has contributed greatly to the increased efficiency of the pastoral industry in the last decade. Generous gifts from individuals, and from organizations such as the George Aitken Pastoral Research Trust and the Australian Wool Board have augmented the funds provided by the Government.

In 1935 the Wool Use Promotions Act rendered available approximately £350,000 per annum for scientific research concerned directly with the production and utilization of wool. This, together with the sums previously available, brings the total sum expended on research to about one per cent of the value of the wool clip.

Chapter VII

THE PLACE OF WOOL IN THE AUSTRALIAN ECONOMY

BY IAN CLUNIES ROSS

Professor of Veterinary Science, University of Sydney, formerly Chairman, International Wool Secretariat, London

WOOL IS WOVEN into the whole fabric of Australia's economic life. Although, as the wheat and dairying industries have expanded and vigorous secondary industries have developed, wool growing is no longer of such dominating importance as formerly, vast tracts in the drier inland areas still depend upon wool for profitable occupation. For much of the interior there is no other use than for wool growing. Upon wool hundreds of small inland towns as well as many large ones depend for their existence; railways and roads find justification in wool; banks and other institutions rely upon wool for their stability; the financial system of the Commonwealth rests upon wool as the main source of its overseas funds.

Before the war wool made up forty-two per cent of the value of all exports from Australia. In this one commodity Australia holds undisputed primacy both in quality and quantity. Her flocks total about 120 millions, or one-sixth of all the world's sheep. They grow more than a quarter of all the world's wool, one-third of the world's clothing wool, one-half of the world's merino wool—the most durable and satisfactory natural fibre for clothing yet produced.

The main sheep zone, containing eighty-five per cent of Australia's sheep, extends in a great arc on the inner side of the Great Divide in the eastern States. The densest sheep population in this zone is in the State of New South Wales where almost half of all the sheep in the Commonwealth are to be found. Outside this zone the only concentrations are in South Australia and the south-west of Western Australia, which divide the remaining fifteen per cent fairly equally. The Tropical North, the rugged ranges of the Divide, and the higher rainfall areas contain very few sheep. On the other hand, the greatest concentration is not in the arid centre but in regions which, for a continent of generally low and erratic rainfall, would be called the better watered areas between the fifteen- and twenty-inch lines of annual rainfall. A feature of sheep raising in the Commonwealth is the association of sheep and wheat farming. About thirty per cent of all sheep are run on wheat farms, this figure rising to over forty per cent in both South Australia and Western Australia.

THE SHEEP STATIONS

Today the wool industry is no longer based on the great sheep stations of fifty years ago. Subdivision and closer settlement have reduced the size of properties, and today only thirty-eight stations, mainly in western New South Wales and Queensland, carry over 50,000 sheep, 346 carry 20,000 to 50,000, 1,086 carry from 10,000 to 20,000, 3,006 from 5,000 to 10,000, and 9,190 from 2,000 to 5,000. Though 75,000 sheep holdings out of 100,000 average less than 1,000 sheep, approximately eighty per cent of all sheep are carried on the larger properties with more than 1,000 sheep. The number of sheep gives little indication of the size of the property, since country with twenty-five to thirty inches of rainfall may carry a sheep or more to the acre, falling to, perhaps, a sheep to four acres in the fifteen-inch rainfall zone, while out on the saltbush and bluebush plains, with ten inches of rain or less, a single sheep station with 50,000 sheep may cover 1,000 square miles (640,000 acres), or more than twelve acres per sheep. Always, however, where there are sheep, there for most Australians is typical Australian country. There always is the grey-green of the eucalypts, with the glint of green and gold or scarlet as the parrots flash by; or the dove-grey and rose-pink of the galahs wheeling against the crimson sunset. There too, along the unmade dirt tracks of the far-stretching plains of New South Wales and Queensland a driver will often put up a mob of kangaroos which take their fantastic flying course in twenty-foot leaps, or a flock of emus may pace beside the car at thirty miles an hour.

Difficult as the Australian sheep country is with its droughts and bush fires, it has the great merit of a mild winter. Sheep, even on the largest runs, are unshepherded, unhoused, and seldom hand-fed. The industry is based predominantly on natural grass, and only in the winter-rainfall areas of the south-east are many sheep run on improved pastures. In these circumstances sheep can be raised with perhaps the lowest ratio of labour to livestock for any improved animal industry in the world. More and more, however, with greater intensity of stocking, parasitic and other diseases have proved increasingly serious, and always over the great bulk of the sheep lands there is danger of the greatest scourge of the pastoralist, "blow-fly strike."

Australia's flocks are predominantly of the merino breed. In 1939, about eighty-four per cent of the wool clip comprised merino wool and sixteen per cent crossbred, which latter classification includes all wool other than merino, whether in fact true Crossbred, Corriedale, Romney or other. As always during war, the proportion of Crossbred wool has increased and now comprises twenty-three per cent. The percentage of merino and crossbred wool grown varies from State to State, as irrigation or the introduction of sown pastures in the higher rainfall areas of the south-east brings about a transition from wool growing to fat lamb production. Queensland produces virtually nothing but merino wool, New South Wales normally about ninety per cent merino, South Australia about ninety-four per cent and Western Australia ninety-four per cent. By contrast, Victoria prior to the war produced only fifty-five per cent of merino wool, and Tasmania only twenty per cent.

SHEARING TO SALE

Once a year a vast wool clip of about 3,500,000 bales (each approximately 300 pounds) is shorn. This is the climax of the year; and on all properties the sheep are mustered and brought into large wool sheds, which with their mustering "yards" and iron roofs are a feature of the Australian sheep station. Here in orderly sequence the rams, wethers, dry ewes, and ewes and lambs are shorn by teams of professional shearers who move by "flivver" or "motor-bike" from the earlier to the later shearing districts, as from mid-year the season rises to its peak in each.

Shearing in Australia is much more carefully organized than in most other countries. The shed with its holding pens, its shearing floor with machine shears, and its shearers, who in very big sheds may number thirty, is kept spotlessly clean. As the wool is shorn it is lifted by the "picker-up" and thrown by him on the skirting table where the stained, "burry" or less valuable wool is detached. The fleece is then rolled and placed on the wool-classer's table. With uncanny judgment the expert appraises its length, "count" and quality, and places it in the appropriate bin. From this bin, wool, all now of one type, is baled by a press in 300-pound lots, and the bale is branded with the name of the property, the type, and the quality of the wool. So it is that buyers of Australian wool are able to buy with confidence a number of bales of a particular wool clip after examining a sample from a bale of a single large line.

The Australian wool grower is deeply shocked when, let us

say, in Texas he finds a team of shearers working on a board platform in the open; or when he sees the scant regard for cleanliness on an English farm—the bundling together of the whole fleece, stained pieces, dirt and all, and finally the baling of these without regard to quality or type.

Though shearers are paid high wages today, £2:2:6 per hundred sheep, their speed is such (a good shearer should average one hundred per day and may do up to two hundred) that the cost to the owner is only about 7d. to 9d. per sheep, including all charges for classing and baling.

From the sheds the wool bales pour over the dusty plains into the great ports for sale prior to export. Before the war about ninety per cent of the wool clip was sold for export, and ten per cent was bought by domestic processors and manufacturers. During the war expansion of textile production in Australia led to as much as 13½ per cent, or 470,000 bales of 143,000,000 pounds weight, being consumed locally in the peak year 1941–42.

The clip is normally sold by auction at the ports of shipment such as Brisbane, Sydney, and Melbourne, more than a million bales being sold at Sydney during each of the last-mentioned years, or more than in any other centre in the world. Sales took the form of an auction at which, before the war, buyers from all parts of the world competed freely. The amount realized for the wool, less brokerage and handling charges, was transmitted to the grower, who retained ownership of the wool up to the time of sale, the wool-selling brokers acting as agents on his behalf.

IMPERIAL PURCHASES AGREEMENT, 1939

On the outbreak of war the British Government agreed to purchase the Australian wool clip for the duration of the war and for one full wool season after its conclusion, at an agreed average price of 13.4375d. (Australian) per pound, and similar agreements were made with the South African and New Zealand Governments. Wool is no longer sold at auction, but the whole of the clip is appraised to determine the value of each grower's wool in relation to a scale of values set down in what is known as the Table of Limits, in which some 4,000 wool types are listed. The grower is immediately paid the appraised price for his wool; and at the end of the season, after the average appraised price of the whole clip is known, he receives a further payment to bring the appraised price of the clip up to the agreed purchase price. The British Government, after the needs of Australian manufacturers are satisfied, re-sells to its own manufacturers or to foreign buyers. At the end of the 1941–42 season the British Government agreed to increase the purchase price by fifteen per cent, bringing the average price to 15.4531d. per pound.

Under the Imperial Wool Purchase agreement 17,900,000 bales had been sold to the end of the 1943–44 season for £337,551,000. The scheme has been satisfactory to the wool growers, but the disorganization of trade and the closing of wool markets in enemy and neutral countries, together with shipping and manpower difficulties, have resulted in a grave decline in war-time wool consumption. In consequence, surplus wool stocks have accumulated in Australia, the United States, and South America, and today these total probably 12,000,000 bales, or nearly 4,000 million pounds of wool, roughly equal to the yearly world production. This, in spite of very great expansion of exports to and consumption of wool by the United States.

The marketing of these surplus stocks (which are largely owned by the British Government) concurrently with that of the yearly production of all wool-exporting countries has created a problem of considerable magnitude for the Commonwealth. It is unlikely that disposal can be accomplished, without seriously endangering the stability of the wool growing industry, unless it is spread over a period of years. Follow-

Plate 7. Cotton on open forest soil. Cotton is grown in rotation with Rhodes grass in sub-coastal Queensland.

Plate 8. Natural blue grass pasture established on an ironbark ridge, Darling Downs, south Queensland. Australian savannah at its best.

Plate 9. Apple orchards, south-west Western Australia.
Plate 10. Dried fruit industry, Renmark, South Australia.

Plate 11. Subterranean clover sown after burn on Jarrah country, south-west Western Australia.

Plate 12. *Paspalum* pasture, summer rain zone, Queensland.

Plate 13. Sorghum for green fodder, summer rain zone, north Queensland.
Plate 14. Droving sheep on western plains, New South Wales.

ing discussions between British and Australian authorities, machinery has now been set up for this purpose.

There are, however, contrary considerations. Stocks of wool, like those of every other commodity produced under war-time controls of currency, wages and prices, will probably be relatively cheap compared with competitive synthetics produced under post-war inflationary conditions. For some years ahead wool may, therefore, suffer from little disadvantage in price and hold a positive advantage in preference.

Before the war Great Britain took about thirty-five per cent of Australia's wool exports, Japan twenty per cent, Belgium eighteen per cent, France eleven per cent, and Germany seven per cent. Consumption of raw wool by Japan has risen sharply since the last war. From 1909-13 to 1935-36 Japan's average yearly import from Australia rose from seven million to two hundred million pounds. Thereafter, following the Australian-Japanese trade dispute, imports of Australian wool fell sharply.

The United States since 1922 has imposed a tariff of thirty-one cents per pound (clean) on all imported clothing wool, and increased this to thirty-four cents per pound in 1930. In consequence of this high tariff, United States domestic sheep numbers and wool production increased markedly; and in recent years she has been a very erratic operator on the Australian market. Exports to the United States in the four seasons 1934-35 to 1937-38 were 5.4, 24.9, 72.7, and 4.2 million pounds respectively.

THE MENACE OF SUBSTITUTES

There is, however, another problem which has introduced uncertainty into the future of wool, namely the development of staple fibre substitutes, the production of which now equals that of world wool production on a clean scoured basis.

WORLD'S TEXTILE PRODUCTION, 1920–1940
(In millions of lbs.)

Year	Wool (greasy)	Cotton	Silk	Rayon	Staple Fibre
1920	2,960	10,710	46	33	
1925	3,360	14,115	90	185	
1930	3,680	13,120	106	457	6.2
1935	3,600	13,420	88	1,080	139.6
1938	3,920	14,550	123	1,945	957.6
1940	4,070	14,850	127	2,380	1,236.8
1942					2,025.7

Sources: Cotton and Wool: U. S. Bureau of Agricultural Economics.
Silk: Statistique de la Soie, and (1934 to date) Commodity Exchange, Inc.
Rayon: Textile Economics Bureau.
Staple Fibre: U. S. Department of Agriculture; Bureau of Agriculture and Industrial Chemistry.

The great bulk of these fibres are derived from cellulose, originally obtained from birchwood but latterly also from other soft woods such as pine, from cotton linters, reeds, nettles, seaweed and a wide variety of other plant sources. In the early 1930's also, a protein fibre lanital, derived from casein, the protein of milk, was produced in Italy, and more recently a similar milk protein fibre aralac has been produced in some volume in the United States. Another plant protein, that of soybean, was developed in Japan before the war, and finally the protein of peanut shells was utilised for the same purpose in Great Britain.

Fish, feathers, and other sources of animal protein have also been claimed to be capable of conversion for textile purposes. Another group of "true synthetic" fibres also seen as potential competitors with wool is that including nylon, based on coal tar derivatives, vinyon derived from coke and limestone, saion derived from petroleum and salt, and perlan, a German proprietary product.

Though initially the cellulose staple fibres were markedly

deficient in tensile strength and elasticity, particularly when wet, as compared with wool, intensive scientific research has led to continued improvement in quality, and the crimp and "scale" formation of the wool fibre has been simulated, if not completely reproduced.

The present price relationship of the protein fibres with that of wool is not yet clear, but it is not probable—in view of the alternate industrial uses to which casein can be put, and the nutritional value of this high quality protein—that the "milk" fibres will be produced in sufficient quantity to constitute a serious threat to the wool industry. Similarly up to the time of writing the nylon and similar fibres have been widely employed for other purposes, and, as far as is known in Australia, only nylon wastes have been used for the manufacture of "wool-like" fabrics such as "camel hair" coats and bobby socks.

REPRESENTATIVE TEXTILE PRICES
(U.S. dollars per lb.)

	Wool	*Cotton*	*Rayon*	*Silk*
1939	1.23	.37	.52	2.72
1943	1.80	.56	.55	Not available

NOTE: The reader should not attach too much importance to these figures since they are for representative types in each group. Other types might have been selected with equal significance, but the comparison between textiles would give approximately the same result.

On the other hand the cellulose staple fibres (of which by far the most important quantitatively is viscose staple fibre, the others being those produced by the cupramonium and cellulose acetate processes) are considerably cheaper than wool. Standard viscose staple fibre sold in England at 10d. per pound pre-war and in the United States at 25 cents per pound. The comparable price of 64's wool (clean) was about twenty pence per pound in Britain, and owing to the operation of the tariff in the United States the disparity there was somewhat greater. Today wool is at an even greater price disadvantage, since in Britain the price of staple fibre after a wartime rise of seventy per cent has recently been reduced from seventeen pence to fourteen pence a pound, while the price of wool to the British manufacturer is almost one hundred per cent above pre-war values. In the United States during the war years wool (clean) has been from four to five times the price of viscose staple fibre, the price of which has been reduced from 25 cents to 23 cents a pound. Further technological advances in the production of the staple fibre top by the "tow-to-top" process, which eliminates many of the stages involved in carding and in the production of the top, may cut production costs of staple fibre top by a further two pence a pound.

These factors, coupled with improvement in quality (particularly appearance and handle) of pure staple-fibre fabrics and blends with wool for women's dress materials and worsted suitings, have created considerable concern in the Australian and other wool-growing industries. Opinions have, however, varied from the optimistic assumption that until such time as synthetic fibres reproduce the "bio-physico-chemical" structure of wool there is no serious danger, to the no less extreme view that the survival of wool as a major product is threatened. It is as yet not possible to assess the scale on which substitution of wool by synthetics is likely to occur, since the further improvements which may have been effected in the quality of synthetics during the war cannot be measured.

The dual problem of a heavy surplus of wool stocks and the potential competition of synthetics in wool's traditional textile fields is of sufficient gravity, however, to make it necessary to rally to wool's aid the resources of science, which have proved of such signal efficiency in creating wool's competitors. In recognition of this, in May 1945 the Common-

wealth Parliament, with the cordial agreement of the wool industry and the country as a whole, passed the Wool Use
Promotion Bill under which a tax of two shillings a bale is
levied on all wool sold, and the funds so produced are matched
£1 for £1 by the Government. From these funds of £650,-
000 a year, at least half will be spent on scientific research
into the problems of production, processing, and manufacture,
and the remainder on publicity for, and promotion of, wool
in the world's markets.

THE FIELD FOR RESEARCH

What is the field for research, whether biological in relation
to the production of wool, or chemical and physical in relation to the processing and manufacture of wool? Biological
research may have a twofold objective:

(i) the improvement in efficiency of production so lowering costs and enabling wool to withstand any reduction
in price which may be forced by staple fibre competition; and

(ii) an improvement in quality so that raw wool may be
possessed of those properties allowing its more effective
employment in manufacture.

It is undoubted that great opportunity exists for increased
efficiency of production. The Australian merino sheep has
the ability, without breed improvement, to grow at least fifty
per cent more wool per head if adequately fed, so lowering
costs of production. Considerable improvement in nutrition
may be effected, even on natural grass pastures, if the present
serious lack of knowledge of plant and animal ecological rela-
tionships is made good by intensive investigation. It is indis-
putable that much of Australia's grasslands have suffered from
over-stocking with consequent lowering of production, deterioration of pastures, soil erosion, and rising costs. Disease,
in spite of great advances in knowledge, exacts a yearly toll

of millions of pounds sterling. Blowfly strike, which is now largely controllable by the Mules operation, has been estimated to cause losses of as much as £4,000,000 in a "bad fly year."

Similarly there is scope for the application of modern knowledge of genetics to improve the quality of wool, once there is more precise definition, as a result of textile research, of the fleece characters of economic importance to the manufacturers. At the moment there can be no general directive as to breeding policy other than that wools shall be "sound and well grown."

In the field of wool textile research great opportunities exist for improving the efficiency of wool processing, and for modifying the physical and chemical characteristics of wool so as to endow it with new properties and to adapt it to a wider range of uses, whether alone or in mixture fabrics. In no country has the volume of wool textile research been commensurate with the importance of the industry, or with the urgent necessity to supplement the traditional arts of wool manufacture by every possible scientific aid.

Australia will now be enabled to devote a greater sum annually to wool textile research than has any other country, not with any purpose of assisting the Australian wool manufacturer alone, but rather of making whatever results accrue from this research freely available to the wool textile industry of all countries. Similarly greatly enlarged funds will be devoted to wool publicity and promotion. This will include the examination and the active development of potential markets for wool in India, China, and other countries in which post-war industrialization appears likely to lead to rising purchasing power and new consumer needs.

The possibility of a serious decline in wool prices, should the present premium value enjoyed by wool over synthetics fall appreciably owing to the closer approach of the qualities of synthetics to those of wool, has also led to consideration of the extent to which Australia could change from merino wool production to fat lamb and mutton production. Though great expansion of fat lamb production on the irrigated and improved pasture lands of south-eastern Australia is possible, similar trends in New Zealand and South America could lead, in the absence of a general rise in world purchasing power, to over-production of mutton and lamb and a serious decline in price which might be as disastrous as that of wool. In any case such an outlet could not be exploited in much of Australia's semi-arid wool growing country where no adequate alternative appears practicable.

The possibility has also been suggested that wool might be degraded and converted into (a) a protein synthetic fibre, or (b) a source of protein for human nutritional uses. As for the first alternative it is difficult to see how under any circumstances wool as a raw material for synthetic fibre production would enjoy any higher price for this purpose than for employment in its present form. For the second, in a world which cheerfully allows the consumption by pigs of the more valuable animal protein skim milk, from which a return in the form of pig meat of only one-twelfth is obtained, it is highly improbable that any profitable market for wool as a foodstuff will exist.

In short, there can be no future for the major part of the Australian wool industry should wool ever come to be no more than a by-product of the mutton industry. In the long view, however, there appears to be no need to anticipate any such gloomy possibility. Wool has emerged from the war with enhanced rather than lowered prestige. That prestige can be maintained if the industry at all stages of production, manufacture, and consumption is seen as a unity, and intensive scientific effort is devoted to the more effective employment of those inherent properties of wool which are still superior for many of wool's traditional uses to those of any of its synthetic competitors. This, coupled with the unsatisfied and immeasurable demand of mankind for textile fibres in a happier and more rational world, gives grounds for hope that further expansion of Australia's wool industry may be expected, and that, in the future as in the past, it will continue to be a major pillar of the Australian economy.

Chapter VIII

THE CATTLE INDUSTRY

BY R. B. KELLEY

Officer-in-Charge, F. D. McMaster Field Station (C.S.I.R.), Badgery's Creek, New South Wales

DEVELOPMENT OF THE cattle industry in Australia has not been comparable with that in other countries of similar area. The first limiting factor in the control of grass growth, upon which the industry depends, is the prevailing aridity that has been described in Chapters II and IV. In Australia, moreover, beef production has been forced to compete for the land with a more profitable rival—the sheep industry. Beef cattle are to be found mainly on the hot savannah areas of the monsoonal north, where pastures are too strong or harsh and seasonal conditions are unsuitable for sheep, whilst dairying has been concentrated in areas that are in general too wet for successful sheep raising. This allocation is, however, true in a broad sense only; and as the accompanying maps show, there is much beef raising in the better rainfall areas of the south-west, south-east and east.

These two facts, of aridity and the greater earning power of sheep over most of the pastoral area of the continent, go far toward explaining the relatively small cattle population. Australia depastures about 13,000,000 head of cattle, whereas the United States, with approximately the same total area, contains 67,000,000, and the United Kingdom, with only four per cent of Australia's area, supports 9,000,000. If, for these three countries, sheep population is converted (at five sheep to a beast) to the equivalent of cattle in the three countries, the respective carrying capacities would rank at about 78,000,000 head for the United States, 37,000,000 for the United Kingdom, and 44,000,000 for Australia. It has taken eighty years for the cattle population of Australia to grow from four million to its present figure of thirteen million—a fairly significant index of the geographical and economic difficulties faced by the industry. Periodic droughts have caused serious losses in all parts of the continent. In Queensland, which contains about half of Australia's herds, more than sixty per cent of the whole cattle population of the State was wiped out between 1892 and 1902 by severe droughts and the ravages of cattle ticks.

Relative importance of cattle and sheep in the principal countries has some interest for this survey. The contrasted positions, of Australia on the one hand and of the United States, Brazil, and Argentina on the other, deserve notice:

LIVESTOCK IN SOME OF THE PRINCIPAL COUNTRIES

Country	Year	Cattle millions	Sheep millions	Beef Exports Aver. 1936–38 (million lbs.)
Argentina	1937	33	44	1307
Australia	1938	13	113	250
Brazil	1935	40	13	129
Canada	1938	8	3	5
Russia	1938	63	84	...
South Africa	1937	11	41	13
Uruguay	1937	8	17	264
U.S.A.	1938	67	54	40

Distribution of cattle in Australia shows in an interesting way the close association of animal industries with water supply. In general, areas which receive twenty inches of rain or more a year support the greatest concentration of cattle. Dairy cattle are confined mainly to areas receiving thirty inches or thereabouts, and to irrigation areas. Distribution of human population as well as of cattle must of necessity be controlled by water resources. Both are more densely concentrated in the heavier-rainfall areas, although the pattern of distribution for dairy cattle is very different from that for

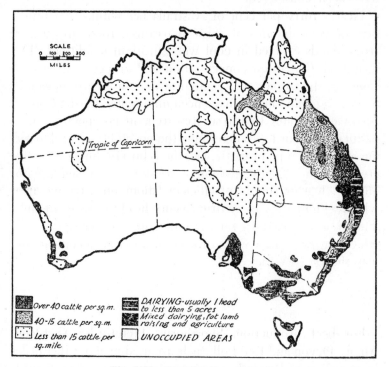

Fig. XII. Distribution of cattle.

either sheep or beef cattle. The reasons will be apparent when the climatic controls and the availability of artesian water from different areas of the continent are studied.

In southern and south-eastern areas there are stud herds of European beef and dairy breeds of cattle attested by overseas judges, who have acted at Australian exhibitions, to be equal to any in the world. Further, world's records of dairy production have been established by cows in these areas on more than one occasion. But this review has been made principally to disclose Australia's position as a possible source of world supplies of food having origin in cattle. Exporting areas, therefore, have been isolated and problems of those least developed have been considered.

Nearly forty per cent of Australia lies within the tropics, but the four millions of cattle depastured there are derived from breeds evolved in cool wet European conditions. This is, indeed, the largest concentration of European cattle to be found in the tropics, and ecological disabilities are inevitable. Since 1933, experiments have been undertaken by the Council for Scientific and Industrial Research, in co-operation with pastoralists, in order to determine the possibility of acclimatizing a tropical type of cattle, i.e., the zebu (Brahman). Results are promising, but the crossbreds are difficult to handle without an adequate supply of efficient labour on extensive areas which seldom carry more than twenty head to the square mile. This is nearly maximal for carrying capacity per square mile which varies greatly, within the tropics, as the accompanying map shows. (See Fig. XIII.)

BEEF CATTLE

For beef production, Shorthorns, Herefords, Aberdeen-Angus, Devon and Red Poll cattle are used in about that order of importance. Recently there has been an apparent, but as yet ill-defined trend in favour of Herefords. However, much cross-breeding occurs; this is most marked between Devons and Shorthorns, and Shorthorns and Herefords. Many herds are relatively small. One hundred and twenty is about the average size in pastoral districts of Queensland. Although there are over eight hundred herds of a thousand head or more in that State, only about three per cent number more than five hundred. This is small-scale operation in which breeding and fattening are usually carried out on the same holding. Long

distances to the coastal areas are often a severe handicap. Some
of the largest runs "drove" stock, at about two or three years
of age, hundreds of miles to depots which are not truly specialized fattening areas. There are no fattening areas in Australia similar, in nature or extent, to those of the Argentine
lucerne (alfalfa) belt. The cattle are moved towards railways
and the coast so that, when fattened, their condition is maintained during the shorter journey to the meat works. This calls
for judgment and great knowledge of watering places and
pastures.

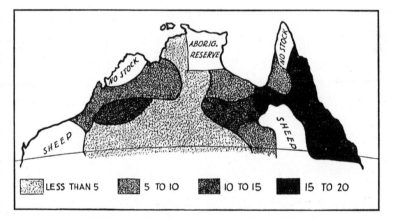

Fig. XIII. Distribution of cattle, northern Australia.

Western Australia, Tasmania, and to some extent South
Australia, are self-supporting with regard to beef. Markets in
Victoria and New South Wales are mainly metropolitan, with
three sources of supply. Beef comes from cattle bred and
fattened in the State, from Queensland cattle fattened locally,
and from chilled beef direct from Queensland meat works.
Approximately a quarter of a million head of cattle leave that
State annually to be fattened elsewhere. South Australia uses
some of these and others from areas more directly north.
Consumption of beef and veal in Australia is about 112 pounds

per head of population. This absorbed approximately seventy-seven per cent of the output in 1937–38, so that the surplus for export is relatively small, as well as comparing unfavourably in quality with highest grades of South American beef.

Meat works which process most of the export beef are on the east coast of Queensland. Slaughter and grading is supervised by veterinary inspectors employed by the Commonwealth Government. Queensland has an almost complete monopoly of the export trade, and provides ninety-eight per cent of the chilled and ninety-four per cent of the frozen beef. This represented seventy-six per cent of 2,600,000 hundredweight, which was the total Australian export of beef and veal for the 1938–39 season.

North Australia, which supplies this high proportion of the export beef, has a highly seasonal rainfall. Grass growth depends on rains in the summer monsoon season, the cool season being dry. Cattle fatten during and soon after the rains. This fixes a peak period of slaughter which reduces supplies at other times.

Irregular production of this kind was less important when beef was frozen for export, because shipment could be safely delayed by holding carcases in store for a considerable time. It is, however, a severe deterrent to continuous supplies of chilled beef, which must be shipped and consumed relatively soon after slaughter. The whole situation is in marked contrast to conditions in the Argentine, which dominates the United Kingdom market for chilled beef. Distance of Australia from Europe is a further serious disability. The sea voyage is longer than the extreme limit for keeping chilled beef in the ship's hold, unless the disability is overcome by use of carbon dioxide gas.

The United Kingdom normally takes more than ninety per cent of beef exported from Australia. In 1938 this constituted about six per cent of the chilled and fifty-two per cent of the frozen beef received by that country.

Chilled beef from Australia was, moreover, subjected to

price discrimination in the United Kingdom. Chilled beef from the Argentine realized prices about twenty per cent higher than exports from Australia on the British market, whilst Australian frozen sold for about twenty per cent less than Australian chilled beef. This price disadvantage for both chilled beef and frozen beef shows the amount of leeway that the Australian product has to make up before it compares favourably with that from the Argentine.

DAIRY CATTLE

Dairy cattle—twenty-six per cent of the Australian cattle total—are restricted to higher rainfall and irrigation areas where, broadly, the objective is to market grass as dairy products. Housing is not necessary and supplementary feeding is not general. In New South Wales only five per cent of dairy farmers on the south coast and one per cent on the north coast conserve fodder. Such conditions represent competitive advantages in production that are of some significance for the production and export of butter and cheese. Victoria with 950,000 dairy cattle in a total of 1,880,000, New South Wales with 1,050,000 out of more than 3,000,000, and Queensland with about 1,000,000 out of a total of 6,000,000 are the chief producers of milk, butter and cheese.

Dairying in Australia is not uniformly mechanized. In areas like Gippsland (Victoria), and north-west Tasmania where electric power is available, milking machines are common. In New South Wales, however, it is estimated that machines are used in only twenty-five per cent of herds as compared with ninety-five per cent in New Zealand. Almost universally, cream is separated on the farms and processed at centralized co-operative butter factories.

Levels of production vary from herd to herd and from season to season. For instance, the average annual production of milk per cow in Queensland varies very widely as the following figures show: southern districts, 226 gallons; central districts, 180 gallons; northern districts, 186 gallons. Similar variations are usual as between States. In 1937–8, for example, the average yield (gallons per cow) varied from 446 in South Australia and 441 in Victoria to 324 in New South Wales and 304 in Queensland. This means, of course, that large margins for improved efficiency exist. The average yield of 350 gallons of milk a year over the whole of Australia is low. In 1941, 2,078 registered cows of all breeds under standard herd test in Victoria averaged 345 pounds of butter fat over a period of 273 days. Converted to volume of milk having four per cent

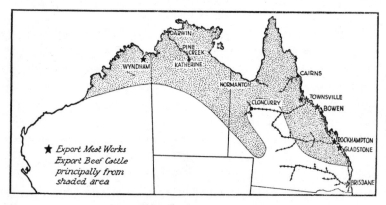

Fig. XIV. Beef export industry.

of butter fat the figure represents 862 gallons per cow. The average production of all dairy cows in New Zealand during 1939–40 was 224 pounds of butter fat, which represents 560 gallons of milk, and the figure for average production of milk per dairy cow in England is of the same order. In the United States it is of the order of 450 gallons.

DAIRY PRODUCTS

Whole-milk consumption is estimated to be 3.5 pints per head of population in Australia. This absorbs a high proportion of milk produced, particularly on dairy farms near the big cities. The remaining output is manufactured into condensed or concentrated milk, butter, and cheese, and a large proportion of these is exported. War conditions have altered the pattern both of production and trade considerably, and the following survey is, therefore, mainly confined to the pre-war period.

The total production of condensed or concentrated milk in 1937–38 was about 78,000,000 pounds. Twelve million pounds of this was manufactured in New South Wales, the remainder coming from Victoria. The largest production of butter in Australia was recorded in 1934–5 when, as a result of a favourable season, 469,000,000 pounds were manufactured. Average production is about 436,000,000, of which Australians consume about 33 pounds per head annually. This absorbs

PRINCIPAL DAIRY PRODUCE BY STATES
(millions of lbs. approx.)

Year	New South Wales	Victoria	Queensland	South Australia	Western Australia	Tasmania	Australia
BUTTER							
1937–38	121	142	118	22	15	12	430
1939–40	117	165	143	23	16	12	475
1941–42	90	141	99	21	17	11	378
1943–44	92	112	103	20	15	8	350
1944–45	72	105	95	16	13	8	309
CHEESE							
1937–38	8	16.5	12	15.5	.9	3.8	56.6
1939–40	7	24.5	14	20.5	.9	3.2	69.8
1941–42	5	22.3	16	18.6	1.3	3.0	66.6
1943–44	5	25.6	25	19.7	1.8	2.2	80.0
1944–45	4.4	27.6	22.7	18.5	1.7	2.3	77.2
BACON AND HAM							
1937–38	21.3	16.7	19.6	6.2	4.0	2.5	70.3
1939–40	26.0	17.9	20.0	7.0	4.7	2.9	78.6
1941–42	34.2	19.2	24.4	8.9	6.1	2.1	95.0
1943–44	31.6	20.8	28.1	11.4	9.7	3.0	104.9
1944–45	42.8	22.1	31.8	10.4	11.2	2.5	120.8

from 200 to 230 million pounds, leaving the remainder, some 200 million pounds, for export.

Butter and cheese are manufactured in all States, but not in proportion to the number of dairy cows in them. This is shown by the figures in the following table. Local consumption of cheese fluctuates and is about four pounds per head of the population. This absorbs from twenty-three million to thirty-one million pounds, whilst the remainder, averaging about thirty million pounds, is exported.

CATTLE DISEASES

Australia has relatively few cattle diseases. Aphosphorosus is not uncommon in both beef and dairy cattle. Rinderpest has occurred once in Western Australia, but it was immediately and completely eradicated at the site of outbreak. Cattle ticks (*Boophilus australis*) are the outstanding ectoparasites of the North. They extend as far south as the northern border of New South Wales, and arid conditions check their spread westward at about the mid-line of the continent. The Buffalo fly (*Lyperosia exigua*), which is similar to the horn fly (*Lyperosia irritans*) of the United States, has moved eastward from the Northern Territory to the east coast at Townsville, and continued movement southward appears inevitable. Pleuropneumonia, which first occurred in Victoria in 1858, has moved north throughout the continent. It has been eradicated from the southern States, but is endemic in the North. Tuberculosis, contagious abortion (*Brucellosis*) and mastitis are more prevalent among dairy cows in this country than elsewhere. It is believed that their incidence is lower because the cattle, while in the paddocks, are not often in contact with one another. Cows producing whole milk for the capital cities are compulsorily tested for tuberculosis, and most States have programmes for eradicating and controlling this disease in dairy cattle.

POSSIBILITIES OF EXPANSION

This survey has treated only broadly important aspects of the cattle industry. It has given no opportunity to answer two critical questions: (1) Have the limits been reached? and if not, (2) How can (a) beef production, and (b) dairy production be increased? A statement on possibilities in the light of present knowledge is, therefore, necessary.

1. Even if the number of cattle remained stationary, output of beef or dairy produce has not yet reached its maximum. Expansion is possible in both branches of the cattle industry, if (1) prices for cattle products are sufficiently favourable to producers and (2) methods of husbandry are improved.

2. (a) *Beef cattle:* Improved watering and other facilities for droving stock from the interior to rail heads would prevent wastage (shrink) and make larger numbers of cattle available at coastal meat works or fattening depots. Alternatively, meat works could possibly be established closer to centres of production in Northern Territory or nearby districts, but overhead costs and intermittent killing periods at such works would be critical factors.

Although extensions of railways would benefit the industry, military roads, as such, are unlikely to affect the cattle position. Their usefulness would principally be to provide greater amenities for producers and to facilitate transport of goods which, possibly, might include fodder. Cattle movements from the interior require avenues of outlet (stock routes) well equipped with watering and resting points, or organized systems of transport capable of lifting hundreds, perhaps thousands, of head at one time, and road vehicles have not yet been adapted for such work.

Increased output requires an objective. Northern cattle, which provide the export beef, are grown and fattened under extensive rather than intensive conditions in tropical or subtropical areas. Despite many difficulties some chilled beef has

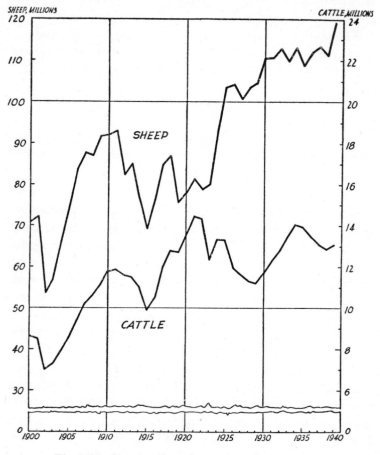

Fig. XV. Sheep and cattle numbers (1900–1940).

been exported. It has so far competed with difficulty against highest grades at Smithfield, the world's most discriminating market. The method of preservation and the competition emphasize all Australian disabilities in production, transport, and sale. However, retailers in the United Kingdom prefer to handle chilled rather than frozen beef because, among other reasons, stocks on hand do not require to be given time to thaw. Thus, to reduce their overhead, they discriminate against frozen beef as such.

This discrimination is critical, and, associated with the quantities of chilled beef available in Argentina, it appea that, to compete in England, Australia will be forced to adop. the chilling process which makes possible the sale of otherwise unsalable beef. Failing that development, Australian exports of frozen beef on pre-war markets would probably be restricted to Army, Navy and municipal contracts. Nevertheless, much of the beef that has been chilled and exported should be distinguished from the grade that is "true chiller quality" which competes with beef home-grown or fattened in the United Kingdom. Argentina can and does produce this quality, and, without the Ottawa Agreement or some similar control, could and would saturate the United Kingdom market.

Natural conditions in the greater part of north Australia are not ideal for producing "true chiller" cattle. Further, only twenty-three per cent of the Australian output of beef is available for export; and southern States are becoming increasingly dependent upon beef or beef-cattle from the North. Australian purchasing power is arbitrarily maintained at a sufficiently high level to absorb the better types available from favourable areas and in good seasons in the North. That this demand will persist and grow as population in the south and east of the continent increases is, at least, highly probable.

It appears likely, therefore, that the bulk of Australia's export beef will continue to come mainly from cattle that are not of "true chiller type and quality" by Argentine standards. It can be chilled and sold as such; but the freezing process is better adapted to spread maximal seasonal supplies over the longest sales period.

Realistically, Australian beef should be regarded not as a superlative product but as an admirable source of animal protein for those, in reorganized Europe or elsewhere, whose income restricts their purchasing power. If this were acknowledged, and acted upon, Australian cattle could be held to optimal weights. Other steps could also be taken to produce, at lowest possible cost, much larger quantities for sale upon a specialized market. Organization of such schemes will become necessary to correct malnutrition in Europe; indeed, such measures are implied in the Atlantic Charter. Continuance of selective trade agreements within the Empire (likely to be more difficult after the war) and costly idealistic attempts to lift the standard of Australian export beef-cattle to "true chiller qualities"—difficult in the face of efficient South American production—are the rather unhopeful alternatives. On the other hand, a large and rapid increase in the population of Australia would place the industry in a very different situation. There is also a potential market in South-eastern Asia. But its purchasing power is and must remain low until improved by large-scale manufacturing industries; a process which will involve complete re-education and re-orientation of millions of people.

Increase of quantities for any objective requires control of disease, notably pleuropneumonia and tick, eradication of malnutrition among herds and breeding-types suited to specific producing areas. Within such plans, better bulls, better feeding, additional watering points, and improvement of subtropical and other pastures will undoubtedly all play parts in extending the industry.

More extensive use of Zebus for crossbreeding provides an opportunity for considerable expansion of output in the North. Their management may require more labour, but an increase of eight thousand tons of beef annually, estimated to be possible by this procedure alone, does not exhaust all the advantages of the crossbred cattle. Even at chilling weights, crossbreds provided suitable carcasses at least twelve months earlier than the British-bred cattle with which they were compared.

(b) *Dairy output:* Although new or extended irrigation

systems would provide further dairy areas, the greatest possible number of dairy cattle, in districts now regarded as safe for the industry, is either in sight or has been reached. Nevertheless, total production could be increased by more extensive applications of herd testing and culling, by supplementary feeding and by the use of progeny-tested bulls as distinct from those judged on appearance only. "Better breeding and feeding" is the line of attack. Levels of production already reached in some areas, and the increasing number of farmers who conserve fodder make possibilities of expansion by those methods abundantly clear. A larger rural population is, however, required to provide economically the farm labour necessary and to plant and harvest appropriate crops.

The official figure for milk production per cow in North Queensland is stated as 186 gallons per annum. This was probably estimated by using the number of all dairy cows and heifers, regardless of age or of how many were actually in-milk. If an average were determined, using total production and the number of cows shown as being in-milk, the figure would become 283 gallons per annum. It can be assumed that a figure somewhere between those two is a generous estimate of production. Further, it must be remembered that the cows were within the tropics. Their situation adds weight to a comparison of the corrected estimate with production of Sahiwal (Zebu) cows on approved dairy farms in India. In 1938–39, 112 head, regardless of age, averaged 546 gallons of milk, and in the following year 169 head, also regardless of age, averaged 510 gallons. One cow averaged 874 gallons for her first four lactations, and another 994 for her first seven lactations. This comparison and experience of zebu cross-cattle in Queensland disclose a means whereby dairy production in Australia could be increased far beyond its present figure.

The coastal high-rainfall belt of North Queensland and potential irrigation areas of the north and north-west of the continent, but particularly the former area of about 18,000 square miles, should be regarded as one of the inadequately developed dairying regions of the world. Properly managed crossbred (Sahiwal British) dairy herds, provided that an adequate labour supply is available, would markedly increase the volume of Australian dairy production. In addition, an expanded dairy industry in the North would supplement the sugar industry, which is now restricted to fixed acreages, and would serve as a development basis for a larger population in Northern Australia.

Chapter IX

THE AUSTRALIAN WHEAT INDUSTRY

BY W. S. KELLY

Adviser to Commonwealth Prices Commissioner on Prices for Primary Products

ALMOST SINCE settlement began wheat has played a dominant part in the cropping programme of Australia. Wheat was the early settlers' most urgent need, and for long was the only food which would command a regular export market. More-over, it could be grown and harvested under Australian climatic conditions with relatively little labour, so that in many farming areas the cultivation of wheat has been prac-tised almost to the exclusion of other crops. Even as late as 1940, when the wheat acreage had been severely reduced, the proportion sown to wheat was approximately sixty per cent of the total area cropped.

Wheat-growing in Australia is something of an enigma to many in other parts of the world. It is widely known that the yield per acre is very low—the average for the last decade has been about twelve bushels. It is known, too, that financial loss and disaster have been the reward of many of our settlers; that much of our sub-marginal wheat land could be bought before the war for £2 or £3 per acre—far less than it cost to clear the land and effect the improvements. On the other hand, the price that has for years been paid for the more fortunately situated farm areas challenges comparison, for example, with wheat lands in England. How is it that good farms in the Wimmera district of Victoria, or on Yorke's Peninsula in South Australia should sell in the late thirties for from £15 to

£20 per acre, when wheat land in England, say, East Anglia, could then be bought for less? Why should wheat farms 13,000 miles from the world's greatest market for its produce bring more money per acre than land almost in the market? East Anglian yields would be equal or greater, and the farms would almost certainly be more improved than comparable farms in Australia.

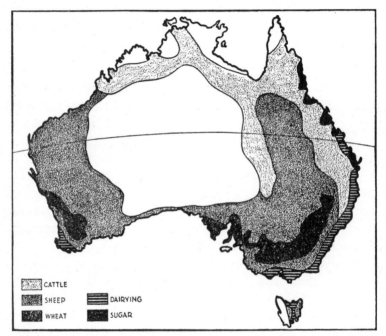

Fig. XVI. Relation of wheat belt to other rural production (adapted).

The high land values of these better-class farms must be a measure of some natural advantages Australian farmers enjoy in the areas favourable for wheat production. These advantages include:

(1) The more effective use which can be made of big agricultural implements by reason of the size of the fields and the predominantly level nature of the land.

(2) The climatic conditions, though unfavourable in some regards, help greatly in this mechanisation—

(a) The plough furrow need not be so deep nor need it be turned so thoroughly, for weeds are killed much more readily under Australian conditions. This makes the ploughing operating quicker and less costly. The stump-jump ploughs evolved in Australia have made it possible to cultivate land still carrying submerged roots and rocks. Except for implements of this nature the costs of clearing virgin country would have been much heavier.

(b) The drier climatic conditions also enable the weeds that germinate on the ploughed land to be killed by subsequent surface cultivation. This makes possible the use of the combined drill and cultivator, which destroys the weeds and sows the seed and superphosphate in one operation. One man with a tractor-driven "combine" will commonly cultivate and sow thirty acres with seed and fertilizer per day.

(c) Cost of drainage, often so heavy in other countries, is seldom incurred in Australia. This, however, is offset by the urgent need to provide drinking water for the stock by means of large dams, or wells and windmills. The drier conditions also necessitate a big proportion of bare fallow in order to better conserve the moisture for the following wheat crop. This requirement of bare fallow before the wheat crop reduces the gross returns off any given acreage.

(d) The long, hot, and dry summer days permit very effective use of combined harvesters. These are commonly operated from sunrise to sunset, during which time one man would harvest more than two hundred bags per day.

(e) When bagged, the wheat is sufficiently dry to be marketed at once, and is carted from the field direct to the silos.

The combination of these conditions makes possible a remarkable economy in man-power, so that frequently one man and a boy will till and harvest up to four hundred acres per year, as well as care for a small flock of sheep and the few cows needed to maintain the home in dairy produce. It must be granted, though, that the small amount of employed labour used on wheat farms too often leads to neglect of improvements and not a little untidiness.

There are other advantages. The pastures grown in rotation with wheat comprise chiefly annual grasses and clovers. Unfortunately, these are frequently mixed with undesirable weeds; but where hardy reseeding annuals such as Wimmera rye grass or the better clovers and medics are established, they persist without being resown, so that when the field is left out to pasture the heavy recurring expense in other countries of sowing down the small "seeds" is saved, and the cost of the subsequent pasture is limited to the fertilizer applied.

The prevalence of medics and clovers in the pastures goes far towards maintaining the nitrogen content of the soils where pasture rotations are regularly adopted. The normal fallowing operation also increases the available nitrogen. As a result, the Australian farmer is relieved of the heavy expense of applying nitrogenous fertilizers, nor is it necessary to apply potash which is present in adequate supply over nearly all the cultivated areas. If the farm is reasonably divided (before the war sheep-proof wire fences could be erected for about £50 per mile), and if stock water is available, a flock of breeding ewes can be very economically associated with a typical wheat farm. In fact, as will be shown later, it is important to combine, in a much greater degree than has usually been done in the past, the keeping of sufficient livestock with the growing of wheat. A ewe flock mated to early maturing rams to produce fat lambs, not only adds materially to the income of the farmer, but also aids greatly in the control of weeds and the maintenance of the fertility of the farm.

The gross return from a well-situated farm of, say, 1,000 acres, of which 300 acres might be sown to wheat at four shillings per bushel and 150 acres to oats and fat lambs bringing twenty shillings at the siding, might be expected to average something in the nature of £2,500 per year. This would seem a very modest gross return per acre as compared with the return from farming in many parts of the world, but in Australia it can be won by the owner and only one man (except for shearing) and, if interest and depreciation are excluded, with no heavy outgoings except for fertilizers, corn sacks, and fuel oils. In other words, while the return per acre is low as compared with figures in England and Europe, the return per man on the more efficient Australian wheat farm is often very high. This applies more particularly to the larger farms, where sufficient cropping can be secured to make full use of the large labour-saving plant now available. To do this and maintain reasonable rotation to safeguard the fertility of the soil, the acreage per farm needs to be a thousand acres or more. It is because the bigger farmer can produce more cheaply that land values are maintained at the high level in the areas of more reliable rainfall. On good farms of around two thousand acres, and yielding from twenty-five to thirty bushels per acre, the actual costs other than interest are often under three shillings per bushel of wheat. The return including the earnings from wool and lambs on such farms would often exceed £1,500 per man. Thus it is that the larger and more efficiently run Australian farm, in areas with reliable rainfall of from eighteen to twenty-two inches, can often show profits which justify prices for land that appear very challenging to British farmers, whose earnings per acre are much higher but whose outgoings are also much heavier.

But that is only one side of the picture. The other side is a very unpleasant one. When the price of wheat rose to eight shillings a bushel at Australian ports in 1920–21, and returned soldiers were searching anxiously for land, the stage was set for an unhealthy boom in land values and for an unwise expansion into areas unsuitable for wheat growing. Some of the land was unsuitable because of the nature of the soil, which is often of a light sandy texture and very liable to drift when the covering vegetation is removed and the land cultivated. Other areas were unsuitable because of low and variable annual rainfall, sometimes below twelve inches. In parts the limited rainfall is too often concentrated into a few winter months, so that the spring is frequently dry and hot, causing failure in spite of reasonable winter rainfall. The men and women who have undertaken this second phase of Australian pioneering have put up a brave fight, comparable with that of the early settlers who first developed the wheat lands. They purchased plant at inflated prices and incurred debts often carrying interest rates from six to eight per cent. Much of the country was rough or was made difficult by stumps or stones, and this caused the wear on implements to be exceedingly heavy. Many of the men were unfamiliar with agricultural plant, particularly with tractors, which were then greatly inferior to modern types. The result of all this was heavy loss and indebtedness.

The Royal Commission on the Wheat Industry reported that by 1935 the total debts of wheat growers amounted to £150,000,000. The debt was heavy even while the price of wheat remained relatively high. The low yields, often under six bushels in those sub-marginal areas, make the cost per bushel very heavy. But from the time when the price began to fall in 1929, till it reached the disastrously low level of 2/4½d. at Australian ports in 1931, the position seemed hopeless. In an attempt to maintain total income, despite the fall in prices, the farmers in 1930 increased production so that the wheat area which before 1914 was around eight million acres and had risen to fourteen million acres in 1929, rose again to the record figure of eighteen million acres in 1930. That crop had to be marketed at an all-time low price-level! It is hard to exaggerate the hardship and privation that many of this second band of pioneers suffered. Even prior to this their living standards were low. Their homes were often mere huts with no means of keeping food fresh in the blistering heat of the summer, and usually possessed a most meagre water supply. Often their land when cleared became subject to wind erosion, so that even when growth was healthy it would frequently be cut off or buried by drifting sand.

Since then much has been done to retrieve the position. Extensive schemes of debt adjustment have been operated. The Commonwealth Government has found money to subsidise the price of wheat when unduly low, and later a flour tax was imposed to support the price level. Money has also been provided to move farmers on the worst areas to land suitable for intensive farming.

The record drought of 1944 reduced yields to a little more than fifty million bushels, less than one-third of normal production. This crop failure in conjunction with the heavy use of wheat for stock feeding resulted in severe wheat shortage in Australia.

The lowering of soil fertility has not been limited to the sub-marginal areas. Many of the farms more favourably situated have been over-cropped, and here water erosion has washed away much of the precious surface soil. A Rural Reconstruction Commission has reported upon this and other problems, but it seems certain that the wheat area which between 1931 and 1938 had fluctuated around 14,000,000 acres, but fell to 8,300,000 acres in 1944, should not be allowed to exceed 12,000,000 acres.

Such a policy may be resented as restrictive by some, and it will certainly need careful administration, for it is important not to knock out the larger wheat farmer. Operating in suitable wheat areas, he is often one of the most efficient producers of wheat in the world. Even so, there are very few farms which cannot with advantage extend the rotations between their corn crops.

Generally, rotation of crops in Australia has been sadly lacking, and where practised has been of a very simple nature. Gradually, however, the advocacy of the Departments of

Agriculture and the experience of the more successful farmers have caused a more general adoption of rotation practices. The rotation now being increasingly adopted is fallow, wheat, oats or barley, followed by one or two years of grazing. Because of the widespread presence of medics and clovers, land left out for grazing quickly builds up its fertility. In fact, seriously wheat-sick land can be greatly improved in texture and fertility by simply leaving the field for grazing for three or four years, provided legumes are present in the pastures and phosphate is applied.

Many farmers on wheat areas are now successfully using peas in their rotation. Thanks to the ingenuity of our agricultural implement manufacturers, these peas, like wheat, can now be reaped, cleaned, and bagged in one operation. The pea crop improves the physical condition of the soil and also builds up the nitrogen content.

Already the partial adoption of better cultural practices is safeguarding the wheat areas from the frequent recurrence of widespread failures such as used to operate at the beginning of the century. Too often then the average yield fell below ten bushels. Now, despite the frequent failure of the poorer Mallee lands and excepting so severe a drought as 1944, the average yields are more consistent and most of the wheat is grown in country where from twenty to thirty bushels are common.

The farmers' policy in the future must inevitably follow the established practices in the older farming countries of the world, found essential to maintain fertility and lengthen the periods between the wheat crops. Fortunately, in areas of even low rainfall, good stock feed can be grown on the pastures in the years between the wheat crops. The grazing after barley or oats, and particularly after peas, will fatten lambs very successfully through the winter months without any supplementary feeding. Where good feed is available, well-bred lambs weighing about thirty-six pounds dressed weight can be made ready for market in four and a half months, such lambs being worth about twenty shillings at sidings on export basis. It is this ability to make profitable use of the land between crops which is the most hopeful feature of Australian wheat farming.

In many areas lucerne is lightly sown with the wheat. From two to four pounds of seed sown in this way will provide good auxiliary feed for from three to five years, and will greatly increase the fertility of the soil.

Providing the fields are well fenced and water is available in each paddock, the labour required to care for a line of, say, five hundred ewes is very small, except at lambing and shearing time. An hour or so on a horse a few times a week to look over the small flock is all that is required. Even in lambing time a couple of hours per day is generally sufficient. Thus it is that the raising of fat lambs fits in well with the wheat farmer's programme.

Prior to the war Australia was exporting some five million lambs a year. With sound farming practice and reasonable conservation of fodder, this number can be increased by fifty per cent. To the extent that Australia can find a market for lambs at seven shillings per pound, or if need be for wethers at four shillings per pound, we can well afford to reduce our wheat acreage. If this is done by cutting out the poorest of the sub-marginal areas, and improving our cultural practices and thus the fertility of the soils of our better lands, we should be able to materially increase our average yield per acre and establish our wheat farming on a sound and permanent basis.

If there is an especial requirement for wheat for a year or so Australia could increase production considerably, but over the years a contracted acreage well farmed will be better from all angles.

People who judge from the car windows often say that Australian lands are lying unused. Most people say that about lands other than their own. There is certainly room for much intensification of production in many of our areas; but as regards wheat, there is no area of any significance where there is a dog's chance of success where Australians have not already given wheat-growing a good go. Kipling says of the engineer that one cannot raise a stone or cleave the wood "to make a path more fair and flat" except he find that the job had already been tackled by some other "son of Martha." It is like that as regards wheat-growing in Australia. Our farmers have not lacked courage nor enterprise; they have, in fact, been reckless in taking risks, jeopardising their health too often in the attempt to push forward the edge of cultivation. This policy of unwise expansion into unsuitable areas has brought a difficult problem, and much of these lands must revert to light grazing. There remains the great bulk of our wheat-growing areas where with sound farming practice we should be able to maintain a healthy and permanent agriculture. The moral to be drawn from all this is that we can look forward hopefully to a modest programme of wheat production which can be produced for a price that will compare well with other countries, but if we continue to overreach ourselves, permanent loss will ensue.

Chapter X

THE FRUIT AND SUGAR INDUSTRIES

BY S. M. WADHAM

Professor of Agriculture, University of Melbourne, and Member of the Rural Reconstruction Commission

WITHIN ITS boundaries Australia, like the United States, has such a variety of climate and soil that all the commercial fruits can be produced somewhere. Queensland is Australia's Florida, where tropical types such as pineapples, bananas, and paw-paws (Amer. papaia) can be grown. Southern California has Australian counterparts in South Australia, Western Australia, and the Murray Valley where citrus fruits, grapes, peaches and figs (and the corresponding dried and canned fruits) are extensively produced. Washington and British Columbia—the apple, pear, plum, apricot and berry-fruit regions—are represented by Tasmania, southern Victoria, and the south-west of Western Australia. Fruit-growing for home and export markets, especially since the introduction of cool-storage and refrigerated shipping space after 1887, has become a widely established industry. In the British market Australian apples, pears, and canned fruits compete with the products of Canada and the United States, though at a different season, while the competition between Californian and Australian dried fruits is very keen.

The World War of 1939–1945 greatly disorganized the Australian export of fruit; but, after the entry of American forces into the south-west Pacific, a large part of the exports, other than apples, which formerly went to the British market

FRUIT PRODUCTION 1939–40
(Figures approximate)

	New South Wales	Victoria	Queensland	South Australia	Western Australia	Tasmania	Total Commonwealth
Vineyards (acres)	17,000	43,000	3,000	58,000	6,500	.....	127,000
Wine ('000 gals.)	2,090	1,126	43	11,180	336	.....	15,000
Table Grapes (tons)	3,975	4,107	2,118	1,046	2,523	.....	14,000
Dried Fruits..Sultanas and Raisins (tons)	6,600	47,500	.....	15,000	700	.....	69,800
Currants (tons)	1,500	10,500	.....	10,500	3,000	.....	25,500
Orchards and Fruit Gardens (acres)	85,000	70,000	33,000	29,000	22,000	31,000	271,000
Apples ('000 bu's.)	616	1,603	247	589	1,118	5,148	9,320
Apricots ('000 bu's.)	195	486	11	438	63	74	1,270
Bananas ('000 bu's.)	1,655	.....	844	.....	24	.....	2,520
Oranges ('000 bu's.)	1,945	532	350	754	343	.....	3,930
Lemons ('000 bu's.)	211	121	41	49	70	.....	490
Peaches ('000 bu's.)	532	1,211	69	173	89	7	2,080
Pineapples ('000 doz.)	39	.....	2,382	.....	.....	.....	2,420
Pears ('000 bu's.)	276	1,299	23	279	96	.....	2,290
Berries (cwt.)	198	12,500	6,300	6,200	727	133,334	159,260

found a new outlet in supplying the Allied Services. The pre-war situation is best shown by the statistics of production and export:

Fruit growing for export has gone through severe trials in the last fifteen years. The year 1933 was one of great crisis, especially for apple growers. Under the Ottawa Agreement, Australian orchardists, in common with those of the other British Dominions, were given free entry for their fruit into the United Kingdom, whilst non-British exporters had to meet a tariff of about 1/7d. a bushel. The Australian apple crop for that year was a record, and more than six million bushels were shipped in the hope that the new tariff would have eliminated competition from the United States and elsewhere. The results were otherwise, the North American growers obtained sub-stantial reductions of freight and continued their shipment, prices fell disastrously, and growers suffered severe losses. While some recovery took place in succeeding years, con-ditions have never lifted the apple trade to its former security and prosperity. The home market is much too limited to absorb the whole of the Australian apple and pear production, while about ten per cent of the citrus crop is exported, mainly to New Zealand.

In addition to high transport charges owing to the distance from the British market, exporters of all fruits, fresh and dried, have had to combat difficulties associated with long periods of storage on board ship. It is only in comparatively recent years that researches have disclosed the causes of the various types of breakdown which occur in fresh fruit in transit, but it takes a considerable time for orchardists to learn when to pick and how to pack safely for export, and for the refrigera-tion engineers on ships to understand their responsibilities in connection with maintaining the fruit in good order. Apart from such matters the conditions in markets on the other side of the world, several weeks after despatch, are difficult to estimate, and the co-ordination of supplies when they are carried as part cargoes by ships going to various ports at different speeds and following several routes has so far proved impossible. The cessation of export since the outbreak of war made Federal assistance necessary to prevent disaster to the apple producers in those States which rely mainly on export, namely Tasmania and Western Australia.

Even before the war the apple export markets were limited, and it is probably too much to expect that post-war Britain will be able to take the 5,000,000 bushels which was about the pre-war maximum which could normally be absorbed in the three months which form the Australian apple season. Fruit picked in February, March, and April in southern Australia competes on the British market in April, May, June and July with stored fruit from New Zealand, S. America and the United States. The later shipments meet with much competition from berry fruits which are then in season. After July the appearance of English and Canadian fruit practically closes the market to Australian apples and pears. During the late winter and spring northern Europe could, of course, consume all the fruit that could be exported, but the reduced purchasing power of those countries is now the barrier. There is little chance of opening new markets elsewhere.

During the war citrus growers were temporarily in a happier position. The urgent requirements of many thousands of American soldiers and sailors in tropical areas, and the added emphasis on citrus for nutritional reasons, absorbed at a fair price most of the available fruit. Except at peak periods of production the local market was very short of oranges and other types, and it is fair to assume that growers enjoyed prosperous times. With the war over, the supply will probably be fairly balanced with demand, especially if the New Zealand trade is resumed.

The prospects for fruit-growing have a close bearing upon Australian reconstruction plans. After the war of 1914–18 many returned solidiers elected to go on the land, and State governments developed irrigation areas, especially in the Murray Valley. With the help of British preference for Australian dried fruits, and assistance to soldier settlers, plantings were accelerated until markets became a serious problem. Moreover, some citrus trees and vines were planted on unsuitable soil, or in areas where soil troubles developed as a result of irrigation; but most of these difficulties have been overcome in recent years.

The development of further irrigation areas in the future will lead to possibilities of expansion in fruit production, but the lessons of the past suggest that caution should be observed. Most irrigation districts have a variety of soils, some of which are eminently suitable for citrus, others for vines, and some, where water is cheap, can be effectively used for pasturage on which dairying or fat lamb production can be carried on. The outlook for citrus is limited by the size of the home market and by the possibility of arrangements with New Zealand. The home market is not well supplied with high-grade fruit at certain seasons of the year, and oranges when reasonably cheap are becoming more popular, so that a moderate increase in citrus plantations, if located on the right soils and in the correct districts and if of types in which the market is deficient, would be justified. On the other hand, increased dried fruit production is more difficult to justify. The ratio of export to home consumption is very high in sultanas, and if the American home market does not absorb the American production world prices may easily fall to a level which would be disastrous to Australian growers. Australia finds its chief competitors in the production of currants in the Aegean, and is in no better position to justify an expansion. In all these fruit industries the importance of efficiency among the producers has become more apparent in recent years. The power to compete on home or world markets is greatly affected by the level and regularity of the crop, and there is always a tendency to assume that the returns have to be sufficient to render production profitable in the less satisfactory districts and on the poorer types of farm.

Canned fruits are in much the same position as dried fruits. During the war their output was largely acquired by the armed forces, but the export ratio is high and the future will be determined by the extent to which international trade becomes buoyant and standards of living high.

The production of tropical fruits could be expanded, but improved production and continuous supervision and technical efficiency at all stages between the farm and the consumer are essential. If these fruits are to become articles of diet among the southern population, they must be landed in the capital cities in good condition and at reasonable prices. So far bananas and pineapples are the only fruits in which this has been realized.

Berry fruits are most effectively grown in Tasmania, although most other States have small upland areas in which they can be grown during limited periods. Probably aeroplane transport will be used in future for small parcels to luxury markets at special times.

The general position of the fruit industries is that they are more dependent on general conditions of employment and prosperity than any other form of farming, but the outlook for the apple growers is particularly difficult. Growers of fruit for export will, in every country, be facing the future with some trepidation, and it could scarcely be expected that the Australian growers, with disadvantages due to transport costs, would be in any favoured position.

Compared with the cane-sugar production of other countries, that of Australia makes a modest showing. The average annual yield of raw sugar for the years 1935 to 1939 was about 800,000 short tons, compared with 3,000,000 tons for Cuba, 1,200,000 for the Philippines, 990,000 for Porto Rico, 960,000 for Hawaii, and 496,000 for continental United States, which produced in addition 1,600,000 tons of beet sugar. Australian production of beet sugar is almost negligible. Average annual world production for both cane and beet sugar for the last four pre-war years was about 34,000,000 tons.

The sugar industry ranks after dairying and wheat growing, but has a peculiar significance in the Australian economic and political system. It was established in Queensland by private enterprise in the 1860's. The work on plantations was done by "indentured" labour recruited from the Pacific islands by methods which are said to have often been less than creditable to employers and their agents; and public opinion in Australia became very hostile to the system. When federation of the colonies took place in 1901 and the policy of a "White Australia" was adopted, the kanakas, as the islanders were called, were gradually repatriated and the industry was placed on a new basis. Succeeding Federal Governments recognized that the industry was essential to the development and settlement of coastal Queensland. Of all tropical products it offered the best chance of yielding profits sufficiently attractive to induce white people to work in the tropics, but the level of profit necessary required protection.

A great developmental phase began during World War I. The Commonwealth Government assumed control of the industry, bought the Australian crop at a fixed price, restricted imports, and placed an embargo on exports. As the war proceeded a world sugar shortage developed, the Commonwealth Government was forced to raise the guaranteed price, and by 1920 the price per ton of raw sugar in Australia reached £30:6:8, the Government was paying £80 a ton for imports and the retail price in Australia was 6d. a pound. At this time, therefore, sugar growing was of considerable financial assistance to the national economy.

After the war the Commonwealth Government agreed to continue to support the industry by regulating importations and by fixing the retail price within Australia. With this support it expanded rapidly, and further settlement based on sugar growing proceeded in new northern areas. The general geographic movement has been northward, and today Queensland produces about ninety-five per cent and New South Wales five per cent of the cane-sugar output.

Since 1923 the industry has been virtually controlled by the Queensland Government. The Sugar Agreement has been renewed from time to time after discussions between the Commonwealth and Queensland Governments, and between representatives of growers and refiners. The present price of raw sugar for home consumption ensures a retail price of four pence a pound for refined sugar in the capital cities. The price for the portion of the output consumed in Australia is £24 per long ton (2,240 pounds) of raw sugar; and when this is averaged with the world price received for as much as fifty-eight per cent of the output in some years, the over-all price is about £15:12:0 per ton. During the war the industry has had many difficulties owing to shortage of labour, essential fertilizers and transport. Its production has consequently varied, but although costs have increased slightly it is not otherwise impaired.

The rate of expansion could not be maintained after the point where production largely exceeded home consumption, and where large exports became necessary. Heavy losses were sustained on the export of sugar after 1929, when the world price fell to £5 sterling per long ton. The industry recognized the need to check further expansion in view of the world sugar surplus. This control took the form of restrictions on the acreage cropped by assigning to each sugar farm the right to grow cane only on a specific designated area. This led to a great improvement in efficiency of production on the farms, since growers wished to maximise income from the fixed area. In view of the fact that the volume of Australian exports is now restricted by the International Sugar Agreement total production of sugar was limited to 737,000 tons. This quantity was rationed among the mills, and through the mills among the growers. Production in excess of this is paid for at a penalty price of ten shillings a ton.

Most of the cane is grown in scattered districts of rich soil which occur along the coastal zone, the intervening areas of which are generally poor in character. The whole zone is seldom more than fifty miles wide, and it would be quite erroneous to assume that the whole of the Queensland littoral has either the rainfall or the soils suitable for high-grade cane production. In one area where the rainfall is lower and badly distributed, the crop is irrigated by water pumped from the underground gravels of a river delta.

Most of the cane is grown on small holdings worked by intensive methods. The average area of cultivation on each farm is about forty-five acres, and a Government Research organization carries out many investigations ranging from the type of cane grown to methods of controlling insect and other pests, and from fertility maintenance to methods of cultivation. This organization is effectively decentralised and has the confidence of growers. It is probably the most efficient extension service to farmers in Australia.

In such a humid climate the conditions are arduous for white workers and wage rates are high. In 1938 a man cutting three and a half to four tons a day earned up to thirty shillings a day for about five months of the year. The cane is crushed at thirty-six mills throughout the sugar zone and the crude sugar is shipped to the refineries situated mainly in the capital cities. The concentration of refining at a few points makes control of the industry relatively easy. Technically there are three criticisms which can be levelled at the present organization. First, by insisting on the designation of specific pieces of ground which are to be cropped it is probably undermining the fertility of those particular areas; secondly, mechanization of the cutting should have been pursued more vigorously than has been the case; and thirdly, some of the southerly and older sugar areas are scarcely economic, but land holders have continued to grow the crop because of their rights in the matter, whereas crops other than sugar would probably have given better results. However, similar criticisms can be urged against almost every type of farming in every country.

It would be idle to deny that the development of the sugar industry has been free of criticism from the States which are not sugar producers. The subsidy is, however, now generally regarded as the price which the Commonwealth is paying for a great experiment in tropical settlement by white people. Tropical Queensland now supports about 130,000 people, many of whom are third-generation residents. So far as medical research can discover, the climate has not led to deterioration in the stamina of the residents in the tropical belt; indeed, the health statistics are very satisfactory. The sugar industry as the mainstay of white settlement in the Australian tropics is regarded as an integral part of Australian developmental policy; and it is not likely that any substantial change will be brought about by political disagreement.

Chapter XI

DIFFICULTIES OF SMALL-SCALE FARMING IN AUSTRALIA

BY S. M. WADHAM

Professor of Agriculture, University of Melbourne, and Member of the Rural Reconstruction Commission

FROM 1788, when British occupation of Australia began, up till the present day the field of land legislation in Australia has been the happy hunting-ground of the theorist. In the early days the Governors and those in Britain who were responsible for deciding the shape of things in the new colonies, in later years the Governments of the States, the political parties who controlled them and the official heads of various departments charged with the administration of land matters, have all had their views as to how the ownership or occupation of the land should be arranged. Time after time, legislation has been enacted to encourage this or that social scheme in the countryside. Frequently the desired pattern was based on some concept derived from conditions in over-seas countries, or upon some economic theory which had little relationship to the realities of the country. The inability of the advocates of many of these schemes to take account of the facts of the Australian environment and the wrongly conceived policies which resulted, lead one to marvel that the damage to the land, its soils, and its vegetation is not much greater than it actually has been.

Of all the foolish policies of land settlement which have been advocated for general application in many parts of Australia, the endeavour to create systems of small-scale or peasant farming is probably the most stupid. Millions of money have been wasted on it; countless years of human toil and vast amounts of material have been spent in fruitless endeavours to build rural societies on that basis—and there is every reason to suppose that similar endeavours will be made in the future in some districts with results which will be similar.

SKETCH OF DEVELOPMENT

Phillip, the first Governor, started it. He came from England in 1788 when there were still many yeoman farmers and many small rented farms employing a few labourers. Few of the soldiers under his command or of the other men of the community had experience in farming; but as the new community was likely to be short of food, Phillip had to develop a local agriculture. He, therefore, wrote home asking the Government to send out free settlers in the form of "landed proprietors," who could "bring with them people to clear and cultivate the lands and provisions to support those they bring with them." He realised that under the circumstances which prevailed ordinary settlers lacking capital could easily become a charge upon the settlement, because, as he put it, they "want that spur to industry" which is provided by the possession of capital. Some few settlers in the very early days were successful in farming ventures because agriculture in the new colony had not progressed far enough to become embarrassed by surpluses of its products.

Phillip's requests for free settlers were unavailing, but, in fact, they were not likely to have induced farmers to migrate from Britain, where an agricultural boom was in full progress owing to the inflation of the Napoleonic wars, coupled with a shortage of farm products.

Succeeding Governors found this problem increasingly difficult. When seasons were good, the crops were heavy and there was no market for the surplus, export being impracticable. When seasons were bad, there was little crop and the price became sufficiently high to be a social menace. This state of affairs was partly the result of the variable rainfall and of the season at which it fell, and was partly due to the poverty of the soils which required building up in fertility and the development of systems of agriculture not then fully understood. The usual devices were tried by various Governors—storage of surplus grain, alternative uses, e.g., distilling, guaranteed prices for part of the produce, and assistance to the settlers. They were quite unavailing; and, agriculturally, the new colony made little progress until the development of the production and export of wool gave it a new life and a new hope about 1820.

Similar developments took place in Western Australia where in 1829 the young "Swan River Colony" was started on an area of soils most of which were very light in character and low in fertility, while practically all were low in phosphate content and many had deficiencies in other minerals which have only recently been demonstrated. In these circumstances profitable farming development was automatically slow; and, although administrators and writers deplored the rate of settlement, this was but the logical result of the nature of the soils. Progress could not be made until the ranges were crossed and various tracts of better land were found. Widespread progress was not possible until superphosphate came into general use at the end of the century.

This first period of Australian agricultural development is a typical cycle of events which was repeated between 1820 and 1840 in each of the Australian colonies as it started near the coast; later similar troubles occurred in many parts of the interior. The problem has always been that of devising a way in which a community could grow up and expand agriculturally when it had no large centre of population capable of absorbing the production of that agriculture.

The development of the grazing industry was extremely rapid. When a reasonable prospect for the overseas sale of wool at an attractive price had been established, and the existence of large tracts suitable for sheep-grazing had been demonstrated, the squatters spread far and wide wherever there was water and the timber was not too dense or the country too rugged. Although many of the men who ultimately succeeded did not start with much capital it was not a small man's game, and it could not be considered as occupation on a peasant basis. At first each squatting unit had to rely on the coastal settlements for supplies of all kinds. Gradually each began to grow as much of its food as possible; but the need for continual purchases of all sorts of equipment remained. This involved a considerable turn-over in money and could only be maintained by selling the produce of hundreds or thousands of sheep. There was little opening for casual labourers on their own holdings living in the sheep districts because, as the flocks had to be relatively large and the carrying capacity of the country was not heavy, the stations had to be far apart and the casual worker could not get enough work near to any point to start a permanent home.

THE URGE FOR SUBDIVISION OF ESTATES

The gold diggings, for example at Ballarat and Bendigo, started a few settlements with a prosperous agriculture because they offered a good local market at very high prices. In most cases the gold-rushes were transitory and many mining areas were poor country. However, some of those on alluvial flats in areas of good rainfall gave rise to numerous small farms, some of which have persisted, mainly as homes. The gold-rush development (1850–70) had secondary consequences. In the difficulties after the diggings were exhausted an anti-squatter sentiment appeared and often took the form of a demand for subdivision of large holdings for closer settlement. By this time Lands Departments were so imbued with the desirability of preventing aggregation that they usually made the holdings too small, 160 acres being a common allotment. When the wheat industry developed in the nineties, many of these were taken up; but, except in the districts where both soils and rainfall are good and crops heavier and more reliable, these were unsuccessful. As wheat machinery became larger the farms necessarily had to be larger also if they were to use it efficiently. Dairying has ultimately followed much the same course. In general it is clear that all attempts at making small farms have been a failure, except in certain cases around the various cities on certain specially favoured patches of soil, or where conditions particularly suitable for small-scale farming have been produced, as for instance in the dried fruits irrigation areas.

DIFFERENCES BETWEEN EUROPEAN AND AUSTRALIAN CONDITIONS

Possibly those who have encouraged the establishment of small farms of a peasant type in Australia have not realised that in those areas of the world where such farming has been developed with success it has come about by a process of gradual growth. In such regions there were, in the first place, small centres of settlement often connected with a feudal or manorial estate, and when the local population expanded new land was broken in, families usually being prepared to assist their younger members to establish themselves. Assistance was given by various members in clearing the land, and in establishing new farming units hacked out of the forest or scrub. Alternatively, men took small areas from waste ground, settled on them, and by carrying on various occupations such as charcoal-burning, wood-cutting or doing casual work, they were able to eke out a difficult living during the period of their establishment. In the meantime they could grow vegetables and small acreages of crop, they kept a few fowls, a pig or two and possibly a cow.

In Australia the room for this sort of development was very small indeed, and for a variety of reasons. In the first place, ready supplies of water were often scarce, the number of reliable running streams being very small except in some regions near the coast. Secondly, the native timber was usually hard and required much toil before it could be controlled; many of the species sucker freely from the roots when ring-barked and most of them do not burn down to the root. Thirdly, many of the soils were not inherently rich and as soon as the small amount of fertility represented by the humus in the top few inches had been destroyed by cultivation, their productive capacity became low. Fourthly, the rainfall in most districts was erratic, quite apart from any question of its being deficient in total amount. This erratic nature of the rainfall made it necessary to conserve and hold much greater quantities of foodstuffs for livestock than was necessary in most parts of Europe.

One further aspect of the comparison between peasant farming under European conditions and small-scale farming in Australia seems entirely to have escaped attention. In most parts of Europe the period of scarcity for the farm family is the winter. All through the Middle Ages the struggle was to grow enough food during the spring and summer and to conserve it in the autumn, so that the winter, the lean period for man and beast, could be passed satisfactorily. All sorts of devices were used for overcoming this period of five or six months of critical nutrition. It was possible to put by grain in the dry form; meat could be salted or smoked; butter also was salted; farm cheese, if properly made, would keep; certain vegetables such as pumpkins and turnips and, latterly, potatoes could be put by and protected against frost. Others could be pickled or turned into sauerkraut. Some varieties of fruit would keep through the winter, others could be preserved.

Eggs could be put down in lime. All these devices were developed as methods of conserving food against the cold period.

In most parts of southern Australia the position is reversed. The annual period of scarcity starts rather before the period of maximum temperature. Smoked meats stored at the high temperature of an ordinary room will not keep. Butter and cheese are little better. Vegetables cannot be grown without subsidiary water supplies, and those which have been grown in the spring will not store during the summer. It follows that a peasant family trying to establish itself in Australia in regions with hot, dry summer conditions was liable to malnutrition. They might not realise that condition, but the gradual loss of energy and mental poise which is due to inadequate diet would automatically destroy that spirit of mutual forbearance which is essential to successful family life —and therefore to peasant settlement. In the northerly regions, where the rain falls mostly in the summer, the winters are sometimes dry; but usually their average temperature is too high for effective conservation of food and the maintenance of a good diet without irrigation.

Around the large cities a certain amount of successful settlement on the small-scale farming plan has been developed, because vegetables and fruit-growing or poultry-keeping or dairying could be carried on and the grower could carry his own produce to the city markets and thus virtually earn part of his living as a transporting agent. In some of the better rainfall areas men have kept going on small holdings by selling their labour during part of the year for shearing or for other casual work, but the number required for this is relatively small, and any attempt to encourage the development of farms of this type on the grand scale has only ended in failure and will continue to end in failure in the future, despite all the propaganda and good wishes of those who seem to feel that there is some special virtue in peasant farming.

The locations in which success may be expected are—

(1) Those districts which have a well distributed and reasonably high rainfall with low variability and good soils not markedly deficient in plant foods.

(2) River alluvials where underground waters are available for plants.

(3) Areas around cities where there are special opportunities for casual work and good local markets.

(4) Irrigation areas of a type suited for fruit culture which cannot be readily mechanised or where water is cheap.

In other parts of this continent farming must be on a more or less commercialised basis, depending on the sale of produce rather than on self-sufficiency on the holding. These are the inescapable facts of the Australian environment from the point of view of land-use and land-settlement. The desires of would-be reformers may lie in other directions but attempts to ignore the basic facts in the future will be as costly and disastrous as those of the past.

Chapter XII

THE FORESTS AND FOREST INDUSTRIES OF AUSTRALIA

BY S. L. KESSELL

Formerly Conservator of Forests for Western Australia,
Commonwealth Timber Controller

THE AUSTRALIAN bush is a land of sunshine where the grey-green foliage of widely spaced trees casts little shade. It is the home of the gum tree and the wattle. Both are members of very large plant families which extend over the whole continent and are responsible for the characteristic Australian landscape. Many members of both families have been transported to other continents where they have flourished and multiplied so freely that their Australian origin is being rapidly forgotten.

The gum tree belongs to the genus Eucalyptus, of which there are more than 600 species. They range in size from the stunted mallee of the arid interior to the giant mountain ash of the extreme south-east, and the towering karri in the extreme south-west of the continent, of which many specimens exceed 250 feet in height. There are reliable records of Victorian mountain ash more than 300 feet in height; but none to equal the tallest of the California redwoods, which are now accepted as the tallest trees in the world.

Gum trees, or eucalypts to use the contraction of the generic name favoured by foresters, differ greatly in size, shape, and type of bark. Those carrying a dark, thick, persistent bark with deep fissures are generally referred to as ironbarks, and the term gum tree in most parts of Australia is reserved for those members of the family with a smooth clean bark, the outer layer of which is shed annually. There is an intermediate group of eucalypts known as stringy-barks, with a softer outerbark which peels off readily in layers. All these and many other types, however, share a foliage very characteristic

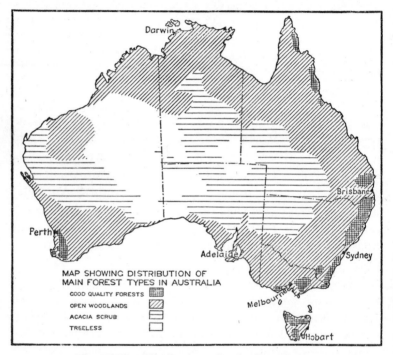

Fig. XVII. Distribution of main forest types.

in design, texture, and oil content, which even the most casual observer is able to recognise.

The other great Australian plant family of wattles or acacias has 629 members on the Australian mainland, which range from small thorny bushes to large forest trees of which the largest and best known is the Tasmanian blackwood. For the most part members of this genus in the better rainfall regions grow as shrubs or small trees among the taller eucalypts;

but in the semi-arid interior there are vast areas of pure acacia "scrub" generally known as mulga, much of which is being used for sheep raising. The leaves of the acacias may vary from soft feathery types to hard thorns; but all share the little yellow balls of blossom and the flat pods with small hard seeds. The floral emblem of Australia is the fragrant yellow blossom of the Golden Wattle (*Acacia pycnantha*) of the Adelaide Hills.

Although the eucalypts and acacias predominate, very many other families are represented in the tree flora of Australia; and the most satisfactory approach to any discussion of the forest industries of Australia is a brief description of the main forest regions, the position and extent of which are shown on the map (see Fig. XVII).

The principal commercial forests of Australia are located in the regions of high and regular rainfall adjacent to the eastern coast line, extending with some breaks from Cape York Peninsula in the north to Tasmania in the south, and in a comparatively small isolated region in the south-western extremity of Western Australia.

Apart from the sandy and stony deserts of the "dead heart of Australia," the balance of the continent is comparatively well wooded considering the low and irregular rainfall which characterises so much of it. The open savannah woodlands of the dry inland areas are of great value to the farming, pastoral, and mining industries which have been established in these regions.

In Queensland the best of the forests follow the eastern slopes of the coastal ranges, where the heavy summer rainfall is responsible for the development of tropical rain forests. These are typical tropical jungles, with ropes of climbing vines and with ferns and orchids growing in the forks and on the trunks of many different species of trees. Important members of these mixed forests are hoop and bunya pines (*Araucaria spp.*), and kauri pine (*Agathis sp.*), and many broad-leaved trees yielding decorative cabinet woods. These forests support a considerable sawmilling industry, and are the main source of both rotary-peeled and sliced plywoods.

Tropical rain forest types continue over the border along the coastal ranges in New South Wales, and extend to the limit of the summer rainfall belt south of Sydney. South of the Queensland border they are referred to generally as brush forests; and, while many of the same species persist, the average size of the trees is smaller and utility timbers tend to replace the highly figured cabinet woods. It is in these forests that valuable stands of coachwood are found, which have proved of special importance during the war. Coachwood logs are being peeled into veneer for the manufacture of aircraft plywood which is equal to the best birch and spruce plywood produced in England and America, and is now being used for the manufacture of Mosquito aircraft in Australia. The wooden parts of rifles and other small arms are also made from this timber. The sawmill output of this forest region was stepped up very considerably during the war to replace softwood supplies no longer obtainable from overseas.

Scattered through and surrounding the narrow belts of rain forest on coastal ranges of New South Wales, there are more open stands of tallowwood, ironbark and other eucalypts, most of which have dense and durable timbers widely used for general structural purposes. From these forests are being obtained most of the long piles and heavy timbers to build wharves and jetties in new naval and military bases being developed in New Guinea and other Pacific Islands.

Entering the winter-rainfall zone south of Sydney the tropical rain forest type fades out, and the forests on both the eastern and western slopes of the coastal ranges consist of practically pure eucalypts with an under forest of acacia species. These forests all have commercial possibilities, and many are being worked for the supply of shipbuilding and general structural timbers.

Over the Victorian border, in the south-east corner of the continent, the rainfall increases to a maximum of approximately fifty inches per annum; and there is a corresponding change in the character of the forest which, in favoured localities of this region, is of a temperate rain forest type consisting of very tall and straight eucalypts with an under storey of tree ferns. The principal tree species is mountain ash (*Eucalyptus regnans*), which is a stately tree with a straight bole reaching to 150 feet before the first branch. Odd specimens more than three hundred feet in height have been measured. These towering trunks rising above the delicate fronds of tree ferns fifteen to twenty feet in height, with a canopy of delicate tracery of eucalyptus leaves far overhead, provide some of the most beautiful forest scenes anywhere in the world. Unfortunately, heavy fires have played havoc with these forests, a large proportion of which were killed in the disastrous fires of January 1939, which it is estimated killed 2,000 million super feet of log timber. Government-sponsored salvage operations have recovered nearly half of this timber, which has been stored in log dumps, or left lying on the floor of the forest where a quick growth of bracken fern and low scrub has prevented sun-cracks developing. These fire-killed logs have provided the bulk of wartime timber supplies in Victoria, and will continue to be the mainstay of the sawmilling industry in this region until 1948, a period of ten years after the fires. The timber of these forests is hardwood, light both in colour and in density, and is extensively used for boards, joinery and building scantling.

The principal commercial forests of Tasmania are of similar temperate rain forest types to those on the ranges of the mainland opposite the island, and support an extensive sawmilling industry mainly producing boards and general building timbers. On the west and north-west coast of Tasmania there are areas of temperate rain forest where myrtle beech (*Nothofagus*), and sassafras (*Atherosperma moschata*), are the dominant species. These evergreens of the so-called myrtle forests have a denser foliage than the eucalypts; and the branches and boles of the trees are covered with lichens, while the floor of the forest which the direct sunlight never reaches is permanently moist and covered with moss and small ferns.

After leaving the south-eastern section of Victoria, there are no forests of commercial importance along the whole two thousand miles of the southern coastline until the extreme south-west of Western Australia is reached. Before moving to Western Australia, however, some notes on the hardwood forests of the hinterland of the east coast are necessary to complete an account of the commercial forests of that region. On the west of the mountain ranges which follow the coastline are eucalypt forests, those in the north are of low milling value, but south of Maryborough they increase in quality and depth. In New South Wales these inland forests of ironbark and other dense-timbered eucalypts extend for a hundred miles or more west of the coastal ranges; and have provided in the past very large quantities of railway sleepers and timber for bridging, building and general farming purposes. Much of this land has been cleared for wheat growing and grazing.

Another interesting forest type rapidly disappearing from this region as a result of clearing for agricultural purposes is cypress pine (*Callitris spp.*). This so-called pine grows in open parklike stands, and the timber is highly valued on account of its resistance to termites. Regrowth is prolific; but the rate of growth is disappointingly slow, as might be expected in view of the low annual rainfall and the long dry summers. There is still a considerable sawmilling industry operating on the remnants of cypress pine forests on private property and forest reserves which have been retained by the Crown both in Queensland and New South Wales.

South Australia is a State without indigenous forests of any great commercial importance, although large quantities of timber for domestic requirements are obtained from the second-class eucalypt forests of the ranges which follow the eastern coast of St. Vincent's Gulf, more particularly from the Adelaide Hills and portions of the State south of Adelaide.

Western Australia has a vast area of 625 million acres, of which less than four million acres in the extreme south-west corner carry commercial forest. This small and compact forest region is State-owned and is permanently dedicated to timber production. It is possibly one of the most valuable hardwood forests in the world, and consists of three million acres of almost pure jarrah forest and 350,000 acres of karri forest. Jarrah is a rough-barked eucalypt (*Eucalyptus marginata*), which grows to 150 feet or more in height and has a clear bole of up to eighty feet. The timber is durable, red in colour, and dense (weighing fifty-one pounds to the cubic foot when air-dried); but it is easily worked and takes a fine finish. In consequence it has a wide range of uses, extending from railway sleepers and street-paving blocks to fine carving and cabinet work. It is the general utility timber of Western Australia, where it is used to build homes and to furnish them throughout. It is also exported in considerable quantities to England and countries around the Indian Ocean. Karri (*Eucalyptus diversicolor*) ranks second to jarrah as a timber in Western Australia. It has the same red colour as jarrah and is stronger for superstructural work; but it does not work so easily to a smooth finish. As a forest tree it is much more impressive, rivalling the mountain ash of Victoria in height and grandeur. It has a clean grey-white bark; and a pure forest of karri, towering more than two hundred feet in total height with tall glistening trunks six to ten feet in diameter at the base and rising straight as a gun barrel to the first branch 100 feet to 150 feet above the ground, is a memorable sight. The beauty of the forest is enhanced by the open nature of the stand and the absence of any dense under storey, so that long vistas extend in all directions, framed by white tree trunks patterned with sunlight, and carpeted with bracken fern and soft-foliaged plants six to eight feet in height. In the spring many of these plants carry masses of blue and yellow flowers. Some day these forests will be numbered among the tourist attractions of the world.

The jarrah and karri forests of Western Australia are among the few forests in the Empire which are managed on a basis of sustained annual yield. Regeneration operations are regulated to keep ahead of exploitation. Management plans also aim to maintain a permanent rural industry engaged in the protection, tending, and working of these valuable forests. Intensive fire-control has been developed to protect the forests from the summer fires, which were threatening twenty years ago to reduce them to waste land carrying only malformed regrowth. Those responsible for their protection and management have to contend every year with four or five months of summer drought. Except in the karri forest near the south coast all the rain, which varies from thirty-five inches annually in the north of the belt to fifty inches in the south, falls in the winter months. A compensating advantage is that the land is generally fairly level, and lends itself to easy access and cheap road construction.

East of the jarrah and karri forests the average annual rainfall decreases very rapidly. In many places the distance between the forty-inch isohyet and the twenty-inch isohyet is no more than twenty miles; which, in the absence of mountain ranges and any marked changes in elevation, is rather remarkable. In this belt the forest becomes more open and jarrah gives way to wandoo, a eucalypt having a denser and harder timber. In colonies throughout the wandoo belt occur another interesting group of eucalypts known as the mallets, whose bark is very high in tannin content and is stripped for use by the leather industry in Australia and Europe. The original scattered stands of mallet have all been destroyed by bark stripping, but the species is being preserved and its habitat extended in large plantations established by the Western Australian Government during recent years. Many of the hard woody perennials which grow on the floor of the wandoo and mallet forests are toxic to stock; and this fact, associated with the generally poor nature of the soil, has limited agricultural and pastoral development in this region to the broad belts of alluvial soil which follow the ancient river systems which appear as dry watercourses for most of the year.

Lying inland from the commercial forests already described along the east coast and in the extreme south-west, are vast stretches of open eucalypt and acacia forests, which extend from the stony or sandy deserts of the interior to the coastline in the north and north-west of the continent. The open forests of these regions are, for the most part, a parklike growth of trees with a ground cover of grass or low herbage such as salt-bush and bluebush, which have a considerable value for grazing. These dry-country eucalypts have solved the problem of existing on a minimum of water. How they grow to a height of sixty to seventy feet with twenty or more trees to the acre, in regions having intermittent rain averaging only eight or ten inches per annum, with drought periods of two or more years during which practically no rain falls, is one of the problems which botanists have not yet been able to solve. A good example of this type of forest stretches around Kalgoorlie, the inland gold-mining town of Western Australia, where the sun shines brightly nearly every day of the year and the temperature in the shade is around 100° F. on most days in summer. The solution of the problem of forest growth in this desert region is not to be found in underground water supply, since it is necessary to sink 150 feet or more before reaching water, which is invariably more highly mineralised than sea water. The happy circumstance that these forests do exist has been an important factor in making gold mining economically possible; and special railway lines have been run in all directions for a radius of one hundred miles from Kalgoorlie to bring firewood and mining timber from these forests to the mines.

The other typical forest of the dry interior consists of various species of acacia commonly referred to as mulga, which may range from shrubs ten feet high to trees forty feet in height. In mulga country good stock water is usually obtained by boring. This fact, coupled with the value of the ground herbage and the seed pods and even the leaves of the mulga as stock feed, has resulted in most of this country being used up for sheep grazing. In favourable years a good growth of grass follows any heavy rain, with the result that a series of good years generally leads to over-stocking; and, in many parts of the dry interior, there is a steady deterioration taking place in vegetative types owing to this cause.

An interesting small tree scattered through many of the dry inland forests in Western Australia and South Australia is sandalwood. A close relative of the royal tree of India whose timber is so prized for small carvings and for burning as incense in temple braziers, the Australian sandalwood has the same aromatic wood. It is one of the romances of modern commerce that sandalwood should have been discovered on the early wheat farms of Western Australia, when trading junks from China could no longer secure sufficient supplies of the precious wood from the Pacific Islands. It was one of the first exports from the port of Fremantle, and for the past sixty years most of the sandalwood burnt in the temples in China has come from this source.

Sales of sandalwood helped many a struggling farmer in the early days of the Colony, and as supplies were no longer available from the wheat lands the sandalwood-getter pioneered tracks into the waterless interior, and blazed the trail for the prospectors who discovered many of the gold fields in the eighteen nineties and early nineteen hundreds.

In the year preceding the war Australia used approximately 1,000,000,000 super feet * of timber. Of this quantity about 650,000,000 super feet were produced locally and 350,000,000 super feet were imported.

The graph (see Fig. XVIII) showing (a) local production, (b) imports, (c) exports, and (d) consumption, illustrates

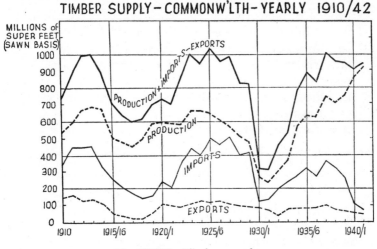

Fig. XVIII. Timber supply.

some interesting features of the timber industry which may be summarised briefly as follows:

1. Timber consumption is a remarkably accurate index of general prosperity. Demand for timber fluctuates with the "ups and downs" of business activity. During the 1914–18 war, construction in Australia fell and the timber trade slumped. The trade boom which developed after the war and continued until 1929 with a series of new high peaks in timber usage, the economic depression between 1930 and 1933, and the recovery up to the outbreak of the present war are clearly shown.

* A super foot is the same unit of volume as the American board foot. Twelve super feet or twelve board feet equal one cubic foot.

Of special significance is the manner in which timber consumption has been maintained since the war commenced in 1939. In this war not only has Australia provided an Army, Navy, and Air Force of considerable magnitude in comparison with her population, but she has set out to equip both her own fighting services and to help her Allies with large quantities of equipment and foodstuffs. As a result there has been little decline in the demand for timber since the outbreak of war, although private building has been practically prohibited.

2. Local timber production and timber imports are complementary, and these lines in the graph show similar trends from 1910 to the outbreak of the recent war. Since 1939, principally owing to shortage of shipping, imports were no longer available to meet the continuing war demand. This has thrown a great strain on the local sawmilling industry, which in spite of serious shortages of manpower and transport difficulties has responded in a remarkable manner and provided the bulk of urgently needed timber supplies.

3. Over the 33-year period shown in the graph, exports have shown a gradual downward trend. These exports, mostly of hardwoods from Western Australia, have been supplied as railway sleepers, wharf timbers, mine guides, waggon scantling, telegraph crossarms, flooring and general building timbers to countries around the Indian Ocean (particularly South Africa, Ceylon, and Egypt) with lesser quantities to England and European countries. The only other timber export of any importance is that from New South Wales of durable hardwoods for public works in New Zealand in exchange for softwoods from that country.

The sawmilling industry in Australia is for the most part in the hands of small operators who work mills producing from one million to three million super feet of sawn timber per annum. One reason for this is that the forests, with few exceptions, do not carry a high volume of merchantable timber per acre, and it must be hauled to the mills over roads or tramlines.

Timber, therefore, cannot be assembled cheaply in large quantities as is possible with water transport of logs down rivers. Another reason is the class of log which has to be sawn. Nearly all eucalypt logs, which are the principal species milled, have a "pipe" through the centre or some other form of faulty heart with "star shakes" radiating out into the solid timber. This means that the sawing of every log is a problem which has to be given some care if a satisfactory recovery of sawn timber is to be obtained.

The bush sawmill, therefore, although often somewhat primitive in appearance and lacking the air of efficiency associated with a modern industrial plant, is effective for the class of forest and type of log treated. There is, however, plenty of scope for improvement in sawmilling practice in Australia, as in most other countries where virgin forests are being worked to supply distant markets.

The following is the output of sawn timber by States in 1938–39, divided into main classes already described in the section dealing with forest regions:

Queensland:	Super Feet
Eucalypts	66,500,000
Hoop, bunya and kauri pines	108,200,000
Scrubwood including N.Q. cabinet timbers	19,700,000
Cypress pine	7,900,000
Total	202,300,00

The 1941–42 total to meet wartime requirements was 228,300,000 super feet, or about 25.5 per cent of total production.

New South Wales:	Super Feet
Eucalypts	104,500,000
Brushwoods	16,500,000
Cypress pine	33,000,000
Hoop pine	7,100,000
Exotic pines	200,000
Total	161,300,000

By 1941–42 this had been increased to 218,500,000 super feet (24.5 per cent).

Victoria:	Super Feet
Eucalypts	126,200,000
Exotic pines	7,800,000
Total	134,000,000

The 1941–42 figure was 216,200,000 super feet (24.1 per cent).

Tasmania:	Super Feet
Eucalypts	55,800,000
Other species	5,800,000
Total	61,600,000

The 1941–42 total was 94,000,000 super feet (10.5 per cent).

South Australia:	Super Feet
Eucalypts	4,600,000
Exotic pines	9,700,000
Total	14,300,000

The 1941–42 total was 14,100,000 super feet (1.6 per cent).

Western Australia:	Super Feet
Eucalypts	
Jarrah	105,800,000
Karri	18,500,000
Other eucalypts	4,700,000
Exotic pines	200,000
Total	129,200,000

The 1941–42 total was 124,200,000 super feet (13.8 per cent).

Australia has now no vast unused tracts of virgin forest. Sawmilling has been developed beyond a safe limit in all the best commercial forests, with the possible exception of North Queensland. Only in the jarrah and karri forests of Western Australia has the output of the sawmilling industry been restricted by regulation to the calculated yield capacity of the forest; and it has been necessary to close sawmills to attain this objective.

Other States have small areas of virgin forest still to be developed, and many mills have a long life ahead of them; but, for the main part, the forests of Australia are a wasting asset which will require very careful management and silvicultural attention before the increment overtakes the annual loss through fire damage and exploitation. Measures being taken to correct this position are dealt with under the heading of Forest Conservation and Development.

THE PLYWOOD INDUSTRY

The plywood industry is well organized, and under normal conditions produces more than 130 million square feet of utility plywoods per annum. During recent years steady progress has been made in the manufacture of resin-bonded plywoods for special industrial uses, and in the production of sliced veneers from highly figured timbers for furniture and panelling. Many of the sliced veneers, particularly Queensland "walnut," cut from the stumps of large trees from the rain forests of North Queensland, are very beautiful, and were finding a considerable market in the United States as well as in Australia and New Zealand before the war. During the war all production of fancy veneers has been prohibited; and the labour used in the forest and plywood factories has been diverted to the production of utility plywoods required for war purposes.

PULP, PAPER, AND WALLBOARDS

Thirty years ago the manufacture of paper from eucalypt timber was considered impracticable. Today, as a result of research work by Australian chemists, there are large modern factories in Australia producing newsprint, fine printing and writing paper, and brown wrapping paper from eucalypt pulp, mixed with a small percentage of long-fibred imported pulp in the case of newsprint and wrapping paper. The log intake of the Boyer Newsprint pulp and paper plant in Southern Tasmania is 21 million super feet per annum, and the production of paper is thirty thousand tons per annum. The pulp and paper mill at Burnie on the north-west coast of Tasmania uses seventy thousand cords of timber a year for pulp and fuel for the production of twenty thousand tons of paper. The Kraft Paper Mill at Maryvale, which uses eucalpyt thinnings from the Victorian forests, requires 48 million super feet of wood per annum for pulp and fuel, and has an output of thirty-one thousand tons of pulp and twenty thousand tons of paper per annum. A new pulp and paper plant to operate on thinnings from pine plantations in the south-east of South Australia is nearing completion. In the Newcastle district of New South Wales there is a plant making wallboards from eucalypt pulp only and producing 28 million square feet per annum.

Other forest regions in Australia where large quantities of thinnings are becoming available from regeneration operations offer scope for considerable expansion of pulping and other chemical industries using wood as a raw material. These forests have the advantage that regrowth is prolific and grows rapidly to pulpwood sizes, so that ample supplies of raw material in reasonable proximity to the mill may be assured for all time.

OTHER FOREST INDUSTRIES

In Australian forests there are many minor forest products with commercial possibilities awaiting development. Useful industries have been established in the distillation of oil from the leaves of certain eucalypts, and sandalwood oil from the timber of that species. Wattle bark from certain species of acacia rich in tannin has been used extensively by the leather industry, mostly as raw bark. Mallet, a Western Australian eucalypt very rich in tannin, has been exported mostly to Germany as a tanning bark.

Within the last few years a new industry has been developed in the south-west of Western Australia—making a tanning extract from the wood of wandoo, a very dense eucalypt timber containing about eleven per cent of tannin. This extract produces a soft pliable leather, and is finding favour as a substitute for chestnut extract from Central Europe. By mixing it with extracts of mallet bark which grows in the same locality, blended extracts suitable for the production of any class of leather can be obtained. The quantity of wandoo timber used by the single plant now operating amounts to 61,000 tons per annum and there is scope for a number of additional plants.

To study problems of forest utilisation, the Commonwealth Government established in 1928 a Forest Products Laboratory as a Division of its Council for Scientific and Industrial Research. During the war this institution has proved a handsome investment of public funds, because scientific data accumulated in pre-war years has enabled many essential war industries to be supplied from local sources. Important instances of the substitution of Australian-grown timbers for previously imported material include scented satinwood (*Ceratopetalum apetalum*) for birch (*Batula sp.*) in aircraft plywood, and for walnut (*Juglans sp.*) in rifle furniture, hoop pine (*Araucaria cunninghamii*) for Port Oxford cedar in battery separators, Queensland maple (*Flindersia brayleyana*) for mahogany in aircraft propellors and boatbuilding, white birch (*Schizomeria ovata*) and radiata pine for aspen in matches, spotted gum (*Eucalyptus maculata*) for hickory in axe and hammer handles, silver quandong (*Elaeocarpus grantis*) and hoop pine for spruce in spoon-bladed oars, Queensland maple and scented satinwood for Gaboon mahogany (*Aucoumea klaineana*) and birch in plywood panels, and she-oak (*Casuarina sp.*) and myrtle beech (*Nothofagus cunninghamii*) for maple (*Acer. sp.*) in boot lasts.

FOREST CONSERVATION AND DEVELOPMENT

As in all countries developed by British stock, the early settlers did not bring with them any tradition of forestry as an occupation or forests as a crop. Trees were an encumbrance on the land hindering the development of food crops or pasture. In the pioneering stages clearing was necessary and inevitable; but, in many areas, destruction of the indigenous forest went too far. The Australian community is now forced to repair the mischief as far as possible, and to strike a balance between the various forms of cultivation including forests.

In one respect Australia has been fortunate. Although many of its best forest areas have been thrown open to grazing and made available for sawmilling on very easy terms, the tenure given to grazier and sawmiller has been leasehold for a fixed term of years with the State retaining the title to the land. This has meant that after years of maltreatment by burning and uncontrolled exploitation, the land and the timber remaining on it have reverted to the State. All States of the Commonwealth now have legislation dedicating timber areas as State Forests in perpetuity; and the total area of commercial forest dedicated is approaching the target figure of 19 million acres set nearly twenty years ago by a conference of forest authorities from all the States.

Each State now has its own Forest Service, staffed with professional officers; and considerable progress has been made in the rehabilitation of indigenous forests and the establishment of softwood plantations. However, the leeway resulting from a century of indifference or neglect cannot be made good in one or two decades; and there is great scope for productive work of national value in post-war years, in extending measures for the protection and regeneration of indigenous forests, and establishing plantations of pine to make good Australia's serious shortage of softwood timbers.

Australia is a country with many trees, but a relatively small area of dense forest. It has abundant hardwoods of great strength and durability but is deficient in general-utility softwoods. For many years to come it will need to import a considerable volume of timber to meet its industrial requirements, for the principal reason that forestry as a rural industry has not kept pace with the rapid development of other primary and secondary industries. There is now a much keener appreciation than formerly of the importance of the protection and development of the national forest estate. Accelerated progress on this work offers great scope for remunerative employment of labour under healthy and congenial conditions in post-war years, particularly in the transition period immediately after the war when other industry is being adjusted to a peacetime basis.

Chapter XIII

WATER CONSERVATION AND IRRIGATION

BY LEWIS R. EAST

Chairman, State Rivers and Water Supply Commission, Victoria

THE average annual rainfall over two-thirds of Australia's total area of three million square miles is less than twenty inches, and as a consequence there are few great inland rivers, and even these are very intermittent in their flow. Fortunately, underground water of good quality can be obtained over large areas at reasonable depths, and the pastoral occupation of many thousand square miles of country depends almost entirely on artesian and sub-artesian supplies. Apart from comparatively short coastal streams, the only more or less permanent rivers are the Murray and its tributaries which, during the winter months, take a large volume of water through the sub-arid inland areas of the south-east.

THE MURRAY-DARLING RIVER SYSTEM

The catchment of the River Murray and its tributaries comprises some 414,000 square miles extending from Victoria across New South Wales and into Queensland. Only 159,000 square miles of this area can, however, be regarded as contributing to the river-flow, and some of it to a small degree only. Part of the catchment has a heavy rainfall ranging up to seventy inches per annum, and some of the mountainous areas in the south-east are covered with snow for several months in each year, but the average annual rainfall over the whole area is only seventeen inches. The rainfall, moreover, varies considerably from year to year, with consequent great variation in the stream-flow. The fluctuation of flow from month to month may also be very marked.

In other inland streams seasonal variations are even greater than with the Murray, and in dry periods large streams frequently dwindle to mere chains of water-holes. Quite a number of Australian rivers, after leaving the hills as considerable streams, traverse hundreds of miles of non-contributing plain country in the passage of which their flows are diminished by evaporation and percolation to such an extent that, save in occasional years of exceptional rainfall, they disappear altogether. Examples of these are the Lachlan River in New South Wales, whose waters seldom reach the Murrumbidgee River to which stream the Lachlan is tributary, and the Wimmera River in Victoria, which, flowing northerly into the sandy Mallee country, does not reach the Murray at all.

IRRIGATION WORKS AND POLICY

It has long been realized in Australia that storages are essential for the economic use of available supplies and, especially in Victoria and New South Wales, all Governments for many years have followed progressive policies in regard to water conservation. Practically all waterworks of importance in Australia have been constructed and controlled by public bodies, either State or local. Earlier works were confined almost entirely to storages and distributary works for the domestic and industrial requirements of growing centres of population; irrigation on a large scale was not seriously considered during the first hundred years of Australia's history. In 1882 two Victorian municipalities, the Echuca and Waranga shires, combined to initiate what has now become the Goulburn-Waranga irrigation system, which, with its twenty-four hundred miles of irrigation channels, waters a third of a million acres of Northern Victoria.

Before this irrigation scheme was begun, the problem of maintaining water supplies for stock requirements in these areas had become increasingly urgent, and after the 1877 and 1881 droughts it was clearly seen that, without artificial means of water supply, the Victorian northern plains could not be developed. The Victorian Government then began the systematic regulation of the north-flowing streams by weirs in order to provide supplies for stock on waterless plains. The

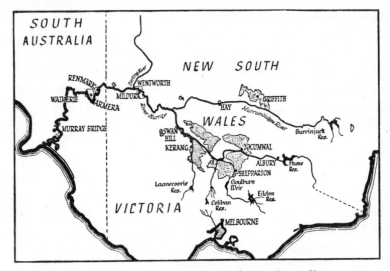

Fig. XIX. Irrigation areas, south-east Australia.

whole position, however, in regard to water supply was still far from satisfactory, and in 1886 Parliament passed an Irrigation Act which marked a new era in the history of water-supply legislation. This revolutionary act vested in the Crown the right to the use of water in any stream, lake, or swamp; provided that no riparian rights could be established in the future that might prevent the use of water for irrigation; authorized the construction of national works by the State; and enabled directly elected trusts to carry out their schemes with money advanced by the Government.

Then followed a period during which local trusts were constituted and irrigation projects undertaken in all parts of Victoria. The Government itself constructed an irrigation storage on the Loddon River and a substantial weir on the Goulburn as national works, the latter to divert water to the Waranga channel system. Works were also carried out to take water from the Murray River for the irrigation of lands between Kow Swamp and Kerang.

A particularly interesting development was the establishment of irrigation settlements at Mildura and Renmark by the Chaffey brothers, who came to Australia from California and saw in what was then a desolate remote corner of the State the possibilities of irrigation. To their genius and vision we owe the thriving settlements that in Victoria today supply nearly two-thirds of Australia's dried-fruit production, which for 1944 reached 104,000 tons, valued at nearly £6,000,000.

By 1900 there were nearly ninety irrigation and waterworks trusts in operation in Victoria, but it was not until the constitution of the State Rivers and Water Supply Commission in 1906 that these trusts were taken over and a State policy inaugurated. Realizing that sound irrigation and water-supply development in Victoria must always be dependent upon the availability of water supplies, and that these could be assured from intermittently flowing streams only by the storage of winter flows for use in summer, the Commission from its inception has followed a progressive policy of water conservation.

At the time of the great drought of 1902, which so clearly demonstrated the necessity for water conservation, the total capacity of storages in Victoria was 172,000 acre-feet. The construction and subsequent enlargement of the Waranga Basin, the completion of the Eildon Reservoir and of numerous smaller storages, and the additional supply made available to Victoria as its half share of the Hume Reservoir have now increased this to 1,908,900 acre-feet, or 530,000,000,000 gallons. Plans are ready for a large increase of the total storage after the war. The major storage is now the Hume Reservoir on the Murray River just below its junction with the Mitta Mitta near Albury. The structure itself—a joint work with New South Wales—provides for an ultimate height of 118 feet and a total length of a little more than a mile.

The capacity of the storage to the spillway crest is now 1,250,000 acre feet, and provision has been made for the installation later of twenty-nine vertical-lift steel gates twenty feet in width to raise the water level a further twenty feet, thus increasing the storage to two million acre-feet.

Increases in water storages have been followed by a vast increase in irrigation. The total area of lands in Victoria commanded by irrigation channels (of which there are more than five thousand miles) is now two million acres, and the area actually irrigated is nearly seven hundred thousand acres as against one hundred thousand acres when the Commission was constituted in 1906.

Practically one-half of the total area is supplied from the Goulburn system, whose two storages—Eildon and Waranga Reservoirs—hold between them nearly two-thirds of a million acre-feet. Water released from Eildon Reservoir finds its way down the Goulburn River for 150 miles to the Goulburn Weir, where a portion of the flow is diverted into the eastern channel to irrigate Shepparton and Katandra, but the greater part into the western channel and on to Waranga Reservoir, whence it can be distributed throughout the northern plains between the Goulburn and the Loddon Rivers. The Waranga Western Channel now crosses the Loddon River and goes on to Birchip, a distance of 230 miles, to supplement the Wimmera-Mallee domestic and stock-supply scheme.

The supply for another great gravitation system—the Torrumbarry system extending from Cohuna to Swan Hill—is drawn from the Murray River at Torrumbarry, fifty-two miles downstream from Echuca, where a weir raises the summer level of the river some sixteen feet and thus enables water to be diverted from the river throughout the year. A lock provides for the passage of river craft while the weir is in operation.

The weir itself—an original design evolved by J. S. Dethridge, an eminent Australian engineer—comprises a series of movable steel trestles running on a concrete foundation and provided with wooden drop-bars to keep the river up to diverting level. In times of flood the bars are removed, and the trestles themselves drawn right out of the stream on to the river bank.

Other gravitation schemes of note are the Bacchus Marsh and Werribee schemes supplied from the Pykes Creek and Melton Reservoirs, and the Maffra-Sale scheme supplied from a large storage on the Macalister River at Glenmaggie. There are as well a number of important irrigation schemes supplied by pumping from the Murray River. Of these, the most important are the Red Cliffs, Mildura, and Merbein group, which form a compact area of thirty thousand acres of vineyards, citrus groves, and orchards. At Nyah, also, some three thousand acres are similarly supplied.

Irrigation development is still proceeding. The limit will not be the quantity of land that is suitable for irrigation— such land can be measured by millions of acres—but will be the total amount of water which can be conserved and distributed to these lands.

THE WIMMERA-MALLEE OPEN-CHANNEL SYSTEM

Work of no less importance is represented by the extension of domestic and stock-supply channels throughout the Wimmera and into the Mallee wheat-growing areas. Since 1906 the area served by the Wimmera-Mallee scheme alone has been more than trebled, until now more than eleven thousand square miles are supplied by its channels. To serve this area, which includes forty-three townships, and has a population of 120,000 persons, more than sixty-six hundred miles of channels have been constructed. The longest channel carries water a distance of 375 miles from the storages in the Grampians into the far north. The total capacity of the storages of the scheme, Lake Lonsdale, Wartook Reservoir, and others, is now two hundred thousand acre-feet, of which slightly less than one-half is required for watering the whole area in an average year. The system is safeguarded against any possibility of shortage even in an exceptionally dry period by an extension of the Waranga-Mallee channel which enables supplies to be brought to it from the Goulburn system if required.

There are, in addition to the Wimmera-Mallee gravitation system, several independent schemes where large areas totalling more than a thousand square miles are served by channels filled by pumping from the Murray River.

In domestic and stock-supply districts, farmers are required to provide excavated earthen storages on their farms of sufficient capacity to meet all their water requirements for twelve months, and the channels are run once only each year to fill them, generally during the winter months to reduce evaporation losses.

Outside the channel areas, a million acres of Mallee lands lying near the South Australian boundary are supplied by sub-artesian bores. In this area 110 five-inch bores have been put down, and by the aid of large windmills and storage tanks local farms are supplied.

The magnitude of the task of supplying rural Victoria with water may be appreciated when it is recognized that, by channels, bores, and other methods, approximately one-fourth of the whole area of the State is now artificially supplied with drinking water for domestic and stock purposes, and that the

State has, as a direct result of its expenditure on water supply, added to its productive area whole provinces which would otherwise have been practically non-productive. A weir has been constructed across the Murray at Yarrawonga, from which channels will convey water to an area of four hundred thousand acres at present unsupplied.

WATER CONSERVATION IN NEW SOUTH WALES

In New South Wales, the history of irrigation is very largely the history of the conservation and distribution of the waters of the Murrumbidgee River from the great 232-foot-high masonry dam at Burrinjuck, which forms a vast artificial lake of 771,600 acre-feet capacity. Water released from this storage finds its way down the Murrumbidgee River for 240 miles to a movable weir where it is diverted into an artificial river—the Murrumbidgee main canal—which conveys it to the irrigation areas. The main canal itself is ninety miles in length, and the area irrigated from sixty thousand to seventy thousand acres, utilised chiefly for rice, fruit, and fodder crops. It is of interest to note that the twenty thousand acres devoted to rice growing produce the whole of Australia's requirements of this commodity, and that Allied troops in the South-west Pacific have been largely supplied from this area.

Other irrigation schemes in New South Wales, though on a much smaller scale, are the settlements on the Murray at Curlwaa and Coomealla, and the Hay irrigation area on the Murrumbidgee devoted to citrus and dried-fruit production.

The most recent development in New South Wales has been the construction of works for the distribution throughout the southern Riverina of that State's share of the Murray waters. Already a weir and channels have been completed for the purpose of irrigating some forty thousand acres in a total area of 537,000 acres known as the Wakool district, and a canal to carry 5,000 acre-feet a day has been built from the Murray River to the Berriquin district of 605,000 acres, of which it is intended to irrigate fifty-six thousand acres. The Berriquin and Wakool areas are limited to fodder crops, it being specially stated by the irrigation authority that water will not be provided for rice culture or for commercial orchards and vineyards.

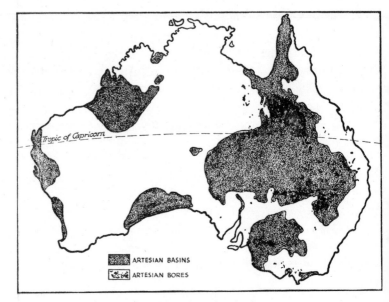

Fig. XX. Artesian basins.

In New South Wales, as in Victoria, there are extensive works for the provision of domestic and stock supplies in rural districts, and several million acres are supplied with water from bores or from artificially regulated streams controlled by Trusts. An interesting development is the project to pipe water for domestic supplies from a low-level lock at Menindee on the Darling to Broken Hill seventy-two miles distant in the arid inland area.

In South Australia, irrigation is confined to a number of settlements supplied by pumping from the Murray River, the total area irrigated being in the vicinity of forty thousand acres, of which the greater part is devoted to fruit and vine cultivation. An interesting development is the scheme, now completed, for taking water from the River Murray at Morgan 230 miles to Whyalla, a steel-making centre on Spencer's Gulf.

Rural domestic and stock-supply works are quite extensive, and large areas of farm lands are reticulated with pipe-lines through which water for drinking purposes is supplied under pressure. The Tod River scheme supplies nearly ten thousand square miles west of Spencer's Gulf through a 240-mile-long main and more than a thousand miles of distributary pipes.

The first pipe-line scheme in Australia, if not the world, was that constructed in Western Australia in 1906 for the supply of the Kalgoorlie gold fields. The works of this extremely bold and ambitious scheme comprise the Mundaring Reservoir in the coastal ranges, and a series of eight pumping stations which force five million gallons per day through a thirty-inch diameter steel pipe-line across 350 miles of arid and semi-arid country to deliver it at a level 1,290 feet above the reservoir.

On the decline of the demand for water for gold-mining purposes, a new and increasing demand has arisen for domestic and stock supplies to wheat lands adjoining the pipe-line, and extensions of the scheme are planned to supply additional areas. Some of these are already in operation. Another scheme near Denmark, in the coastal area south of Perth, has mad Western Australia self-sufficient in butter and cheese.

Other interesting water-conservation works are the rock catchments in Western Australia, and the galvanized iron or "ironclad" artificial catchments in the Victorian Mallee.

Apart from the Inkerman irrigation area, where some six thousand acres of sugar cane are irrigated by water pumped from wells in the Burdekin River delta inland from Towns-ville, and some development in the Dawson Valley, irrigation in Queensland has not yet gone very far. The total area of agricultural land artificially watered in that State is about ninety thousand acres. For the watering of stock, however, a vast area is supplied from nearly five thousand artesian and sub-artesian bores, which range in depth from a few feet up to seven thousand feet—the total depth drilled being over 780 miles, and the daily flow more than 300 million gallons.

The basin from which these bores are supplied—the Great Artesian Basin—is said to be the largest discovered, and covers an area of six hundred thousand square miles, one-fifth of the whole area of Australia. The greater part of this basin is in Queensland, but it includes 118,000 square miles in South Australia, eighty thousand square miles in New South Wales and twenty-five thousand square miles in the Northern Territory.

Other extensive artesian basins known to exist are the Murray River Basin, the Eucla Basin bordering the Great Australian Bight, and the Coastal, North-west, and Desert Basins of Western Australia, all of which have been utilized to some extent.

It has not been possible in this article to cover all aspects of water conservation in Australia, or to deal at all with town supplies or inland navigation, but it will be seen that, in the conservation and distribution of water both for domestic and stock use and for irrigation, the water supply engineer has had to play and is yet to play a most important part in con-quest of the climatic vagaries of the continent.

Chapter XIV

MINERAL RESOURCES

BY AUSTIN EDWARDS

Research Officer, Council for Scientific and Industrial Research, Melbourne

AUSTRALIAN mining began with the opening of copper mines at Kapunda and Burra Burra in South Australia after 1840, but it received its real impetus from the gold rushes that followed the discovery of gold in 1851. In those days, Australians and the world at large were dazzled by the discovery, in quick succession, of a series of rich and varied ore deposits that immediately made Australia one of the chief mineral-producing countries of the world. These discoveries, stimulating settlement of the back country, resulted in the establishment of mining towns and so influenced the development of the railway systems. A number of the chief towns of the Commonwealth still depend on mining, such as Broken Hill, Kalgoorlie, and Queenstown, or are metallurgical centres, like Newcastle, Port Kembla, Whyalla and Port Pirie. Many of the mining towns faded with the mines that called them into existence; but some like Bendigo and Ballarat remain as agricultural and pastoral centres, so that the print of the mineral deposits is stamped upon the pattern of the Australian economy.

Gold occupies a special place in the Australian imagination because, following wool, gold gave the country its second great fillip and provided the most colourful period of its history. Ballarat, Bendigo, Mount Morgan, the Kalgoorlie Golden Mile became names to conjure with. The base metals also provided bonanza mines such as Mount Bischoff, formerly the

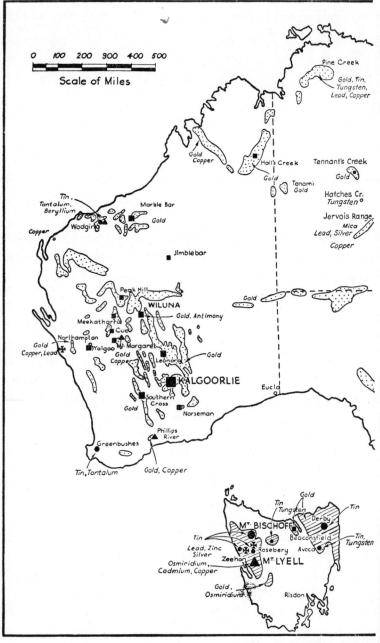

Fig. XXI. Mineralisation

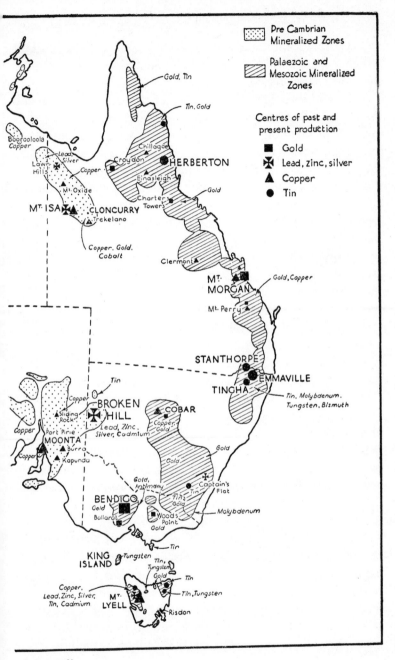

Pre Cambrian
Mineralized Zones

Palaezoic and
Mesozoic Mineralized
Zones

Centres of past and
present production

■ Gold
✠ Lead, zinc, silver
▲ Copper
● Tin

Gold, Tin

Tin, Gold

Boorooloola
Copper

Lead,
Silver

Lawn
Hills

Copper

Mt. Oxide

Mt. ISA   CLONCURRY

▲Trekelano

Copper, Gold,
Cobalt

Chillagoe

Croydon   HERBERTON

Einasleigh

Charters
Towers

Gold

Clermont   ▲

Mt.
MORGAN

Mt. Perry   ▲

Gold, Copper

STANTHORPE

EMMAVILLE

TINGHA

Tin, Molybdenum,
Tungsten, Bismuth

Tin

Copper

Sliding
Rock

BROKEN
HILL

COBAR

Copper

Port Pirie

MOONTA   ▲Burra

Copper   ▲ Kapunda

Lead, Zinc,
Silver, Cadmium

Copper,
Gold

Gold

Gold

Gold,
Antimony

Captain's
Flat

BENDIGO

Gold

Ballarat

Tin,
Gold

Tin

Woods
Point

Gold

Molybdenum

Tin

KING
ISLAND

Tungsten

Tin,
Tungsten
Gold

Tin

Copper,
Lead, Zinc, Silver,
Tin, Cadmium

Mt.
LYELL

Tin, Tungsten

Risdon

of Australia.

179

world's richest tin mine, and the famous mines of Broken Hill which still, and will for many years, take pride of place among the world's non-ferrous deposits.

With the invention of the Bessemer process in 1858, which marked the beginning of the age of cheap steel, the world's mineral production rose steeply. Australian production of lead, zinc, and silver has kept pace with world production; but the other metals, particularly copper and tin, have failed to show a comparable increase. For these metals production has either been maintained at its pre-1900 level, or has declined, so that Australia now contributes a relatively minor share of the world's mineral production. The value of production per head of population, however, still stands amongst the highest, especially if coal is excluded, the output of which is set by the needs of the community and certainly does not measure the productive capacity of Australian coal fields. The total realized value of minerals produced from the beginning of mining to 1940 was £1,500 millions, of which about one-half was paid for gold. The average annual value of mineral production is now about £40 millions in Australian currency.

Mineralisation is widely spread throughout the old Pre-Cambrian and Palaeozoic rocks which come to the surface, or close to it, throughout a large part of the continent but are often masked by desert sands or surface detritus. Many ore bodies have probably disintegrated during the prolonged erosion to which these ancient rocks have been subjected, and their mineral content has been dispersed, except for gold and tin which collected in numerous placer deposits.

The Pre-Cambrian mineralisation is exposed in three broad regions which lie to the west, east, and north of the Eucla basin, coincident with the outcrops of the older Pre-Cambrian rocks (the Archaeozoic and Lower Proterozoic groups). The western region embraces the series of gold fields that extends at intervals through the western half of Western Australia, from the Pilbara district in the north to the Phillips River field in the south. (See Fig. XXI.) These include the highly productive gold fields centred on Kalgoorlie, Leonora, and Cue. The region is predominantly a gold province with minor deposits of copper, tin, lead, chrome ore, and the rarer minerals of the pegmatites.

The eastern Pre-Cambrian region lies on either side of Spencer's Gulf in South Australia, and extends north-eastwards into New South Wales. It includes the copper deposits of Wallaroo-Moonta, Kapunda, and Burra, the iron deposits of Iron Knob, and the great lead-zinc lodes of Broken Hill. The northern region includes the Kimberley Gold Field, the Yampi Sound iron deposits in Western Australia, the scattered gold, tin, copper, lead and tungsten deposits of the Northern Territory, the copper deposits of the Cloncurry district, the important lead-zinc-copper lodes of Mount Isa, and the smaller lead-silver veins of Lawn Hills in Queensland.

The Palaezoic mineralisation occurs in a more or less continuous belt, about two hundred miles wide, around the whole eastern margin of Australia (see Fig. XXI), and down into Tasmania; and shows a more varied mineralisation than the pre-Cambrian regions. In western Tasmania are found the lead-zinc deposits of Zeehan and Rosebery, the copper deposits of Mount Lyell, and the tin lodes of Mount Bischoff, Renison Bell and Heemskirk. In north-eastern Tasmania are rich alluvial tin deposits, and some tin, wolfram and minor gold-quartz veins. In the central district of Victoria, particularly at Bendigo and Ballarat, is an intense gold-quartz mineralisation, the alluvials shed from which provided the highly spectacular finds after 1850. Widespread gold-quartz veins occur, of which the saddle reefs of Bendigo and indicator veins of Ballarat are best known. In eastern Victoria in the Woods' Point belt, the gold veins are associated with basic dykes, and in the north-east of the State a sparse tin-molybdenum mineralisation is associated with the gold, and extends across into New South Wales.

Southern New South Wales is in the main an area of small deposits which contain variously gold, copper, tin, bismuth, molybdenum, except at Captain's Flat where there is a silver, lead, zinc deposit of considerable dimensions. The gold mineralisation is more intense in the Cobar and Mudgee districts, with copper also prominent in the Cobar area. In the north-east corner of the State the formerly rich alluvial tin deposits of New England, now almost exhausted, extend into the Stanthorpe district of Queensland. Small rich tin veins with molybdenum and bismuth as minor constituents also exist.

The Palaeozoic mineralisation is almost continuous along the mountainous eastern margin of Queensland, with gold and copper predominating in the south, as at Mount Morgan— notable for its remarkable surface enrichment of gold— Gympie, and Charters Towers. Mercury ores occur at Kilkiven. In the north, at Herberton, Mount Garnet, and Cooktown, tin is the principal metal, gold becoming prominent again at Croydon and the Palmer River.

The history of mining in countries of wide mineralisation has been generally one of a series of booms, as prospectors spread over the country and found lodes outcropping at the surface. As the surface becomes explored the rate of new discovery, depending as it then does on more systematic efforts, falls off. Australian mining was no exception, and mining output began to fall away about 1907. The decline was accentuated by economic causes after the 1914–1918 war as national policy began to emphasise the development of secondary industries. Mining was confined to the slow development of the known deposits, the few new ventures being in the main based on improved metallurgical technique making payable previously known but refractory ore bodies. Prospecting for base metals almost ceased and only one new large deposit, the Mount Isa field, and a few individual lodes have been found for many years. An exception to this general statement occurred in gold mining following revaluation of

Australian currency in 1931-32. Prospecting immediately revived, and gold mining has continued actively ever since until checked by organization for war.

Whether improved economic conditions for mining generally would lead to new discoveries and greater output depends on many factors. Mineralisation in Australia is widespread, but it is often sparse. There are, however, several mining districts both extensive and highly productive. In few places has prospecting gone much beyond surface examination, except in the important districts; and even there the mines have mostly developed from the original outcrops, the amount of drilling in the area being limited. There has been little of the organized prospecting with intensive diamond drilling campaigns which has marked exploration in the United States and Canada during the last two or three decades. Moreover, large sections of the mineralised areos in Australia are extremely arid and difficult of access.

Although the chances of finding major new ore bodies outcropping at the surface must now be considered relatively remote, the resources of a country with Australia's mining history must still be regarded as very far from exhausted. The metal mines of the future now lie hidden beneath surface detritus, or concealed underground within the enclosing rocks. The recently found copper ore body at Mount Isa in north-western Queensland, for example, does not come within a thousand feet of the surface. It was discovered by chance during drilling. The difficulties of finding such concealed deposits are admittedly great; but constantly improving equipment and scientific methods coupled with improving transport, are steadily increasing the range and effectiveness of prospecting, and there is no reason why methods that have found deposits elsewhere should not be successful here. Thus it may be that new ore bodies will be found both in the older productive fields and in new and more remote areas of the continent.

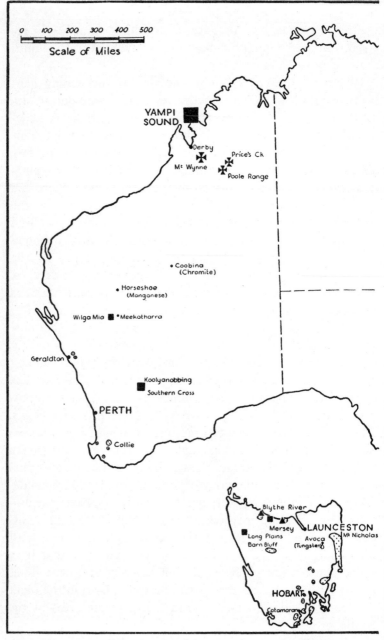

Fig. XXII. Coal and

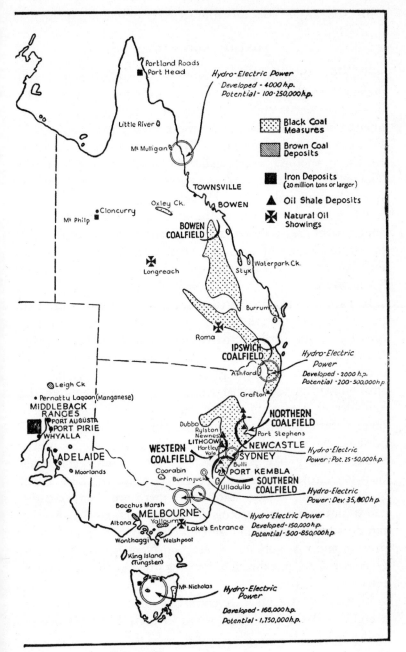

iron resources of Australia.

MINERAL FUELS: COAL

Supplies of both black and brown coal are ample, and greater than for any other country in the South Pacific. The black coals occur chiefly along the eastern edge of the continent and in Tasmania, though there are small isolated beds in Western Australia (see Fig. XXII). The brown coals occur chiefly in Victoria, with smaller deposits in South Australia. The major coal fields lie close to the metropolitan centres and along the seaboard—which facilitates interstate carriage. The traffic is necessary because the coals of Western Australia, South Australia, Victoria, and Tasmania are not suitable for the manuufacture of town gas or of metallurgical coke, and their steam-raising capacities are inferior to those of New South Wales.

In 1929 a committee of the Standards Association of Australia estimated that the coal resources of Australia were as follows: Black Coal—actual [1] 5,806,000,000 tons, probable 10,645,000,000 tons; Brown Coal—actual 59,000,000 tons, possible, 40,500,000,000 tons. Estimates of the coal available in any country are somewhat hazardous, owing chiefly to the difficulty of predicting quality and thickness of seams where there is little information available either from workings or borings. As the committee observed, "In a comparatively young country like Australia, this is even more applicable than in European coal fields, for here there has been much less exploration of the seams, and there are, consequently, many more uncertain factors in the calculations." However, the coal measures are more extensive than the areas already proved, and the workable reserves in New South Wales and Queensland are possibly five times as great as the brown-coal reserves in Victoria.

In assessing Australian reserves it is important to note that a number of the black-coal seams in New South Wales are

[1] Actual=proved. Probable=near-proved.

exceptionally thick (up to forty-three feet), and that, at present, only a portion of the seam is mined. In the thick Greta seam, which is the most productive, less than one-half of the total coal is extracted under present methods of working, and this is true in lesser degree of several of the other seams. In the Northern Field, where annual production is about 6,500,000 tons, another 5,500,000 tons is left unworked. The whole thickness of the seams could be worked by filling the open spaces as is done in metal mines, but the expectation of added costs has until recently deferred the introduction of this method of working. Practical tests on mining the full thickness of coal, using filling, are now in progress.

The brown-coal reserves of Victoria occur in seams from fifty to five hundred feet thick; and on present knowledge these must be worked by open cut if the bulk of the coal is to be won. The ratio of overburden to coal is about one of overburden to three of coal for some twenty-five per cent of the known reserves which can be exploited by open-cut methods. The rest of the coal is at greater depths and remains an engineering problem for the future. The estimates have therefore only a qualitative meaning; but it is clear that Australia has coal resources equivalent to those of some of the major European powers.

New South Wales

The main coal measures of New South Wales form an elongated basin truncated by the coastline, so that part of it lies beneath the sea. The other part occupies an area of about 16,500 square miles. It extends two hundred miles along the coast from Port Stephens in the north to Ulladulla in the south. The deepest part of the basin is near Sydney, where the uppermost seam has been worked at a depth of 2,884 feet. From this point the coal measures rise towards the north, south, and west, to outcrop at Newcastle, Bulli, and Lithgow respectively. The coal fields centre about the outcrops.

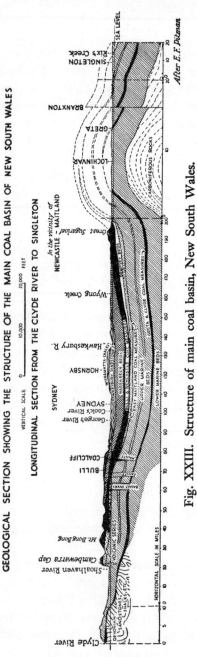

GEOLOGICAL SECTION SHOWING THE STRUCTURE OF THE MAIN COAL BASIN OF NEW SOUTH WALES

VERTICAL SCALE 0   10,000   20,000 FEET

LONGITUDINAL SECTION FROM THE CLYDE RIVER TO SINGLETON

In the vicinity of NEWCASTLE - MAITLAND

After E. F. Pitman

Fig. XXIII. Structure of main coal basin, New South Wales.

188

In the northern (Newcastle-Maitland) field, the greatest production is from the Greta seams at Maitland, where two seams are worked, the upper from fourteen to thirty-two feet thick and the lower from three to eleven feet thick. The Greta seams contain a hard cannel coal, which is used for gas-making, steaming, and domestic purposes, and is the most useful of the New South Wales coals. At Newcastle, production is chiefly from the Victoria Tunnel (Burwood) seam (six to thirteen feet thick), and the Borehole seam (four to twenty-two feet thick) which yields an excellent coal for gas-making and domestic purposes. In the southern field, centred about Bulli and Port Kembla, the coal is a steam coal, which yields an exceptionally strong coke highly suited to blast furnace operations. In the western field at Lithgow a steam coal somewhat inferior to the southern steam coals is worked. The annual production of the three fields is between nine million and ten million tons, of which the northern field contributes about 6.5 million, the southern field about 1.9 million, and the western field about 1.5 million. Coke is produced at Newcastle and Port Kembla, and annual output now exceeds one million tons. About ten per cent of the coke is shipped, chiefly to metallurgical works at Whyalla and Port Pirie in South Australia, and to the nickel smelters in New Caledonia.

Queensland

In Queensland the coal fields have an extent of twenty thousand square miles, and the coal measures extend over another fifty-three thousand square miles which are not yet proved. The coal occurs chiefly in the southern and central parts of the State, with a few smaller areas in the northern part (see Fig. XXII). Coal fields exist for a distance of two hundred miles along the south-eastern seaboard, and the coal measures extend to a distance of six hundred miles inland.

The Bowen coal field (fifty-three miles from the port of Bowen) promises to be the most important field of the future.

The coal is of excellent quality and the field covers an area of four hundred square miles, of which an area of only twenty square miles has been fully prospected. The reserves may exceed a billion tons. As at present known the other coal fields are of lesser importance, either on account of their small size, their remoteness or the disturbed state of the coal. The annual production from the State is slightly over one million tons. The coal seams of New South Wales and Queensland appear to offer an excellent opportunity for testing the merits of combustion in situ.

Victoria

The brown-coal deposits of Victoria rank among the largest known deposits of this type in the world. The main deposit, which aggregates twenty-seven billion tons, lies in a trough-faulted area forty miles long and twelve to eighteen miles wide, extending from Yarragon to Rosedale in Gippsland, Victoria. Similar coal, in seams seventy to one hundred feet thick and aggregating over two billion tons, occurs between Welshpool and Gelliondale in South Gippsland, and another area containing about fifteen billion tons extends from Altona (near Melbourne) to Bacchus Marsh, but the coal here is at considerable depth. Smaller areas occur at Lal Lal and Deans Marsh.

Production of any note is confined to Yallourn, where the State Electricity Commission mines some 5.5 million tons annually for its power-house and briquetting works. The coal seam is from 100 to 240 feet thick with an overburden of clay and gravel thirty to forty feet in thickness. The coal contains as much as sixty-five per cent moisture.

Small areas of black coal in the South Gippsland Highlands are worked by the State Coal Mine at Wonthaggi, and by private collieries at Kilcunda and Korumburra. The annual production is about 350,000 tons.

Other States

Tasmania has an annual production of about ninety thousand tons from the St. Mary's district in the eastern part of the State.

Western Australian production is about 550,000 tons a year of sub-bituminous coal from the Collie coal field, near Bunbury, 124 miles south of Perth. Collie is so placed that it could play a part in Western Australia similar to that of Yallourn in Victoria.

The South Australian Government has begun to mine deposits of sub-bituminous coal at Leigh Creek, 170 miles north of Port Augusta. The deposits may prove of considerable importance to South Australia.

OIL

Practically all the petroleum products used are imported. The search for oil in Australia and the nearby islands has been going on for the past fifteen years, but so far the results have been disappointing. The most intensive studies have been made by private companies in Papua and New Guinea, Queensland and Western Australia, and considerable sums of money have been expended by the Commonwealth and some States in assisting companies to prospect for oil.

On the mainland the most promising areas are:

1. Southern and Central Queensland.

2. The Kimberley district and north-west basin of Western Australia.

3. South-eastern South Australia and adjoining parts of western Victoria.

4. Eastern Victoria.

In Queensland a number of bores sunk in the Mesozoic strata of the Roma-Arcadia district have yielded showings of oil and petroliferous gas. The oil is thought to have migrated to its present position from Permian marine sediments that outcrop to the north of Roma. Bores in these rocks at Arcadia and Hutton Creek, ninety-five and sixty-five miles north of Roma respectively, have yielded quantities of gas, but no oil.

Oil showings have also been found at Longreach, where a heavy oil that solidifies to wax at ordinary temperatures comes to the surface along with hot mineralized waters in many bores in the Mesozoic rocks of this area.

In the Kimberley district, North-west Australia, a quantity of heavy oil occurs in the vesicles of basalt lava-flows, but the cost of extraction would be prohibitive so that it cannot be counted even as a potential reserve. The oil is not indigenous to the basalt, and an extensive search has been made for the source rocks. Showings of oil were obtained from bores put down in Devonian limestones at Price's Creek, and in Permian strata at Mount Wynne and in the Poole Range (see Fig. XXII). Gas showings were obtained in a number of bores put down for water in these regions.

Considerable thicknesses of sediments of Permian, Cretaceous, and Tertiary rocks occur in the north-west basin, and it is known that many anticlinal structures exist there. No positive evidence of the existence of oil has, however, been discovered in the region.

Deep boring is in progress in the Tertiary basins of south-western Victoria, close to the South Australian border. So far there is no evidence that oil occurs in this region, but as there is a considerable thickness of Tertiary sediments present, the area is worth testing.

In Victoria, near Lakes Entrance small quantities of oil have been found at a depth of twelve hundred feet. The oil-bearing horizon is a layer of glauconitic sandstone about thirty-two feet thick, which occurs over an area of ten miles long by two miles wide. The oil is heavy and devoid of light fractions. Pumping or baling operations are required to bring it to the surface.

Undoubtedly Papua, New Guinea, and possibly Timor,

offer the best prospects of obtaining oil in commercial quantities. Developments in Dutch New Guinea have already been important, and geological work was stopped by the war. The production of oil in New Guinea, Papua, and Timor, from an industrial point of view, would be nearly as valuable to Australia as production within the Commonwealth itself.

NATURAL GAS

No sustained attempt has been made to explore natural-gas possibilities, though the geological conditions are favorable in several of our major sedimentary basins.

The main interest attaches to possible supplies near existing industrial centres or in localities suited to industrial development, e.g., the Permian-Triassic basin in eastern New South Wales, and the Triassic-Jurassic basin in Queensland, south of Brisbane. The most important yields of gas so far obtained from bores have been in localities remote from the larger centres of population, e.g., Arcadia, Queensland.

An interesting experiment is in progress at Balmain (a suburb of Sydney) where methane gas from disused colliery workings is being used as a substitute motor fuel. The rate of gas drawn off has gradually been increased and is now (July 1944) about 1,000,000 cubic feet per month.

OIL SHALE

Deposits of oil shale are associated with the coal measures in New South Wales, Queensland, and Tasmania. The yield of crude oil from these shales varies from twelve gallons per ton to one hundred and fifty gallons per ton. The principal deposits are in New South Wales, chiefly in the Newnes-Glen Davis district, where reserves are estimated at twenty million tons, roughly equivalent to about two thousand million gallons of crude oil. Although of value in an emergency, these deposits are only a minor factor in meeting Australia's oil fuel requirements.

IRON ORE

Australia's iron-ore resources, while not commensurate with her coal resources, are more than sufficient for estimated domestic requirements. The size and quality of two known deposits are adequate for an iron and steel industry. These are the Middleback Range deposits in South Australia and the Yampi Sound deposits in Western Australia (see Fig. XXII).

Australian production, which amounted to 2,570,000 tons in 1939, is drawn, in the main, from the deposits of the Middleback Ranges about twenty miles inland on the western side of Spencer's Gulf. The ore is high grade hematite (sixty-four per cent to sixty-six per cent iron). The bulk of production has come from the Iron Monarch at the northern end of the ranges, the largest of several bodies. A proportion of this ore carries from eight to eleven per cent of manganese. The small Iron Knob body is half a mile north of it, and the Iron Prince, Iron Baron, and several other deposits lie at varying distances to the south.

The ore is shipped 1,170 miles from Whyalla to the steel-works at Newcastle; and since 1938 back-loading of coke has enabled a blast furnace and shipbuilding yard to be established at Whyalla. Since 1915 when the Newcastle steelworks commenced operations, to 1939, the tonnage of ore mined was more than twenty million tons. Production of pig iron in 1938 by the steelworks at Newcastle and at Port Kembla was 900,-000 tons, and steel ingots and castings more than a million tons. Output of iron and steel products later sharply increased to meet war needs; and it is fair to say that those activities of "B.H.P." (Broken Hill Pty. Co.) have become the backbone of Australian industrial development.

Yampi Sound is a channel in the Buccaneer Archipelago on

the northern coast of Western Australia, about two hundred miles north-east of Broome (see Fig. XXII). The deposits are on Koolan, Cockatoo, and Irvine Islands. The ore is hematite and extremely high grade (sixty-eight per cent iron). The ore bodies are estimated to contain eighty million tons of ore above high-water mark. The structures of the ore bodies indicate that they may persist below sea level.

Of the many other deposits of iron ore known in Australia, seven have reserves estimated in excess of 20,000,000 tons. Of these, three are in the main too siliceous for present smelting methods, and the other four too remote for economic working.

FERRO-ALLOYS

Manganese

Each ton of steel requires about fifteen pounds of manganese, so that to meet the needs of her steel industry Australia requires a manganese deposit of at least half a million tons; but no known deposit approaches this tonnage. A deposit with reserves approaching this quantity has been reported at Horseshoe, Western Australia, eighty-five miles from the railhead at Meekatharra, but subsequent investigations have not confirmed the earlier reports.

Recent production has been drawn chiefly from Pernatty Lagoon, on the transcontinental railway line, about sixty-five miles from Port Augusta in South Australia, and from the manganiferous iron ore forming part of the Iron Monarch ore body in the Middleback Ranges. All other known deposits are small and are incapable of meeting the demands of the steel industry over any period of years, though they may provide adequate supplies for the manufacture of dry batteries.

Chromium

The known chrome-ore deposits are small, with one exception, and most of them are relatively low grade. The ore body of significant size is in the Coobina district of Western Australia, 255 miles to the north-east of Meekatharra. Development of the deposit has been handicapped by its isolation, and little is known of its extent and grade.

Cobalt and Nickel

Present production of cobalt amounts to about twelve tons a year, obtained in the electrolytic refining of zinc from the concentrates of Broken Hill and Rosebery. This small amount is consumed in Australia. At two previous periods, 1891 to 1900 and 1922 to 1925, Australia produced a considerable tonnage of cobalt ore from small deposits in New South Wales, and from the Mount Cobalt mine near Cloncurry in Queensland. The Mount Cobalt mine was closed in 1931 and the reserves are unknown.

Prior to the war Australia consumed about one hundred and fifty tons of nickel a year, all of which was imported. There was a small production of ore for export from the small bodies of rich nickel-copper ore near Zeehan in Tasmania, but these deposits are now depleted.

Molybdenum

A number of small ore bodies containing molybdenum occur at various localities in the eastern States. The main production now comes from Everton in Victoria. Australian production, at one time the largest in the world, is now insignificant compared with the production from the Climax mine in Colorado, and from the copper ore bodies in Arizona and New Mexico. Small potential supplies exist in Queensland and New South Wales.

Tungsten

Prior to 1914 Australia was the chief source of the world's tungsten, but by 1939 Australian production had shrunk to four per cent of the world's total production. Consequent upon war demand, Australian production has since increased, and comes mainly from the eastern States. A major producer has been developed in the scheelite mine on King Island, Tasmania, which is one of the largest tungsten deposits known.

Gold

Australia ranks fifth among the world's gold producers after the Union of South Africa, Russia, Canada, and the United States. Of the total production to the end of 1938 (155 million fine ounces) about forty-six per cent has come from Victoria, twenty-eight per cent from Western Australia, thirteen per cent from Queensland, and ten per cent from New South Wales, or about seventy per cent from the eastern States. The 1938 production was one and a half million fine ounces, valued at more than £14 million in Australian currency, of which eighty per cent was mined in Western Australia.

Gold mining in Australia dates from the discovery of rich alluvial gold near Bathurst, New South Wales, in May 1851. Much more extensive deposits were discovered in Victoria later in the year. Production reached a peak in the first decade of mining, and Australia became at once the foremost gold producer in the world. As the alluvial deposits became exhausted and mining turned increasingly to the quartz reefs, the yields declined progressively until the last decade of the century. The discovery of the "Golden Mile" at Kalgoorlie and other Western Australian fields then sent production to a new high level in 1903, after which a rapid decline set in, accelerated by the war of 1914–18. The rising price of gold which became effective after 1931 made much previously marginal ore payable, and enabled many of the old established mines in Western Australia to be reorganized. At the same time a number of old mines were reopened, and some new ones found. The main output still comes from the Kalgoorlie field which has produced in all 26 million ounces, and before 1940 was still producing half a million ounces annually. The bulk of the remainder comes from the Norseman district a hundred miles south of Kalgoorlie, from the Leonora district some 150 miles to the north, and from the Murchison and East Murchison districts further to the north-west. A covering of sands and cemented detritus obscures a large portion of the potential gold-bearing series in Western Australia, over much of which prospecting has been confined to "loaming," i.e., a search for pieces of residual gold-bearing quartz or fine native gold in the surface sands. This is an effective method of prospecting, and a number of mines have been so found; but over much of the country the search has been perfunctory.

Victorian output has also been stimulated by the rising price of gold. Much of the increased output has come from new discoveries in the Bendigo field, where total production has reached seventeen million ounces. More than fifty million ounces have been won from the relatively small area of the Ballarat, Castlemaine, Bendigo, and Maryborough fields. Owing to the prevailing flat habit of most ore deposits in this district, as a consequence of which many do not come to the surface, and to the covering of later basalts over part of the Palaeozoic ore-bearing series, there is still a possibility of new discoveries in Victoria.

The main gold producers of Queensland have been the Charters Towers field, where some six million ounces have been won with an average grade slightly over one ounce per ton, Mount Morgan mine with a production approaching that of the Charters Towers field, and Gympie. Of these, Mount Morgan, which today is also a copper mine, still produces half of the State's annual gold output of 150,000 ounces. The chief other producer is the Cracow field.

Silver

The output of silver rose from over eight million fine ounces in 1931 to nearly fifteen million ounces in 1939. The silver is a by-product from lead-zinc ores. Broken Hill contributed nine million to ten million ounces annually, Mount Isa more than two million ounces, and Rosebery about 900,000 ounces.

LEAD AND ZINC

The great lead and zinc producing countries of the world are, in order, United States, Australia, Mexico, and Canada. In 1938 Australia produced lead concentrates containing over 274,000 long tons of metallic lead in a world production of 1,780,000 tons, and zinc concentrates containing 220,000 tons of metallic zinc in a world production of 1,840,000 tons. Actual metal produced in Australia amounted to 222,500 tons of lead and about seventy thousand tons of zinc. Of this about twenty-five thousand tons of lead and thirty thousand tons of zinc were consumed in Australia, and the remainder exported. Production now comes mainly from Broken Hill and Captain's Flat in New South Wales, Mount Isa in Queensland, and Rosebery in Tasmania (see Fig. XXI).

Of these deposits the Broken Hill lodes are outstanding; and, having regard to the grade of the ore, the deposit is the largest lead-zinc ore body in the world. The field has been in continuous production since 1883; and, to the end of 1943, had yielded a total of more than sixty-one million tons of ore. The concentrates produced in 1938 contained 221,000 tons of lead, 165,000 tons of zinc, 8,736,000 ounces of silver, and 167 tons of cadmium, and in addition minor amounts of copper, antimony, gold, and cobalt. Despite its fifty-five years of active production the full extent of the deposit has not yet been disclosed. Actual reserves of the producing mines are computed at twelve million tons of ore carrying fifteen per cent lead, eleven per cent zinc, and six ounces of silver per ton, with probable reserves of a further twenty-three million tons of similar grade ore, plus possibilities which must still be classed as very great.

The development of this deposit, together with the associated industries that have sprung from it, forms a notable page in the industrial history of Australia. The field has been a centre of continuous metallurgical research and Broken Hill metallurgists number among their achievements the initial development of the flotation processes and, in particular, differential flotation, which revolutionized the mining industry throughout the world. The equipment of the mines has kept pace with the metallurgical development, and is in line with the most modern practice. Much attention has been paid to mining conditions, and Broken Hill compares most favourably with other fields in its means of control and prevention of occupational diseases.

The companies engaged in mining the Broken Hill lode have taken a lead in developing other industries throughout Australia. The Broken Hill Proprietary, the first large company on the field, turned to iron and steel production as its lead-zinc leases approached exhaustion; and it now produces the cheapest high-grade steel in the world. This company also started the smelting of lead in Australia, at Port Pirie. In 1915, following the outbreak of war, this plant was taken over by the other Broken Hill companies and is now the largest lead smeltery in the world. Its practice includes the continuous "desilverising" of the lead bullion, a process evolved by its own metallurgists, and not yet achieved elsewhere; and it treats to finality the whole of the Broken Hill output of lead concentrates.

Shortly after taking over the Port Pirie Smelters, the same Broken Hill companies began experimenting on the electrolytic recovery of zinc from zinc concentrates. This work led to commercial results, and to the formation of a company to build a large electrolytic zinc plant at Risdon in Tasmania. Large-scale production began in 1922; and the annual pre-war output amounted to seventy thousand tons of metallic zinc which has since been expanded. Cadmium, cobalt, and sulphuric acid are won as by-products, the cadmium forming a considerable proportion of the world's output. The bulk of the sulphuric acid is used for the manufacture of superphosphate.

In addition to refining zinc, this company purchased and developed the Read-Rosebery zinc-lead deposits in Western Tasmania, and successfully produced salable concentrates from the rather difficult refractory ore of this field. In 1938 these mines yielded concentrates containing more than nine thousand tons of lead and twenty-five thousand tons of zinc.

Apart from their mining and smelting activities, Broken Hill companies have played a leading part in the development of the metal working and fabricating industries both ferrous and non-ferrous, in the production of paper from Australian timbers, and in the manufacture of aircraft in Australia.

The Mount Isa mine, in north-west Queensland, began production in 1931. Prior to the war its output reached about forty-five thousand tons of lead bullion and seventy thousand tons of zinc concentrates. The company smelts its lead concentrates at Mount Isa to produce lead bullion, which is exported for refining and desilverization. The zinc concentrates are exported for further treatment. The reserves on the lead-zinc deposit amount to about ten million tons of ore carrying eight per cent lead, nine per cent zinc, and six ounces of silver per ton. The Captain's Flat mine near Canberra came into production in 1939, when reserves were quoted at two million tons —7.5 per cent lead, 13 per cent zinc, 0.7 per cent copper, 2 ounces silver and 1.5 pennyweight of gold per ton.

COPPER

Copper is widespread throughout Australia, but the lodes do not compare in size with the great deposits of the Americas and Africa. Subject to economic factors they are, however, able to produce Australia's normal requirements of about twenty-four thousand tons a year, and have been able to keep pace with the increased consumption during the war.

The main fields are Mount Lyell in Tasmania, Moonta and Wallaroo in South Australia, Mount Morgan, and the mines of the Cloncurry and Mount Isa district in Queensland, and Cobar in western New South Wales. Of these Mount Lyell has produced 390,000 tons of copper metal. The field consists of a number of ore bodies; and output at present is coming from large low-grade open cuts where reserves of some fourteen million tons of ore exist. As with other copper deposits in Australia, economic factors are of great importance, since the mine can only with difficulty compete with overseas prices. Up to 1939 production averaged 1,100,000 tons of ore per annum, with a grade of 1.4 per cent resulting in an annual output of thirteen thousand tons of electrolytically refined copper. Since that date output has increased, but grade has fallen. The other large producer today is the Mount Isa mine, which has recently developed a copper ore body parallel to its main lead-zinc lode. Reserves are quoted at three million tons of 3.7 per cent copper. Mount Morgan and the Cobar field are the chief other mines now producing. The output of copper is electrolytically refined at Mount Lyell and at Port Kembla, south of Sydney, where the main part of the copper fabricating industry is situated.

TIN

A great increase of Australian tin ore production began after 1870 and reached a maximum of ten thousand tons per annum in 1883. This followed the discovery of rich alluvials in the New England district of New South Wales and in north-eastern Tasmania, and of the Mount Bischoff mine, from which the total production to date exceeds seventy thousand tons of metal. The North Queensland lode and alluvial deposits in the Herberton district were developed later. With the gradual exhaustion of alluvials, output has declined and production has fluctuated in recent years between fifteen hundred and thirty-five hundred tons per annum. Lode mining for tin also depends on economic conditions. There are lode deposits of significant extent particularly on the west coast of Tasmania, but the grade is marginal and output small.

MINOR METALS

There is a small output of antimony, arsenic, and bismuth from various sources. In Victoria a number of rich but very small gold-antimony veins exist. A more intense gold-antimony mineralization occurs in Western Australia in the Pilbara district and at Wiluna; and there are a number of small antimony mines in northern New South Wales and Queensland. In 1938 the Wiluna production was equivalent to four hundred tons of antimony metal. About three hundred tons a year is recovered in the form of antimonial lead from the lead concentrates of the Broken Hill and Rosebery mines, and this recovery is expected to increase in the future. The other mines in the eastern States yield about one hundred and fifty tons of antimony a year.

The 1938 production of arsenic amounted to four thousand tons, chiefly from the Wiluna gold mines. A small amount is obtained from sulphide concentrates from Victorian gold mines, and there are reserves in Queensland.

Bismuth has been mined at a number of places in the eastern States, chiefly in northern New South Wales and in the Chillagoe district of Queensland, where it occurs in small pipelike deposits associated with molybdenite. Small deposits also occur at Hatches Creek in the Northern Territory, and at Moina in Tasmania.

Cadmium is produced as a by-product of the electrolytic refining of zinc from the zinc concentrates of the Broken Hill and Rosebery mines. The 1938 production of two hundred tons is about five per cent of world output.

The zircon production is substantial, the 1937 production of 5,250 tons amounting to fifty-four per cent of the world output. There is also a considerable production of titanium in the form of rutile and ilmenite concentrates. These minerals are associated in beach sands, which also contain significant amounts of monazite. The reserves are large, and there are unexploited deposits of these minerals elsewhere in Australia.

THE LIGHT METALS

The war has led to a tremendous increase in the production of aluminium and magnesium on account of their importance in aircraft manufacture. World plant capacity for aluminium has advanced from three hundred thousand tons before the war to more than three million tons a year, while magnesium production has grown from twenty-five thousand tons in 1938 to as much as five hundred thousand tons.

Aluminium

Australia at present depends on imports for aluminium; but the Commonwealth Government in 1943 allocated £3 million for the entry into production, and as soon as industrial conditions permit, the construction of the necessary initial plant in Tasmania will be undertaken.

Bauxite of varying grade occurs over a wide area. Deposits amounting to several million tons occur in Tasmania, in the South Gippsland Highlands of Victoria, at Wingello, and in the New England district of New South Wales, on the Tamborine plateau thirty-six miles from Brisbane in Queensland, and the Darling ranges in Western Australia. Alunite deposits in Western Australia estimated to contain three million tons of alumina provide another source of raw material for aluminium.

Magnesium

Production of the metal in Australia began in 1941, the output being equal to domestic requirements. The metal is made from magnesite which occurs at a number of localities throughout the Commonwealth. The chief producing fields are at Fifield and Thuddungra in New South Wales. Extensive reserves of magnesite occur near Copley and Crozier in South Australia, at Bulong and Meekatharra in Western Australia, and at Smithton in Tasmania there is an immense deposit of dolomite. Very large deposits also occur in South Australia. A small production of magnesium salts is obtained in the preparation of common salt from sea-water at Geelong in Victoria.

RARE METALS AND MINERALS

In the deeply eroded Pre-Cambrian rocks there are numerous pegmatites, which in some areas, notably the Pilbara district in the north-west of Western Australia, contain various rare minerals. The most important at present is tantalite, which is found in mixed crystals with columbite in many dykes and in the alluvials adjacent, though usually in minute amounts. The dykes carrying tantalite with a high percentage of tantalates are rare, the chief being at Wodgina in the Pilbara district. Beryl is won from dykes in the Wodgina and Yinnietharra districts of Western Australia and is known in minor amounts elsewhere. Uranium ores have been found in the Copley district and at Olary in South Australia. Australia appears to have supplies of lithium minerals, including spodumene, amblygonite, and lepidolite. Indium is present in several base-metal ores in minute but recoverable amounts, and a small amount of selenium is available as a by-product from the Mount Lyell copper ore. Osmiridium is found in alluvials shed from serpentine rocks in western Tasmania. Small deposits of mercury ore occur in the eastern States, chiefly at Kilkiven in Queensland.

INDUSTRIAL MINERALS

Side by side with increasing industrial development is a growing demand for locally produced non-metallic minerals, some of which may be briefly referred to.

Domestic requirements for practically all types of clay, feldspar, pigment minerals, fluorite and sillimanite are being satisfied from sources within Australia. A large part of the requirements of barytes, talc, diatomite, and graphite are also being met from home sources of supply.

Muscovite and phlogopite mica of commercial size is found in numerous pegmatites throughout the Harts Ranges in Central Australia, and less frequently in Western Australia. Much of the local requirements of mica is obtained from Central Australia.

Gypsum production is increasing, and amounted to 180,000 tons in 1938. The reserves are extensive. The production of common salt is also increasing, and the lately established alkali works at Port Adelaide are capable of converting ninety thousand tons of salt a year into soda ash and caustic alkali.

Large deposits of excellent quality blue asbestos are being developed in the Hamersley Range of Western Australia; and some attention is also being paid to chrysotile asbestos deposits in Tasmania. So far, however, Australia is dependent upon imports for most of its requirements of high-grade chrysotile asbestos. A large tonnage, in excess of 1,500,000 tons, of limestone is used annually for the manufacture of lime and cement, and as flux. There is a tendency to pay increasing attention to the development of non-metallic mineral production work for domestic and world requirements.

Phosphates

Production of rock phosphate ceased in 1922 when supplies of high-grade rock phosphates (98.5 per cent tri-calcium phosphate) from Nauru and Ocean Island became available. The total Australian output was only a fraction of the amount now imported in a single year.

Until Japan temporarily occupied the islands, the production and sale of phosphate rock from Nauru and Ocean Island was controlled by a Board of Commissioners appointed by the Governments of the United Kingdom, Australia, and New Zealand; and the three countries were entitled to allotments of the output of phosphate, for home consumption only, in the proportions: United Kingdom and Australia, forty-two per cent each; New Zealand, sixteen per cent. Production reached 1,247,000 tons in the year ending June 1940. Australian imports have shown a comparable rise, reaching 777,000 tons in 1938. World production in 1938 was twelve million tons, so that Australia normally consumes six per cent of world output. Australian consumption may rise to five times its present volume before a stable fertilizer consumption is reached.

Production of superphosphates has kept pace with imports of rock phosphate, and in 1937 exceeded 1,250,000 tons, so that Australia ranks as one of the larger producers of superphosphates.

Sulphur

So far no commercial deposits of elemental sulphur have been found in Australia, and the bulk of the sulphur used was imported from the United States, Japan and Sicily. Imports have kept pace with production of superphosphates, and in 1938 were nearly 142,000 long tons. Despite the lack of sulphur deposits, Australia has considerable potential resources in the form of sulphide ores. Production from domestic sulphide ores is stimulated by a sulphur bounty and amounts to about forty-five thousand tons a year, chiefly from pyritic concentrates made at Mount Lyell, at Captain's Flat, and at Norseman, and from the zinc concentrates from Broken Hill. With the recent improvements in the production of elemental sulphur from sulphurous gases a much wider use of the by-product gases of the smelting works is contemplated. Australia's present requirements could be fully met by domestic production from such sources.

Potash

Australia imports practically the whole of her potash requirements, and about 10,600 tons of potash salts were brought from overseas in 1938. In future her needs will probably be met by domestic production from alunite deposits at Lake Campion in Western Australia, where a plant has been erected to treat reserves containing about 1,750,000 tons of potash. A further large deposit of alunite exists at Bullahdela in New South Wales. Potash deposits also occur in some of the other dry inland lakes in Western Australia and in the other States, but these have yet to be closely prospected.

Nitrogen

Australia has no domestic supplies of mineral nitrates. Her nitrogen requirements are met by production of synthetic ammonia and by importation of sodium nitrate from Chile, and of ammonium salts. Ammonium sulphate at present is produced as a by-product of coke manufacture. Steps are being taken greatly to expand production, which will involve the utilization, from metallic ores, of sulphur now going to waste.

MINERAL RESOURCES OF THE SOUTH-WEST PACIFIC ISLANDS

Australia is fortunate in that her neighbours have an exportable surplus of most of the minerals in which she is deficient. Moreover, in the main, these island mineral resources are favourably situated in relation to Australia. Thus New Caledonia, which is closer to Newcastle than Whyalla is by sea, has ample supplies of nickel and chromium ores. New Caledonia's nickel production for 1938 was 7,300 metric tons, equivalent to 6.6 per cent of world production, and her chrome ore output was twenty-six thousand tons of high-grade ore. New Caledonia also has reserves of iron ore and of cobalt. Production of iron ore prior to the war was small, but will probably be considerably greater in the future; and, if necessary, it may be possible to supplement Australian supplies from this source. Nickel, iron and possibly chrome ores similar to those in New Caledonia occur in the Celebes.

The petroleum production from the Netherlands East Indies, principally Sumatra, Java, and Borneo, totalled 7,943,000 metric tons in 1939, which was 2.7 per cent of world production, and the bulk of Australia's imports came from this source. The island of Java produces from twelve to twenty per cent of the world's iodine, and contains deposits of manganese ore, sulphur, and mineral phosphates. In 1928 production was five thousand tons of manganese (metal content of ore), sixteen thousand tons of sulphur, and thirty-three thousand tons of rock phosphate. The sulphur and phosphate were consumed in Java, but the manganese was exported. The phosphate reserves amount to 650,000 tons, and there are smaller deposits on several of the East Indian islands.

Deposits of high-grade phosphate rock exist on a number of the islands in the south-west Pacific, but the size of the deposits is very unequal. Much of the largest are on Nauru and Ocean Island, from which Australia's requirements are drawn. These contain between one hundred million and one hundred twenty million tons. A further ten to fifteen million tons occur on Makatea Island in the Society group, and there is a deposit of about the same tonnage on Christmas Island in the Indian Ocean, about 190 miles south of Java. A further 2,600,000 tons exist on Angaur Island and the other islands of the Palau group.

Bauxite deposits, estimated to contain twenty million tons of high-grade ore, occur in the islands of the Riouw Archipelago, just south of Singapore, chiefly on Bintan Island, and production in 1938 had risen to 230,000 tons. Bauxite also occurs in the Johore Province of Malaya. The other important mineral resources of the Netherlands East Indies are the alluvial tin deposits on the islands of Banka, Billiton, and Singkep. Production was limited to nineteen per cent of the world output by the International Tin Control scheme, and has ranged from twelve thousand tons to forty-four thousand tons according to the quota. Banka tin was smelted on the island; Billiton and Singkep tin was smelted in Europe or the Straits Settlements.

CONCLUSION

From this brief survey of the mineral resources of Australia and the adjacent Pacific islands several facts emerge. With some exceptions, notably iron ore, gold,[2] and some non-metallic minerals, the mineral resources of Australia tend to be concentrated on the eastern side of the continent (see Figs. XXI and XXII), so that they reinforce the dominating influence of water supply on the pattern of settlement and development. This is particularly true of coal and hydroelectric power. Whereas coal supplies as at present developed tend to concentrate heavy industry in the Newcastle, Lithgow, and Port Kembla districts of New South Wales, the conversion of

[2] Present-day production. Actually seventy per cent of the total production has come from the eastern States.

the brown coal to electricity in Victoria makes for development of industries other than the heavy industries in the southeast of the continent. This tendency will be strengthened as the hydroelectric potentialities of Tasmania are developed. The coal reserves of Queensland may some day be the basis of industrial activity further north.

Even if plastics and the light metals displace the older mineral products, the pattern of the country cannot change greatly, since plastics are derived in part from the phenols extracted from coal, in part from milk products, and in part from timber, all of which can be obtained in quantity only in the rainfall areas of the east.

The position in relation to petroleum and phosphate calls for special comment. The lack of petroleum is a major strategic weakness. Even if supplies are obtained in New Guinea, they would not preclude a possibility of interruption of supplies to Australia. A local source of oil can, however, be provided by the production of oil from coal, for which the coal resources are adequate.

Supplies of phosphate are very unequally distributed throughout the world. The phosphate reserves of East Asia and the South-west Pacific are only about 200 million long tons, whereas those of North America exceed 6,000 million tons, and those of Europe and northern Africa 9,000 million tons. With increased consumption by Australia to perhaps five million tons a year, and with the possibility of a growing requirement of phosphates in China and Japan, the strain upon Pacific resources will be considerable.

It is also clear that, ample though Australia's coal resources are, they are not comparable with those of Canada and the United States, while her hydroelectric potentialities are insignificant by comparison. Australia cannot therefore expect to rival the United States or Canada either as a mineral producer or as an industrial power. Her mineral resources are such, however, that she should be able to play a leading role in the South-west Pacific. This will be assisted by the possibility of supplying a number of her mineral deficiencies from New Caledonia and the other Pacific islands.

ACKNOWLEDGMENT

I wish to acknowledge my indebtedness to Dr. H. G. Raggatt, Director of the Commonwealth Mineral Resources Survey, and to Mr. G. Lindesay Clark, for their help in the preparation of this review. Much of the data relating to the light metals and the industrial and rare minerals is based on the Summary Reports of the Mineral Resources of Australia, prepared by the Mineral Resources Survey under Dr. Raggatt's direction. This has been supplemented by personal suggestions by Dr. Raggatt following his reading of my manuscript.

Mr. Lindesay Clark has guided the review through its several draft stages, and provided invaluable help and criticism in matters relating to development and prospecting.

Chapter XV

THE HYDROELECTRIC RESOURCES OF AUSTRALIA

BY C. M. LONGFIELD

Chairman's Research Engineer, State Electricity Commission of Victoria

To GENERATE hydroelectric power it is first necessary to impound the water. The areas in Australian territory where rainfall and the terrain make large-scale water storage possible are all in the eastern highlands, including Tasmania, and in New Guinea.

The most extensive application of hydroelectric power has been carried out in Tasmania. Relatively heavy rainfall, natural lakes at favourable elevation, and the shorter summer contribute to make this State the best purely hydroelectric area in the Commonwealth. The great bulk of the power now produced in Tasmania is already applied to large-scale electrolytic refining processes or to industries such as paper-making. The ample water power of New Guinea, on the other hand, is still almost unused; but this area will require great general development before large-scale use of the power resources becomes feasible. In existing circumstances they must be regarded as reserves for long-term industrial development rather than possibilities for the immediate future.

For most countries the estimates of water-power resources, actual or potential, are notable only for wide discrepancies, which makes them almost useless for the purposes of a general survey. The estimates for Australia, for instance, range from nine million to seventy million horsepower, and variance of this order exasperates the layman. Where estimates are not defective because of differences in the basis upon which they are made, considerable discrepancies arise when the manner in which the water power is to be used becomes the criterion. At Niagara Falls, for example, the flow of the vast storage of the Great Lakes is regulated with high natural efficiency, and so the power output can be maintained at a uniform level and the plant used to the best advantage. The regulated flow from the plateau lakes in Tasmania resembles that at Niagara. Where ample storage is not provided the stream flow is "flashy," and a station designed upon average stream-flow conditions cannot be relied upon to give such a regular output. This is the problem for most of the mainland areas in Australia where it is possible to generate hydroelectric power.

The best use of hydroelectric plant where regulated uniform flow is out of the question depends upon its relation to other stations in the system. Where steam stations feed the same network as a hydro station, full use can be made of maximum stream flow by relieving other stations of load at such times. Thus, stream-flow variability, storage facilities, and the existence of interconnected power stations with complementary characteristics, all combine to determine the use that can be made of the hydroelectric potential. These factors all operate very strongly in Australia; and the fact that they have seldom been given proper weight has been responsible for some of the discrepancies in the estimates of potential resources.

In Australia, as elsewhere, water power and steam-generated power are often co-ordinated. The most favourable area for this association is in eastern Victoria, where the mountain catchments and the extensive brown-coal deposits of Gippsland are relatively close together. For these reasons the best conditions in Australia for the expansion of diversified industries by means of electrical power are probably to be found in eastern Victoria.

Australia can be divided into four regions: (i) the *Western Plateau*, comprising a large part of central as well as Western

Australia, at an average height of nearly one thousand feet above sea level; (ii) the *Eastern Highlands*, comprising an elevated and irregular plateau with occasional mountain peaks rising at the highest to 7,328 feet; (iii) the *Central Basin*, generally less than five hundred feet above sea level and sloping

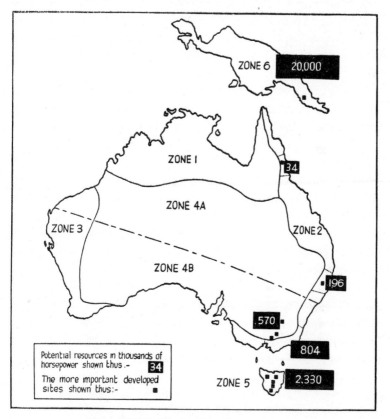

Fig. XXIV. Hydroelectric resources.

into Lake Eyre, which is below sea level; (iv) the *low-lying coastal belt*, whose rivers are not all perennial. The Western Plateau and the Eyre Basin form a vast gently inward-sloping area, for the most part arid and featureless. Hydroelectric possibilities are, therefore, confined mainly to the Eastern Highlands, which form the only significant catchment. It is this highland system, running roughly north and south parallel to the east coast, that provides Australia with its somewhat slender hydroelectric possibilities, which are distributed along a line between and including New Guinea and Tasmania.

Unfortunately for many potential hydroelectric sites in Australia the annual rainfall is highly variable; and the catchment is not high enough to maintain glaciers. Finally, since nearness to areas of demand for current is an important factor in the establishment of a generating station, for some time to come hydroelectric development on the mainland other than for special local small-scale purposes can be considered only in relation to the east and south-east coastal belt.

POTENTIAL RESOURCES

In his presidential address to the Institution of Engineers, Australia, in February 1934, Mr. H. R. Harper estimated the hydroelectric resources of the Commonwealth, excluding New Guinea, to be the equivalent of 4,774,000 horsepower, based on fifty per cent plant-load factor. This estimate is probably conservative.

The distribution of the hydroelectric resources of Australia is shown by means of a map zoned according to the dominant climatic and physical controls, namely, rainfall and main watershed. This is shown in Fig. XXIV, which should be read in conjunction with the map of annual rainfall (see Fig. I).

Zone 1 comprises a tropical belt with a negligible permanent population. As no reliable surveys have been reported, the potentialities are unknown. Rivers draining from the Kimberley Ranges in the north-west have prospects of development, especially if the Yampi Sound iron deposits are opened up. Tidal power has been considered, but the natural features do not reproduce anything like the conditions which form the basis of the proposed Severn Barrage in England.

Zone 2 comprises, in effect, the Pacific slope of the Eastern Highlands. For the present purpose, this zone may be divided into sections as indicated in Fig. XXIV. Practically the whole of the 35,000 hp. of Queensland's resources is near Cairns (Barron, Tully, and Herbert Rivers). The New England Ranges south of Brisbane provide 196,000 hp. of the known resources in the summer rainfall belt of New South Wales, the Clarence River being the most important of the streams. The hydroelectric resources of the rivers draining into the Tasman Sea total some 804,000 hp., of which 349,000 hp. is in New South Wales and the remainder in Victoria.

Zones 3 and 4(a) have no appreciable hydroelectric resources.

Zone 4(b) has a total of 570,000 hp., mainly concentrated in the Murray River basin near the New South Wales and Victorian borders. Of this amount, about 13,000 hp. is accounted for on the Lachlan River east of Sydney, and 27,000 hp. at Burrinjuck Dam. The Mitta Mitta and Kiewa Rivers account for 150,000 hp. and 140,000 hp. respectively.

Zone 5 includes the whole of Tasmania, where precipitation on the western slopes totals up to one hundred inches annually from the prevailing westerlies. The central plateau, with its Great Lakes and the mountainous western slopes, provides about ninety per cent of the hydroelectric resources of the island, and power-station sites are within easy reach of present and prospective industrial sites. As there are no steam stations in regular operation generating for public distribution, Tasmania is dependent upon its hydroelectric system; and consequently the potential resources, which are estimated to be 3,480,000 hp., should be de-rated to conform with a load factor of approximately seventy-five per cent, i.e., the resources should be reduced to about 2,330,000 hp. instead of 3,480,000 hp.

Zone 6 includes the whole of New Guinea, for which the resources have been roughly estimated at 20,000,000 hp.

AUSTRALIA AND NEW GUINEA: HYDROELECTRIC RESOURCES

Zone	Subdivision	Water-power resources on basis appropriate to local conditions	
1	Northern Australia	Not known	
2	North Queensland	34,000 hp.	
	New England	196,000 hp.	
	Tasman slopes of Aust. Alps.	804,000 hp.	1,034,000 hp.
3	....	Negligible	
4	Central Section	None	
	Southern Section		
	Lachlan River	13,000 hp.	
	Burrinjuck Dam	27,000 hp.	
	Alpine Streams and Murray River	530,000 hp.	570,000 hp.
5	Tasmania		2,330,000 hp.
6	New Guinea		20,000,000 hp.
	Total		23,934,000 hp.

NOTE: A plant load factor of fifty per cent has been assumed as a basis of estimate, except in the case of Tasmania where local conditions demand a seventy-five per cent load factor. The estimate for Zone 6 is somewhat speculative.

ECONOMIC PROSPECTS

In any survey of resources the cost of production, including transport to the market, cannot be neglected. The decision of the Commonwealth Government to sponsor the establishment of the aluminium industry in Tasmania presupposes a satisfactory price of electricity in that State for electrochemical industries of that type. The existence of the refineries of the Electrolytic Zinc Co. and of the Carbide Co. proves that the Hydroelectric Commission can distribute in bulk at a satisfactory price. No detailed estimates of the cost of electricity in New Guinea have yet been attempted, but it is safe to express the opinion that it will be lower than in any other part of the territory under review, if development is undertaken upon a big enough scale.

On the mainland, however, no specially cheap source of electricity can be expected, for reasons which are implied in the previous discussion. Reports published as recently as 1937 in New South Wales and Victoria show that Kiewa energy will cost (at 1937 price levels in Australian currency) 0.267d. per kilowatt hour at load centres, while a 220,000-volt transmission system from the proposed Snowy River development could deliver a maximum of 220,000 kw. in Sydney (1,120 million kwh. per annum) for 0.176d. per kwh. Power from the Shoalhaven would cost 0.55d. The estimated cost of energy from other schemes so far closely examined is higher than those quoted above. National necessities and relative urgency of certain types of industrial development, however, may make the cost-accountancy approach relatively unimportant; and it will not be discussed further.

DEVELOPED RESOURCES—STATISTICAL SUMMARY

A comparison between Australian statistics and those of some other countries is attempted below. The extent to which water power has been exploited in Australia is indicated in the following tables:

APPROXIMATE INSTALLED CAPACITY IN HYDROELECTRIC STATIONS, INCLUDING PLANT UNDER CONSTRUCTION—1944

State	Installed Capacity (in thousands of horsepower)
New Guinea	10
New South Wales	42
Queensland	10
Tasmania	202
Victoria	85
Total	350

For the sake of comparison the figures for Great Britain, the United States and Canada are shown in thousands of horse-power, together with other relevant data. These indicate clearly the degree of electrification made possible by available water power and by population density. The comparable per capita figures for Great Britain are somewhat misleading, in that reliance is placed by British manufacturers upon older forms of motive power to a greater extent than in the "newer" countries.

GENERATING CAPACITY 1940 (APPROXIMATE)

Country	Area (million sq. miles)	Approx. Population (millions)	Generating Capacity (in thousands of horsepower)		
			Thermal Stations	Hydro-electric	Total (Approx.)
Australia	2.947	7.07	2,050	350	2,400
Great Britain *.	.0888	46.0	11,500	400	12,000
Canada	3.466	11.4	560	7,600	8,000
U.S.A.	3.027	131.0	40,000	16,000	56,000

* For the year 1937–38.

POWER RESOURCES AND INDUSTRIAL NEEDS

In every country, the possibility of expanding secondary industries depends mainly upon power resources. In Australia these resources are sufficient for the long-term needs of a population at least twice that of the present time, and for much greater intensive development of manufactures. Coal supplies are sufficient, especially if both black and brown coal are included in the total. The concentration of the high-grade coal in two States is the chief difficulty. New South Wales and Queensland are well supplied; all the other States are in a less happy position and, with the exception of Queensland, all are dependent upon New South Wales (Newcastle) for high-grade coal. Victoria's deficiency in black coal is offset by very large deposits of brown coal. Water power cannot, of course, be better than rainfall, even if the topography is favourable for the storage for irrigation, for the generation of electricity, or both.

In relation to area, Australia's water power is far below that of any other continent; and it is singularly unfortunate that two large States, South Australia and Western Australia, are also the driest and poorest in deposits of black or brown coal. The pattern of industrial concentration and of population distribution in Australia is largely explained in terms of this coal-water situation. Nevertheless, in terms of actual or potential power supplies of all kinds, Australia is relatively well supplied, especially in proportion to population; and so far as the power engineer can foresee, there is no obstacle to much greater industrial development because of shortage of energy. The real difficulty is decentralization, which means in this connection the spreading of factory industries more evenly over the Commonwealth, and in each State as well. This possibility turns mainly upon transfer of power resources, and more efficient transport is the best means of supplying coal from New South Wales to deficient States. In general, that must be largely limited to transport by sea.

It may yet become practicable, especially in Western Australia, South Australia, and in the North, to use solar heat for the generation of power. In few regions is a more regular and generous outpouring of sun-heat available than in these States, of which only a small proportion is densely settled. The vast bulk of these States will never be more than sparsely settled, however, even if the utilization of solar energy became feasible. Deficiency of water would still limit the number of settlements which, like Kalgoorlie or Whyalla, could be maintained in the near-desert at the end of a pipe-line. But the scientist and the engineer, doubtless, still have many surprises up their sleeves; and it would be rash to dismiss the possibility of new forms of power generation being perfected and applied. The history of the last century is largely a story of the pessimist confounded, at least in the industrial sense.

Plate 15. Sheep shearing in the Riverina, New South Wales—typical of many hundreds of sheds in the sheep zone.

Plate 16. Cattle droving, Kimberley District, north Western Australia.

Plate 17. Waite Agricultural Research Institute, Adelaide, South Australia.
Plate 18. Drilling for wheat, Western Australia.

Plate 19. Wheat silos at Geelong, Victoria.
Plate 20. Reafforestation. Pine plantation, Federal Capital Territory.

Plate 21. Eildon Reservoir on Goulburn River. Capacity 306,000 acre feet. Proposed future capacity 2,300,000 acre feet.

Plate 22. Yarra Falls wool combing and spinnnig mills, Melbourne, Victoria.

Chapter XVI

THE AUSTRALIAN TARIFF

BY GISELLE SCHNEIDER

International Section, Department of Post-War Reconstruction, Canberra

To AUSTRALIA, as to the United States, the tariff means more than an instrument of trade policy. It has become an organic part of the national economy. In Australia's transition from a young primary to a more mature mixed economy, the tariff has played a constructive part. It is closely tied up both with the desire to reduce the dependence of the country's prosperity upon the export price of a few primary commodities, and with the necessity for providing stable and more diverse employment for an increasing population which mechanized agriculture cannot absorb.

THE TARIFF HABIT DEVELOPS

The first Commonwealth tariff, introduced in 1901, was a mild and straightforward affair, mainly serving revenue purposes; but the first milestone on the road to high protection was the tariff increase of 1908, which left no doubt as to its protective aims. This upward "revision" also saw the first appearance of preference to British goods on the Australian market in the form of a "dual-column" tariff, providing British preferential duties and a higher general tariff for goods from non-British countries. The 1914–18 war stimulated industrial development in a wide range of industries. The tariff of 1920 was intended to protect new industries that had sprung up during the war, and to increase the margin of preference to

British goods. The Industries Preservation Act of 1921 imposed special duties on goods coming from countries with depreciated currencies, and was designed to protect Australia against dumping.

In the same year the Tariff Board was set up to advise the Government on questions relating to trade and customs. The matters which the Minister shall refer to the Board for enquiry and report include the classification of goods for duty and the determination of their value, the necessity for new, increased, or reduced duties, any complaint that a manufacturer is taking undue advantage of the protection given him by charging unnecessarily high prices for his goods, and the granting of bounties. As the Tariff Board acquired more experience and authority, its recommendations were adopted by the Government in most cases; it became a beneficial and moderating influence in trade policy, and the centre of the Australian protective system.

A WARNING VOICE

So far, increases in tariff rates had met with general public approval. The industrial expansion had been spectacular enough to disguise the general economic effects of a rising tariff; but gradually uneasiness about the economic and social costs of the tariff became so pronounced that, in 1927, the Government appointed a "special" committee to investigate tariff policy. The conclusions of that enquiry were published in 1929 [1] in "The Australian Tariff." The committee found that without protection Australia would have been unable to maintain the same population at the same standard of living, that protection imposed "excess" costs, but that these costs had to be weighed against the benefit of providing employment for a

[1] The Australian Tariff: A Special Inquiry made by a Committee of Economists and Others at the request of the Prime Minister. Published by Melbourne University Press.

larger population. The main issue involved was the *degree* of protection and the selection of industries which should benefit from the tariff. The committee calculated the excess cost of protection, i.e., the amount by which prices of Australian products were raised by duties above those of duty-free imports, and arrived at a figure of £26m. imposed by the protection of secondary industries, and £10m. by that of primary industries. It stated that the resources of Australia at that time were sufficient to carry the total cost of £36m., but pointed to the serious dangers of increasing protection. One industry's protection was another industry's cost; higher costs and prices became an excuse for further protection. Moreover, the brunt of the burden had to be borne by the export (primary) industries, competing in the world market, and unable to pass the excess cost on in higher prices. The cost of the tariff in the export industries amounted to nine per cent of their total costs. Australia depended upon the exports of wool, wheat, metals, meat, dairy produce, and fruit to purchase her imports, and to pay interest on her overseas debt. The committee warned that further extensions of the tariff might involve an uncompensated loss, and that costs might overtake the benefits. It stated that the total burden of the tariff had probably reached the economic limits; and no further increases or extensions should be made without the most rigorous scrutiny of the costs involved.

THE SKY IS THE LIMIT

These cool and reasonable considerations were swept aside in the storm of the depression. In the general scramble for safety the tariff became an instrument for fiscal adjustments of emergency. The Australian export price index fell from 1,000 in 1928–29 to 579 in 1932–33. The whole rural economy toppled—and with it the price-income structure of the Commonwealth.

At the same time the stream of overseas loans suddenly dried up, drastic measures had to be taken to diminish imports and to increase exports in order to safeguard the currency. The tariff was revised, and between November 1929 and the end of 1930 no less than seven higher schedules were introduced. Added to that were surcharges of fifty per cent on a number of items, total import prohibitions on others, and a primage duty of ten per cent on all imports. The depreciation in 1931 of the Australian pound in terms of sterling to £A.125 for £stg.100 increased the protective effect of the duties. Imports fell from £stg.143 millions in 1928–29 to £A.55 millions in 1931–32.

IMPERIAL SELF-SUFFICIENCY

Imperial preference has long been a tradition in Australia. When world markets collapsed after 1930 and a wave of economic nationalism swept the world, Australia naturally turned to the only relatively free market—the United Kingdom—and sought shelter within an Empire bloc. It was believed that a revival of intra-Empire trade might help to restore world trade. The Ottawa Conference in 1932 launched a stronger system of "empire preference" under which the United Kingdom gave protection to Australian primary products, and Australia reciprocated by widening the margin of preference for British manufactures. This was achieved at first, not by lowering the British preferential tariff, but by raising duties against non-British imports. Empire preference turned out to be a much more complex affair than had been expected; and it became clear that different sections within the two countries were affected differently. It was true Britain took about fifty per cent of our exports, and Australia bought forty per cent of her imports from Britain; but whilst the dairy, sugar, meat, and fruit industries derived important benefits from a sheltered British market, others including wool, wheat, and metals, which accounted for more than two-thirds of Australian exports, depended to a great extent on markets out-side Britain. A clash of many divergent interests soon became apparent: on the British market between subsidized British agriculture and the Australian primary exporter; on the Aus-tralian market between Australian secondary industry and British exporters of manufactures; in Australia, between pro-tectionist manufacturers and primary producers dependent on the world market; in the United Kingdom, between Britain the World Trader and Britain the Leader of an Empire Bloc.

THE UNITED KINGDOM MARKET AND AUSTRALIAN EXPORTS
1937-38

	Imports from Australia as per cent of total imports into United Kingdom	Exports to United King-dom as per cent of total Australian exports
Wool	39	37
Wheat	22	61
Butter	16	92
Beef	14	99
Mutton and lamb	28	98
Pig Meat	3	98
Dried Fruits	39	58
Fresh Fruits	27	87
Eggs	5	99
Sugar	17.5	98
Wine	..	95

Source: *Commonwealth Year Book*

THE PRUNING OF THE TARIFF

The functions and the importance of the Tariff Board were increased by the Ottawa Agreements, which provided that no new duties should be imposed, or existing duties raised, on products from the United Kingdom without recommendation of the Tariff Board. The agreement laid down certain prin-ciples in determining the measure of tariff protection to be

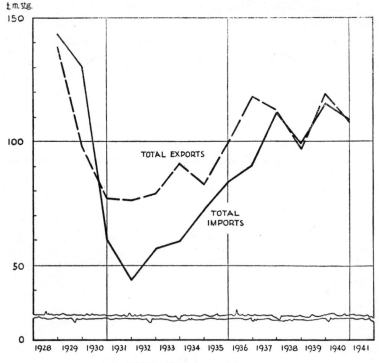

Fig. XXV. Exports and imports.

given to Australian industry. The Board considered a "reasonable" duty was one high enough to raise the landed cost of the overseas products sufficiently to compensate the Australian manufacturer for the higher cost of Australian labour, raw materials, and overhead charges, and to provide a marginal advantage in his favour. This margin should be wide enough to secure the Australian market for goods which could be economically produced in Australia, and narrow enough to preclude inefficiency, uneconomic extension, or undue profit-making. The Tariff Board has been very successful in applying these principles, and has shown sound judgment in its reports. It has used its growing authority to check too costly expansions, and has in many cases recommended the lowering of duties. Up to 1938 three hundred items covering goods which were produced competitively by the United Kingdom and Australia were reviewed by the Tariff Board. Many ad valorem duties were reduced from forty-five per cent to less than thirty per cent and often to ten per cent, and duties on plant and machinery which could not be manufactured economically in Australia were removed altogether. At public hearings all interested parties could give their opinions, and decisions were taken after gathering information from British and Australian manufacturers as to relative costs of economical and efficient production.

In the Exchange Adjustment Act of 1933, duties were reduced to compensate for the protective effects of exchange depreciation, the reduction being limited to goods of British origin, thus widening the margin of preference. It was claimed that this constituted "the greatest single contribution directed towards the encouragement of British trade made by any Australian government since 1907."

The Tariff Board, however, had no counterpart in primary production, and so one of the most disquieting aspects of Australian tariff policy in recent years has been the increasing assistance to primary industries by means of subsidies operated through higher home prices and bounties. Almost the only unassisted primary commodity was wool. This perpetuated and extended non-economic production, and delayed the unavoidable adjustment to changes in world demand.

A COSTLY RELAPSE

The promising developments in tariff-making were unexpectedly interrupted by the "trade diversion" policy of May 1936, a Government measure which significantly preceded the renewal of the Ottawa Agreements, and Anglo-Argentine trade negotiations. Much criticism arose from the fact that the new policy was adopted without reference to the Tariff Board. Its aim was to divert trade away from so-called "bad customer countries" in order to expand the Australian market for British goods, and accelerate the growth of home industries. Duties on cotton and silk piece goods from Japan were increased; a large range of imports mainly from the United States became subject to a system of import license; and the import of motor car chassis from the United States and Canada was restricted to the level of 1935–36. It was true that the Australian balance of trade with the United States had been unfavourable for years, but this was scarcely either the method or the moment for correcting the trade balance. The United States retaliated immediately by placing Australia on the list of countries which had adopted discriminatory trade practices, and "most-favoured-nation" treatment was only restored to Australia in 1938 after the licensing system had been abandoned.

INCREASED INDUSTRIAL EFFICIENCY

After the depression gradual but strong improvement in the competitive power of Australian factory production took place. This was due to keen competition of Australian industries for a reduced market, to a fall in wages not only absolutely but also relatively to wages in Great Britain, and to the depreciation of the Australian currency. Some important manufactures, such as iron, steel, and agricultural implements can now face world competition without protection, and their prices in Australia are mostly free-trade prices. The Tariff Board has contributed to this encouraging development. The considerable growth of secondary industry, in spite of the steady lowering of duties, points to increasing efficiency and reduced costs. The simultaneous increase of imports was due to the greater demand for machinery and raw materials following general recovery. Relative price movements of raw materials, as basic for industrial development as those shown in the table below, are the more significant because of the size of the output involved.

COMPARISON OF IRON AND STEEL PRICES

	June 1930		June 1938		June 1939		June 1940	
	Aust. *£.stg.*	*U.K.* *£.stg.*	*Aust.* *£.Aust.*	*U.K.* *£.Aust.*	*Aust.* *£.Aust.*	*U.K.* *£.Aust.*	*Aust.* *£.Aust.*	*U.K.* *£.Aust.*
Pig Iron...	6.10.0	3. 5.0	4.10.0	8. 0.0	4.10.0	6.17.7	4.10.0	7.17.6
Struct. Steel.....	12.12.6	7. 7.6	10. 2.8	13.15.1	10. 2.8	13. 0.0	10. 2.8	17. 1.6
Bar Steel..	12.12.6	7.15.0	10. 2.8	14. 6.3	10. 2.8	13.11.3	10. 2.8	18. 1.4

Source: Tariff Board Annual Report 1940

THE EMPIRE IS NOT ENOUGH

As the Ottawa Agreement was due for reconsideration, and the Anglo-American trade negotiations were approaching, Australian and British ministers met in London to review the results of empire preference. Their conclusions were summed up in the White Paper of 1938. Both countries reaffirmed their vital interest in their mutual trading partnership. The United Kingdom was the greatest import market for Australian exports, and Australia was one of the largest customers for United Kingdom goods and the domicile of the largest amount of British capital invested in any single overseas country. Nevertheless the experiences of empire preference had revealed the necessity for Britain's measures to safeguard and develop her own agriculture, and the position of the United Kingdom as a great international trader and investor. These facts impose an upper limit upon the extent to which increased markets in the United Kingdom can be afforded to Dominion producers. Any diminution of total exports from the United Kingdom will tend to affect its capacity to purchase foodstuffs and raw materials from Australia. On the other hand, the

United Kingdom had to recognise that it was impossible substantially to increase the population in Australia solely by expansion of primary industries, and that it was necessary to combine with such expansion a sound development of secondary industry. In short, imperial preference had to be qualified by the interests of the home producers of the two countries, as well as by their separate interests as world traders.

WARTIME TRADE CONTROLS

Since the outbreak of war the tariff has been largely eclipsed by a number of more direct measures to control imports. Exchange control was introduced in August 1939, and was supplemented by a system of import licensing to conserve non-sterling exchange and prevent unessential imports. All this led to a great expansion of old industries and the launching of new ones. The Tariff Board divided all industries into three groups:

(i) those desirable for permanent establishment in Australia and assured of reasonable protection after the war;

(ii) those undesirable for permanent establishment, but necessary to meet the exigencies of war, and to which assistance of liquidation should be given after the war; and

(iii) other industries which should get no protection whatsoever.

The wartime imperial purchases schemes arranged for marketing Australian primary products by acquiring surpluses at fixed prices. Trade has become increasingly subject to controls, inter-government transactions, and strategic expediency.

The Mutual Aid Agreement between the United States and the United Kingdom, of February 1942, setting out the conditions of lend-lease assistance to British countries, was followed by lend-lease arrangements between the governments of Australia and the United States. The immediate occasion for this agreement arose from the arrival of United States armed forces in Australia. It provided for reciprocal aid on lend-lease terms so that the need of currency might be reduced to a minimum.

AUSTRALIA'S PARTICIPATION IN POSTWAR WORLD TRADE

Following the war the foremost objective in Australia, as in any other democratic country, must be to provide full employment and improved living standards for her people. Productive capacity has increased, but full employment of men and resources can be maintained only if markets are found for Australian products. Since Australia is a debtor country, the balance of payments is another important consideration in Australia's search for export markets.

Whether immediate pressure to maintain employment and absorb demobilized soldiers can be fitted into a pattern of international collaboration and reconciled with the lowering of trade barriers, turns on a number of factors beyond Australia's control. It will depend on the extent to which the purchasing power of the United Kingdom has been curtailed by the war, on how soon European countries will pass out of the relief period and will be able to pay for imports with their own products; on whether, in a more remote future, new markets in South-eastern Asia could develop from industrialization and from the raising of living standards in that area.

Should the industrially powerful nations try to maintain an excess of exports over imports, should they refuse to lower their own tariff barriers, should they disregard the reality that Australia has come of age industrially, then Australia will be left with no alternative but to maintain her present protectionist policy. But trade is not a one-way traffic. Australia would wish to assist in reviving world trade by making any adjustments which would not prejudice her industrial development. A lowering of tariffs on many commodities would not be regarded as too high a price for participation in an expanding world economy. But it would be futile to deny the possibility of post-war pressure to provide domestic employment by replacing imports and to protect established industries. This will be a political reality of the first importance.

Chapter XVII

WAGES, LIVING STANDARDS, AND THE TARIFF IN AUSTRALIA

BY K. S. ISLES

Formerly Professor of Economics, Adelaide, now Belfast.

and

B. R. WILLIAMS

Lecturer in Economics, University of Adelaide

"STATISTICAL data and the evidence of persons in contact with those in want, lead us to believe that a considerable proportion of Australian citizens are poorly housed, ill-clothed, or ill-nourished—living in conditions which reflect no credit on a country such as ours. . . . No longer can we sustain the claim that Australia is the social laboratory of the world." So wrote the Parliamentary Joint Committee on Social Security at the end of 1941. It is clear that in Australia, no less than in Britain and America, the social unrest which is stirring and the desire for social betterment which is growing, have their origin and their justification in the facts of unequal distribution of the comforts of life and insufficiency of the bare essentials.

WAGE RATES

In Australia the State was early in the field as a protector of wage-earners. Because the workers were roundly defeated in the industrial strife at the close of last century, their growing political strength turned their thoughts to the Government as protector or mediator. The first step in government regulation of wages was taken in 1896, when Victoria instituted a Wages Board. Shortly afterwards industrial courts were established in New South Wales and South Australia. The formulators of the Australian Constitution were likewise influenced by such ideas, and provision was made in the Constitution for Federal arbitration in industry. By 1905 the Commonwealth Court of Conciliation and Arbitration was functioning. In the Act establishing it, trade unions were recognised as natural and legitimate associations performing a necessary function in the economic system.

Set up to maintain industrial peace, but with its jurisdiction limited to disputes affecting two or more States, or referred to it by the employers or employees in the particular State concerned, the Commonwealth Court of Conciliation and Arbitration was soon led to declare a basic or living wage payable to unskilled workers, with added "margins for skill." This court wage is now a major factor determining working-class living standards. Though the States have their own wage-fixing tribunals, the Commonwealth Court has come to exercise through its awards a guiding influence upon them. Moreover, it has been strengthened under national security regulations which give it power to initiate enquiries, even within States, and to declare a common rule.

In determining wage rates the arbitration court has no clearly conceived principles. In making their awards the judges of the court, trained in law but, with few exceptions, ill-equipped for handling this problem in applied economics, have blended expediency with tradition. Their respect for tradition led them to crystallize the standard of living awarded by Mr. Justice Higgins in his Harvester Judgment in 1907; while their willingness to temper tradition with expediency, a willingness strengthened by a conservative Government's choice of judges, led them to jettison the Harvester standard in the hard times of 1931.

The Higgins judgment of 1907 was a forward step. Its purpose was to bring wage rates paid by all employers up to the level of those paid by a few reputable employers, and to prevent backsliding afterwards. Later, however, the mechanism created for maintaining the standard obstructed further improvements in real wages. The prescribed minimum became, in fact, the maximum. Being designed to standardize the best conditions existing when it was introduced, it has tended in practice to standardize them notwithstanding later improvements in productivity.

Changes in the basic wage other than as compensation for changes in the cost of living—i.e., changes in the basic "real" wage—have been made by court award on only four occasions since 1907. The first occasion was in 1921, when Mr. Justice Powers awarded a three-shilling increase. Even then the increase was the result rather of chance than of intention. At that time wages were adjusted for changes in the cost of living only at long intervals, and the "Powers three shillings" was intended merely to compensate for the lag in wages behind the rising cost of living. In 1921 the court provided that cost-of-living adjustments to the basic wage should be made each quarter automatically; and this arrangement was revised in 1939 in such a way as to minimize the lag between price movement and wage adjustment.

The second occasion was in 1931, when the basic real wage was lowered by ten per cent as an anti-slump measure. The third was in 1934, when the ten per cent reduction in the basic real wage imposed in 1931 was nominally restored. The net increase, however, was substantially less than ten per cent, because at the same time the "Powers" three-shilling increase was discarded on the ground that, in the words of Dethridge, C.J., it was an "illogical extension of the basic wage" which had "become quite unjustifiable." The net result was that the real wage was restored to about the level of the Harvester judgment. Almost thirty years of industrial progress and increased national productivity had done nothing to raise the real living standard of the unskilled workman.

The fourth occasion on which the court altered the basic real wage was in 1937. With rising industrial prosperity the court in that year modified its practice by awarding a "prosperity loading" (not to be varied with the cost of living) as an addition to the basic wage measured by "needs." It based this prosperity loading on industry's "capacity to pay," awarding six shillings a week in New South Wales, Victoria, and Queensland, but only four shillings in South Australia, Western Australia, and Tasmania. In determining the size of these increases the court took account of the improvements which had already occurred in profits and industrial activity. But in refusing an application by the unions for a wage increase in 1940, an application based on the fact of increased profits and increased industrial activity, it widened its interpretation of industry's "capacity to pay," and shifted the basis of its assessment by taking into account not only realized facts but also the "economic outlook."

The average real wage earned by skilled and unskilled workers taken together has varied more often, and has risen further, than the basic real wage payable to unskilled workers. It has done so because of changes in the "margins for skill" and in the proportion of workers receiving those margins, and because of other changes such as the introduction of holiday allowances. Variations over the period 1911–1939 are shown in the accompanying chart.[1]

The chart shows the course of: (1) average nominal wage rates earned by adult employed males; (2) the corresponding average real wage rates (average nominal wage rates adjusted for changes in the cost of living); (3) real wages earned per head of all adult male workers, unemployed as well as employed; and (4) productivity per head, obtained by dividing

[1] The figures on which the chart is based are given in an appendix to this chapter.

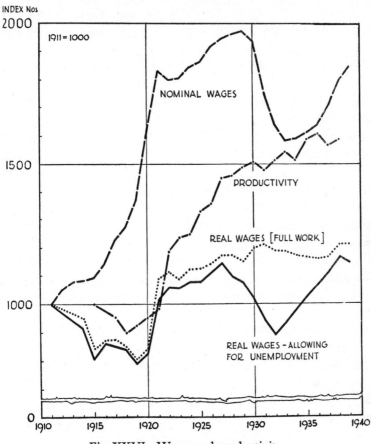

INDEX Nos

2000

1911 = 1000

NOMINAL WAGES

1500

PRODUCTIVITY

REAL WAGES [FULL WORK]

1000

REAL WAGES – ALLOWING
FOR UNEMPLOYMENT

0

1910   1915   1920   1925   1930   1935   1940

Fig. XXVI. Wages and productivity.

the national income produced in Australia by the number of
persons gainfully employed.[2]

[2] The precise figures may be obtained by calculations from data published
in the Commonwealth *Labour Reports* and in Clark and Crawford, *The
National Income of Australia.*

The first series—index-numbers of average nominal wage rates for adult
males in full work—was obtained from the Commonwealth *Labour Reports*
and adjusted where necessary to 1911 as base. The index numbers of the
corresponding real wage rates were obtained by dividing the figures in this
first series by the corresponding figures in the retail price index numbers

It will be seen from the chart that the average real wage paid to employed workmen has risen by about twenty per cent, while productivity rose by almost sixty per cent.[3] On the other hand, the average real wage earned per head of employed and unemployed workmen taken together, though substantially higher during the twenties than in 1911, was lower during the early thirties than in 1911, owing to the much larger percentage of unemployment. In Australia as elsewhere, unemployment as a normal feature of the industrial system has been increasing. Before World War I the average rate of unemployment was about five per cent; from 1920 to 1927 it was between seven and eight per cent; and since 1928 it has ranged between ten per cent and thirty per cent. As can be seen from the growing divergence between curves II, III and IV, as shown in Fig. XXVI, the productivity increase has been largely wasted owing to such unemployment. In 1931, real income produced, measured in 1923–37 prices, was £741 million. Real income produced per person in work was £345, but real income per head of working population, including the unemployed, was only £276. Thus unemployment reduced the average real production by roughly £70 per head of working population.

We can review the changes in real earnings per worker by quoting J. F. Nimmo's figures of the average wage-earner's consumption standard.[4] That standard rose five per cent be-

---

("C" series, adjusted to 1911 as base), and multiplying by 1,000. The third series was obtained by lowering the index numbers of real wage rates in proportion to the trade union unemployment percentages for the corresponding years and by re-computing the resulting series with 1911 as base. The index numbers of real income produced per head of population gainfully employed were calculated from Clark and Crawford, *ibid.*, p. 71.

[3] It should be noted that the rise in productivity as shown here, being calculated on the basis of a 45-hour week, perhaps somewhat overstates the true rise. For (1) if hours in the early part of the period had in fact been reduced to 45, output would not have been reduced proportionately, and (2) if the employment percentage had been as high in the latter part of the period as in the earlier part, output per employed worker in the latter part would probably have been somewhat less than it was.

[4] Cf. *Australian Standards of Living* (ed. G. L. Wood), pp. 173–176.

tween 1901 and 1910, but rising prices thereafter had by 1920 reduced it to between fifteen and twenty per cent below 1911. By 1927, however, after making allowance for redistribution of income through public finance, the standard had risen to fifteen per cent above the 1911 level. From then on until 1932 there was a progressive fall of twenty per cent, but by 1936 the standard was seven per cent above 1911 without allowing for additional benefit on account of public finance. (It should be noted that population in 1936 was half as great again as in 1911.)

LIVING STANDARDS

Adequate appraisement of living standards, however, must go beyond real and money wages and consider the distribution of the national income and the range, quality, and finance of social services. Loss of income through unemployment does not fall evenly on the whole population. Census figures for 1933 show that 392,000 "breadwinners" (including youths and pensioners) had no income at all, and 567,000 others had less than £1 a week. Of the total number of male breadwinners in employment, 1,500,000, or seventy-two per cent, received less than £4 per week, and four-fifths of the remaining twenty-eight per cent had less than £400 per year. About one-tenth of all breadwinners received one-half of the national income. Inequality became less serious as economic conditions improved, and by 1938 roughly fifty per cent of breadwinners had incomes of over £200.

Social services improve the position of those on low incomes. The wage-earning population through old age and invalid pensions, war pensions, maternity allowances, and State social services derived a gross benefit from 1932 to 1936, for example, of over £50 million per annum. After making allowance for their contribution to public revenue, mainly through indirect taxation, the net benefit was about £20 million per annum, which represented an increase of eight to ten per cent of the income of the wage-earning population.

However, the existing social services are inadequate in both scope and content. They lack comprehensiveness in the range both of services included and people catered for, and many of the benefits provided are niggardly. "Once famed as pioneer workers in the social laboratory, we have fallen far behind, smugly satisfied with our achievements, and justifying our complacency on the ground that Australian conditions hardly warrant many services essential in congested industrial countries." [5]

A sense of insecurity is an important intangible element in the standard of living; and, as we have seen, there is a greater chance of unemployment now than there was earlier in this century. This negative element in living standards has been needlessly harsh because of the seriously inadequate provision for unemployment and sickness. Before the war, there was no unemployment or health insurance except in Queensland, and no child endowment except in New South Wales. At the same time expenditure on parks and gardens in densely populated areas, and on education, was miserably low. The inadequate provision for education can be seen when it is realised that expenditure on education was half the national spending on tobacco, half that on liquor, and two-fifths of the gambling "bill."

Provision for social services varies from State to State. For example, New South Wales had a widows' pension scheme but no slum clearance policy, Victoria had the latter and not the former, while Tasmania had neither but had a country medical service. Much the same story could be told about other social services. Yet social service needs from State to State are fairly similar. Until a national policy is developed, Australian provision for social services will remain inadequate.

Housing conditions are worthy of special mention. To quote again from the Joint Committee on Social Security, "No evidence placed before the Committee has impressed it more

[5] A. P. Bland, *Social Services in Australia* (ed. W. G. K. Duncan).

than that referring to the existence of slum conditions in many parts of the Commonwealth, and the general shortage of low-rental houses of satisfactory quality." Surveys in the various States indicate that roughly fifteen per cent of houses embodied the conditions of a sub-standard level of life. The shortage has increased during wartime, and the post-war settlement should include a vast housing programme. To remedy the shortage over a moderately short space of time, however, would imply a danger of too great a concentration of employment in the capital-goods industries, with a consequent difficulty of producing consumption goods.

Since the beginning of the war social services have been considerably improved. Family allowances have been instituted, maternity allowances and pensions increased, and war widows' pensions and disability allowances introduced; while in education there is a wartime scheme for subsidizing competent but needy University students. A comprehensive health and social insurance scheme has been prepared for presentation to Parliament. Providing unemployment can be controlled, post-war Australia will move out of its pre-war doldrums.

Many Australians are fond of saying that the Australian workman is the best-off in the world. But in fact he is not. Mr. Colin Clark's figures of average real income produced per occupied person show that Australia is behind New Zealand, the United States, and Great Britain.[6] Before the war, average real income in New Zealand was 2,040 "international units" but in Australia it was only 1,363 units.

THE TARIFF IN RELATION TO THE STANDARD OF LIVING

Little attention was paid to the general economic effects of the protective tariff, either by parliaments in adopting it and in extending its range, or by the press or the public in form-

[6] Cf. *The Conditions of Economic Progress*, Colin Clark.

ing their opinions of it. Indeed, it grew up with no more logical basis than was provided by traditional arguments put forward in its support by interested parties. But that has not prevented it from being a source of strength and resiliency for Australia in the world economic conditions of the past fifteen or twenty years.

That period has been characterized by a great increase throughout the world in agricultural efficiency, and, at the same time, a growth of economic nationalism leading to a general shrinkage in export markets for primary products. By stimulating the growth of factory production, the policy of protection had already provided Australia with a buffer against a collapse in the prices of her primary exports. It consequently enabled her to maintain a much higher standard of consumption than would otherwise have been possible, in the prevailing conditions of world trade, for a population of the existing size. It is true that, by raising her tariff during the great depression, Australia caused other countries to retaliate, and, like other countries, she thereby aggravated the conditions which she sought to alleviate. Nevertheless the policy of protection was sound in principle even if, in this sense, its application was carried to excess.

This is not to deny that the direct and immediate effect of imposing a protective tariff must necessarily be a fall in the average standard of living, even if only a temporary fall. For the deliberate object is to displace imported manufactures by more costly domestic production. In this connection there have been, and still are, vital differences between the possibilities of expanding primary and secondary industries in Australia. Take first the primary industries. The greater the number of people engaged in them already, the less help can new entrants expect to get from natural resources. They have either to go on to less accessible or less fertile land, or else to intensify production on land already utilized; and the harder, therefore, is it for them to keep up the old level of production per head. Furthermore, the world demand for most primary exports is ordinarily inelastic; and an increase in the output of these goods tends to force down their prices heavily. On the other hand, an expansion of secondary industry tends in obvious ways to increase manufacturing efficiency all round; so that the initial fall in consumption standards caused by a protective tariff has not necessarily to be permanent. Besides, the demand for manufactured goods is generally more elastic than that for primary products. Hence if, instead of encouraging growth of secondary industries, Australia had relied on her great primary industries to absorb a large part of her expanding population, a big reduction in the general standard of living would have been inevitable. Thus in setting out to diversify her production she was causing an obvious though perhaps temporary fall in the standard of living in order to avoid a very much larger fall as population increased. Moreover, by this means she was shielding her economy from the effects of the tremendous variations which occur in the prices of primary products, thus maintaining greater stability of income and employment. Though these were not the clearly conceived aims of Australian tariff policy, they have nevertheless been the results.

There can be little doubt what post-war policy should be. In the first place, unless a great increase should take place in the world demand for primary exports, the present population could not be employed without protection except at a very much lower standard of living. The protective tariff must therefore be retained. In the second place, however, protection should be used with great moderation for several reasons. First, if Australia is to honour her commitments, tariff policy must not be allowed to conflict with the principles embodied in the Atlantic Charter and in Article VII of the Lease-Lend Agreement. Secondly, the lower the rate of protection needed, the less the direct cut in average real income per head involved in securing a given increase in employment. Protection should

REAL WAGE INDEX NUMBERS

Year	I Nominal Wage Index Numbers	II Average for Employed Workers	III Average for Employed and Unemployed	IV Productivity Index Numbers (Year ending 30th June)
1911	1,000	1,000	1,000	....
1912	1,050	....	....	....
1913	1,076	....	....	....
1914	1,081	948	912	....
1915	1,092	842	802	1,000
1916	1,144	867	857	....
1917	1,226	872	850	952
1918	1,270	846	836	899
1919	1,370	808	792	925
1920	1,627	841	825	....
1921	1,826	1,087	1,013	982
1922	1,801	1,112	1,059	1,185
1923	1,805	1,085	1,058	1,233
1924	1,840	1,124	1,075	1,242
1925	1,861	1,125	1,077	1,328
1926	1,914	1,141	1,112	1,357
1927	1,946	1,171	1,143	1,445
1928	1,963	1,172	1,097	1,454
1929	1,972	1,151	1,073	1,487
1930	1,939	1,198	1,015	1,502
1931	1,752	1,210	921	1,476
1932	1,639	1,190	887	1,511
1933	1,584	1,187	933	1,542
1934	1,590	1,173	979	1,511
1935	1,609	1,166	1,022	1,586
1936	1,635	1,160	1,068	1,604
1937	1,707	1,167	1,110	1,566
1938	1,799	1,211	1,161	1,588
1939	1,846	1,212	1,148	....

Explanation:
 I. Index numbers of average nominal wage rates for adult males in full work (Commonwealth *Labour Reports*).
 II. Index numbers of real wage rates for adult males in full work, obtained by dividing each of the figures in Column I by the corresponding figure in the retail price index number ("C" series), and multiplying by 1,000.
 III. The figures in Column II lowered in proportion to trade union employment percentages for the corresponding years, and re-computed with 1911 as base.
 IV. Index numbers of real income produced per head of population gainfully employed, adjusted throughout on the basis of a 45-hour week.

therefore be confined to those industries which need it least. The growing confidence of parliaments and the public in the Tariff Board, an expert body set up to examine and advise the Government on applications for protection, is some guarantee that this principle will be generally followed. Finally, there is the way in which the burden is distributed. The cost of protecting luxuries falls on the purchasers. But luxuries account for only a small part of the total protection. Because most wages vary with the cost of living, the cost of protecting necessaries—and capital goods used in their production—is shifted on to the unsheltered industries, which broadly speaking are the primary export industries. It has been estimated that in 1932–33 these bore more than half the total cost of protection.[7] And since Australia cannot afford to make them unprofitable, especially in view of her heavy external debt commitments, she cannot afford to indulge in extravagant protection.

[7] Cf. L. F. Giblin, *Some Economic Effects of the Australian Tariff* (Joseph Fisher Lecture, University of Adelaide, 1936).

Chapter XVIII

SECONDARY INDUSTRIES

BY WALTER J. ROSE

Member of the Tariff Board, Commonwealth of Australia

THE BROAD FACTS

AUSTRALIA is widely regarded as a country that is limited to rural production; but, in fact, industrial development has gone far and fast. Considering the rapidity of their growth, the remarkable features about Australian manufactures are their concentration, their variety, and the technical advances made during the last twenty years.

To say this is not to claim that the achievements of Australian secondary industry are more spectacular than those of many other countries; but, in a relative sense, and in view of Australia's small population and its distance from world markets, what has been achieved, especially in the last few decades, is remarkable.

The greatest concentration of factory industry has been built up in New South Wales and Victoria. About 2.6 million people, nearly forty per cent of the people of the Commonwealth live and work in two areas totalling less than 1,000 square miles. This represents industrial density which, socially and strategically, is regarded with growing disfavour; even though it is recognized, in the main, as a direct response to the pattern of natural resources. This concentration of New South Wales and Victoria shows plainly in the following statistics:

AUSTRALIA: MANUFACTURING INDUSTRIES, 1941–42

	New South Wales	Victoria	Australian Total	N.S.W. & Vic. per cent of Australia
1. Number employed (thousands)..	298	258	725	76.7
2. Wages paid (£m.)	78	64	180	78.8
3. Value of production (£m.)*.....	139	111	316	78.6
4. Value of Output (£m.)	340	257	773	77.4
5. Value of Plant (£m.)	71	48	169	70.0

* After deducting cost of materials employed. £m Australian.

The extent of this concentration would be even more marked if the highly technical industries were distinguished from processing industries such as food and drink products. A summary of industrial statistics will be useful at this point:

FACTORY INDUSTRIES, 1938–39

(Excluding Food Processing, Wood Working and Clothing)

Industry	No. of Factories	No. of Employees	Value Plant	Value Materials	Value Production
			£A m.	£A m.	£A m.
Rail and tram vehicles	117	27,300	5.390	4.976	8.021
Engineering	1,000	26,200	3.646	7.340	9.250
Motor vehicles	3,232	23,000	1.534	3.650	6.762
Woollen, including scouring..	90	20,000	3.370	7.331	4.790
Iron & Steel	363	19,400	8.611	16.500	10.254
Knitted goods	313	18,000	1.930	4.284	3.809
Boots & shoes	311	17,000	2.632	4.274	3.696
Motor bodies	232	12,000	.630	3.750	3.747
Electrical apparatus	360	11,000	.896	3.195	3.655
Agricultural implements	161	6,563	.9	1.485	1.836
Tobacco	30	5,600	1.095	1.080	2.685
Non-ferrous metal extraction..	42	5,530	3.525	16.844	3.892
Chemicals, drugs, etc.	238	5,400	1.253	3.500	3.830
Tires	262	5,200	1.174	3.646	2.330
Wireless apparatus	72	4,800	.305	1.355	1.123
Tanning, etc.	132	4,400	.919	2.983	1.522
Breweries	36	3,700	2.737	3.418	5.376
Soap & candles	65	2,620	.580	3.530	1.885
Chemical fertilisers	36	2,540	2.353	3.231	1.600

This industrial concentration reflects the "cluster" of natural resources, including rainfall, in the eastern part of the continent. Apart from rainfall, the other factors are the distribution of power resources, the pattern of mineral deposits, and the relation of land routes and seaboard terminals to ocean routes. The main black-coal deposits occur in the rich and extensive coal measures of New South Wales to the north and south of Sydney; and, what is scarcely less important, these deposits lie right on the seaboard. The coal fields are thus admirably placed for export by sea to the other States which are, in fact, vitally dependent upon them for industrial energy. The deposits of industrial metals, upon which modern industry is so dependent, are also mainly concentrated in the east and south-east of the continent.

Outside the east and south-east area (including coastal Queensland and Tasmania) the possibilities of hydroelectric generation are negligible. New Guinea, with the best water-power reserves of any territory under Commonwealth administration, but with unexplored possibilities of industrial development, is as yet in rather a different industrial category.

The transport network, too, is a natural consequence, or rather a natural concomitant, of the resource pattern. The capital cities were founded on the best harbours by the early Governors; and, as the centres of administration, these ports collected population and inevitably became the sites of the earliest industrial enterprises. Naturally, too, roads and, later, railways radiated like the ribs of a fan from the capital cities. As the interior was developed, the steamship companies favoured a policy of concentrating overseas transport upon a few large well-equipped ports rather than on many small ones; and the capital cities thus became ports of trans-shipment for State or other trade, and the great collecting points at the seaboard for exports brought down from the pastoral and agricultural interior.

Finally, as the mechanization of rural industries displaced labour in primary production, a growing proportion of the labour force had to be provided with employment opportunities in secondary and service industries, and the "drift to the cities" intensified the metropolitan concentration. At the census of 1933, 47.5 per cent of the people in New South Wales lived and worked within the metropolitan area; 54.5 per cent of the people in Victoria; 31.6 per cent in Queensland; 53.8 per cent in South Australia; 47.3 per cent in Western Australia; 26.5 per cent in Tasmania. For the Commonwealth as a whole 3.4 million people, or nearly fifty per cent of the total population of 7.1 millions in 1940, lived in the six State capitals. The industrial concentration consequent upon war organization of industry has strengthened still further the concentration of people in the cities. The Commonwealth Government and the State Governments of Victoria and New South Wales have felt impelled to declare that decentralization will be one of the objectives of post-war reconstruction.

The following comparison of pre-war employment figures with those of early 1944 will emphasise changes brought about by war organization of industry:

AUSTRALIA: EMPLOYMENT, 1938–39 AND FEBRUARY 1944

Employees in Factories:	1938–39	February 1944
Males	412,500	515,000
Females	152,500	222,000
Total	565,000	737,000
Governmental		
(Munitions, Aircraft, Ships)	10,100	122,000
Other Factories	555,000	615,000
Total	565,000	737,000
Total in civil employment	2,126,000	1,192,200

FIVE STAGES OF DEVELOPMENT

Australian manufacturing development took place in clearly defined stages. The first was confined to the few crude activities associated with feeding and sheltering the people, repairing mining and agricultural implements and processing some primary products. The great increase of population brought about by the gold rush of 1850–53 ended this phase. In the second phase manufacturing for local needs gradually increased in scope and volume. In 1901 when federation abolished tariff barriers between the States, the markets in all the States were opened to Australian manufacturers who were thenceforward protected by the Commonwealth tariff. This third phase ended with the war of 1914–18, which interfered with overseas trade, threw Australia to a large extent upon her own resources, and forced on the manufacture of many commodities previously imported. The fourth phase commenced after 1920 when there was a strong move to expand manufactures so that the country should not lack many essential commodities if ever a condition of blockade cut off overseas sources of supply. The succeeding decade was a period of considerable industrial expansion accompanied by steadily increasing costs and levels of protection. The fifth phase commenced with the depression. Efficiency was improved and costs reduced, while the depreciation of Australian currency gave manufacturers added protection which enabled them to secure greater proportions of the home market and thus further reduce costs. Australian industry came more and more to stand upon its own feet and a steady reduction of tariffs imposed on British goods was effected.

Generalizing very widely, it can be said that at the outbreak of war Australian imports consisted mainly of raw materials, productive machinery and luxuries. Among raw materials were some partly manufactured goods such as paper pulp, paper and tinplate; and their production had either been commenced, or was proposed under conditions in which prices seemed likely to be little if any higher than those of duty-free imports.

CONTRIBUTION OF OLDER COUNTRIES TO AUSTRALIAN INDUSTRY

In assessing the part played by overseas influences in the development of Australian industry, a clear distinction must be drawn between method and technique on the one hand, and initiative and capital investment on the other. The earliest manufactures in Australia, and a good many of the later developments also, were originated by men from other countries who had acquired skill in the industries they established in Australia. Later developments were to a greater extent the result of Australian initiative, although it was often necessary to secure the assistance of technicians and skilled workers from abroad to train Australian operatives. At all times, indeed, the most progressive manufacturers in Australia were kept closely in touch with overseas developments in their industries. Though Australian manufacturing methods were almost wholly derived from other countries in the first place, much ingenuity and originality have been shown in adapting those methods to Australian conditions. In many cases the methods have been improved considerably in the process of adaptation.

This debt to the industry of other countries must be fully acknowledged; but it remains true that, for the greater part, Australia's industrial development has been brought about by domestic enterprise and investment. In the following broad classifications—cement, glassware and pottery, industrial metals, food and drink products, textiles, leather, clothing, wood-working, paper and paper products—overseas investments have played a relatively minor role. The main classifications in which important sections of industries have developed primarily from the activities of overseas manufacturers are chemicals and oils, tobacco, steel sheet and wire, automobiles, and rubber.

Successive Australian Governments have given a general invitation to overseas manufacturers to establish their operations behind the Australian tariff wall; but most acceptors have allowed Australian capital a share in their enterprise. Some of these industries, indeed, have passed completely to Australian ownership. On the other hand, several Australian companies have sought for and secured the assistance of old-established concerns, mainly in Britain and America, whilst still retaining control in Australian hands. Until quite recently comparatively few overseas manufacturers thought the situation attractive enough to justify establishing their industries in Australia. The main reason was that the market for most commodities is small compared to the total open to manufacturers in Britain and America; and in Britain there was a widespread belief that Australian industry was precariously maintained by high duties. Before 1930, only manufacturers of vision and courage would set up industries in Australia; the remainder preferred to export to this country. Since then, in many cases, overseas manufacturers have found their Australian markets threatened by local enterprises; and, by 1939, a stronger tendency to commence operations in Australia—very often in conjunction with local interests—was apparent.

EXPORTS

Australia's exports of manufactured goods are mostly not highly fabricated, e.g., flour, butter, raw sugar, leather, metals. Manufactures outside this class had, before 1939, found export markets aggregating in value some £4 to £5 million a year, of which machinery accounted for about £750,000. New Zealand is the principal market, though exports are also made to South Africa, Pacific Islands, Netherlands East Indies, and Malaya.

Before the war many of the most progressive manufacturers in Australia had little opportunity to do more than cater for the rapidly growing home demand for their products. Whilst, on the basis of price alone, iron and steel could have been exported in large quantities, in practice exports were limited by Australian productive capacity. In earlier days many serious mistakes were made in the character and quality of exported manufactures, but more recently the export of many items has been established with complete satisfaction to consumers.

ORGANIZATION FOR WAR

The danger in which Australia was placed by geography and world politics was fully recognized by the Australian Government in 1939, when a new department was created under the control of a senior Minister with a Cabinet direction to organize the industrial and trade resources of the Commonwealth in such a way as to "put Australia in a position to withstand a siege" and make it "industrially self-sufficing." The significance of this part of the defence programme was the deliberate drive to organize the whole Australian industrial structure so that it formed the basis of the defences of the continent. One essential feature of the scheme was to gear key industries into a plan for the production of aircraft, motor vehicles, and munitions of all kinds.

The economic as well as the military aspects of the new defence plan emphasized co-operation with Great Britain and the other Dominions; and the British Government in a ministerial statement recognized the necessity for expanding secondary industries in the Dominions, even with the prospect that they would eventually compete with British industries. On the other hand, the Commonwealth has in some cases deliberately refrained from taking advantage of opportunities so offered, when such action was not necessitated by defence requirements.

REVIEW OF SECTIONS OF INDUSTRY

Australian statistics relating to manufactures are divided into fifteen broad classes, which afford a suitable classification for the following review. Some of the less important are omitted.

1. *Non-metalliferous Mine and Quarry Products.* This class, which includes coke, lime, plaster, and cement, is almost completely "sheltered" by costs of importation. An exception is the important chemical, calcium carbide, with which an Australian manufacturer supplies the whole of the market under the cover of high duties.

2. *Bricks, Pottery, Glass, etc.* Whilst the greater part of this group is "sheltered," there were in 1939 some items in which imports were large. The largest of these was table crockery. No serious attempts had been made by Australian manufacturers to enter this field, though local clays are said to be suitable. Fair quantities of ornamental tiles and cut crystal glassware were produced, but importations were considerable in spite of very high duties; in all these lines variety and fashion are important, and Australian manufacturers cannot offer the range available from the rest of the world.

An important wartime development is the production of chemical glassware, optical glass and optical instruments in quality and variety sufficient for all needs.

3. *Industrial Metals, Machines, Implements and Conveyances.* Attempts to develop the steel industry commenced in 1848, but production on highly efficient lines and on an economic scale was not achieved until the war of 1914–18. Until the depression of 1930, heavy imports, in spite of high duties, divided the Australian market with the local manufacturer. Currency devaluation, full exploitation of natural advantages, and aggressive development of processes thereafter placed the Australian manufacturer in a strong position. Of other industrial metals, large surpluses of lead and zinc were exported,

and Australian supplies of copper and most other base metals were, before the war, sufficient for home requirements.

The mining and smelting of non-ferrous metals is now established on a large scale and operated at a high level of efficiency. The industry pioneered in Australia, and in some instances in the world, the use of certain technical processes and operation controls on the one hand, and of methods of improving relations between employer and employee on the other. Most standardised metal articles can now be produced in open competition with the world, or with very low protective duties. There is also considerable activity in the manufacture of art metal ware, plated ware, and other decorative articles. These are protected by average and slightly higher duties, but considerable importations are caused by the demand for variety.

Machines of all kinds constitute both a large item of home production and one of the largest groups of imports. Agricultural and mining machinery is, in general, protected by low rates of duty, whilst other classes have protection ranging up to very high rates. Even in the best established sections, considerable imports bring new designs to Australia from other parts of the world. There is a long duty-free list of special machines; and provision is also made for duty-free admission of machines which are not commercially manufactured in Australia.

Some progress has been made in the manufacture of household machinery, mostly electrical, but large-scale producers in America have a great cost advantage. The tendency is for the agents of several overseas manufacturers simultaneously to commence assembly, and finally to commence manufacturing in Australia. A problem of wide significance is that, whilst the aggregate volume of the Australian market would permit economic methods of production, production costs are seriously increased when that volume is divided among several manufacturers.

Turning to vehicles, rail and tramway rolling stock is almost wholly produced in Australia at reasonable cost. Internal-combustion engines, however, had been produced only in small sizes and in slow-running types up to the outbreak of war. Practically all automobiles in Australia are fitted with Australian bodies, springs, spark plugs, and a few other components. Engines, chassis, and other parts are imported unassembled and the complete vehicle put together in this country. Production of complete automobiles in Australia has been proposed from time to time; and the problems associated therewith are receiving intensive study.

Modern developments of methods of production are forcing on the engineering industry of the world ever increasing degrees of specialization. Australia probably lags behind older manufacturing countries in this matter, though considerable progress has been made. Some firms have specialized in heavy foundry work and some in light; others have developed the production of heavy forgings, others of light, and so on. The machine designer is rapidly becoming a specialist who knows more about the design, say, of mining or sugar milling or other machinery than any individual engaged in those industries. Such a designer in Australia sometimes operates factories in which are assembled castings, forgings, and so on, made to his own requirements by specialist operators. Most are also equipped for a range of other operations; but as equipment, technique, and efficiency of parts manufacturing improves this is becoming less common. Several firms that formmerly maintained large engineering shops to make their own productive machines now depend on specialist suppliers.

The metal-working industries have probably been more greatly altered by the demands of war than any other. These have considerably expanded in size, and production for civil needs has given place very largely to production for war needs. Ferro-alloys and magnesium have been produced on a relatively large scale, and among other smaller developments, the particularly difficult problems associated with the production of tungsten have been solved. Up to 1939, machine tools were produced in small range and of the less accurate types. Since then this industry has been revolutionized and almost all the types needed for production of munitions have been made. A wide range of weapons, munitions, and machines have also been produced, including aeroplanes which are now made with very few imported parts or materials, except aluminum, and the production of this metal is proposed.

In general, Australian manufacturers have adopted, and gained confidence in the use of quantity-production methods and fine limits of dimensions. It cannot, however, be said that precision-repetition methods on the scale and of the kind used in other countries in automobile manufacture have reached a high degree of development.

4. *Textiles and Textile Goods.* As would be expected, the manufacture of woollen yarns and of cloths such as tweeds, flannels, and blankets was commenced early in the industrial history of Australia; the worsted section of the industry was a later development. By 1936 Australian manufacturers had gained most of the local market; and worsted materials in considerable variety and as high in quality and finish as any produced in the world were being made. In the medium-price range, local competition had resulted in prices that were little if at all higher than those of duty-free importations; it was claimed that the bulk of the yarn sold in Australia was at even lower prices. There is little demand in Australia for low-quality, low-priced cloths, and the making of shoddy and mungo has developed only to a small extent.

In the main the Australian industry is organized "vertically," i.e., the largest firms and the greatest number of manufacturers purchase greasy wool as their raw material and perform all operations up to the disposal of the finally completed fabrics, while the largest produce both woollen and worsted cloths.

Early attempts to grow cotton in Australia failed and even

now, in spite of heavy assistance by bounty, the industry maintains only a precarious existence. Cotton spinning commenced in 1924 to supply yarn to manufacturers of knitted goods who had previously used imported material. Two years later the weaving of drills, dungaree, and similar cloths was begun, under the cover of heavy protection. By 1937–38 the position was approximately as follows: Australian production, 5,500,000 square yards; competitive imports, 1,000,000 square yards; non-competitive imports, 190,000,000 square yards.

In 1939 it was found that the high-protection price of Australian cloths had considerably reduced their use in the manufacture of clothing, and that imported fabrics which just avoided the tariff description had largely taken their place. The industry had, however, grown to the extent of providing employment for some 3,600 persons.

Yarn spinning of coarser varieties has been developed to an extent sufficient to supply practically the whole demand of weavers and knitters. In 1939 much of this yarn was sold at prices claimed to be below those of duty-free importations, and many cloths could also have been woven with only moderate protection.

Fabrics for use other than the manufacture of clothing were, in 1939, mainly imported. Felt was produced on a large scale, and a promising start had been made in the production of carpets, though in this field serious difficulties were caused by the wide variety demanded by purchasers. The manufacture of canvas had advanced to the experimental stage, as had the growing of flax to replace comparatively small imports of fibre and yarn. It is hoped that this material will now find an export market. The manufacture of rope, cordage, and twine was well developed, mainly from imported fibres and yarns, and the production of rayon was projected but had not been attempted. Most of the silk yarn needed for women's stockings was spun locally.

During the war the wool spinning and weaving industry

was seriously distorted. Service demands necessitated severe restrictions of supplies for civilians, and the production of more or less standardized cloths in a small range of patterns and qualities. The general effect on cotton spinning and weaving has been to encourage expansion, since the types of cloth for which it was equipped were those needed for war use.

During the war manufacturers extended their activities to the production of other heavy cloths such as cotton canvas and duck.

5. *Leather and Clothing*. Little need be said about leather or clothing; Australia is self-supporting in these, the few imports being mainly dictated by fashion, whilst there are substantial exports of leather. The footwear manufacturing industry is organized in factories that are generally considered too numerous and too small, and, though producing goods of high quality, are unable to compete with mass production in other countries except with the assistance of high duties.

6. *Food, Drink and Tobacco*. In food and drink imports are, with one exception, confined to luxuries. The exception mentioned is canned and preserved fish. Australian fisheries are not well developed. One reason for this is said to be that, as a result of the great development of the pastoral industry, meat has always been plentiful and cheap. In addition, the "continental shelf" near the settled areas of the Australian coast is small and in parts unsuitable for trawling.

Australian-grown tobacco supplies only a small proportion of requirements, and the tobacco manufacturing industry is based mainly on imported American leaf.

7. *Timber*. Australian forests are mostly of the extremely hard eucalypts, and importations of softwoods are large. Artificial seasoning of eucalypt timbers has, however, modified their disadvantages, and during the war their use in place of softwood has extended considerably. In woodware and furniture Australia is practically self-supporting.

8. *Paper, Stationery, Printing and Bookbinding*. Some

wrapping papers and paper boards have long been made in Australia from imported pulp, but lighter varieties of wrapping paper, newsprint, fine printing and writing papers were until very recently imported. Just before the war three factories came into operation, producing paper pulp and paper from eucalypt timbers. Each proposes to produce a substantial percentage of requirements in one of the three main divisions of the industry, namely, kraft papers and boards, newsprint, and fine printing and writing paper. Each of these projects seems likely to develop without heavy protection, except in periods when world prices are very low.

Imports of paper products and printed matter are small, except in books of an educational or cultural nature; before the war these were free from customs duties.

9. *Rubber Goods.* In rubber goods Australia is independent of imports of finished articles, though rubber is not indigenous, and before the war necessary fabrics and yarns were imported. Some years ago it was claimed that, though the cost of producing automobile tires was higher than in Great Britain, selling prices to the public were lower. During the war the spinning of tire cord and the weaving of fabric for the rubber trade have been commenced.

EFFECTS OF WAR DEVELOPMENTS

Though post-war conditions are still unsettled, it is safe to say that the pre-war desire of the Australian public for industrial development will be strengthened. In the decade preceding the war, Australians saw many industries justify their existence which, in the 1920's, seemed of very doubtful value to the country. Again, the many successes of wartime manufacturing have left a conviction that Australia can manufacture anything.

Many new manufactures started during the war will probably survive without governmental assistance; others will show possibilities that will warrant their protection for a time, and others again will no doubt be maintained, although uneconomic, as essential to national security. There will, however, be many wartime activities that must be liquidated, the factories being suitable only for the production of war requirements. Some of the machines in such factories are of "special purpose" types that will have no peacetime use, but many will be adaptable to new uses.

The greatest residual value of the war effort will, however, be the new skills acquired. Technicians and skilled workers have attacked and conquered jobs that would have been considered impossible before the war, and should not lack confidence in their ability to attack the problems of peace. The advance of the greatest future value to the country has been in the field of management. Until quite recently Australian industry has been seriously handicapped by the lack of training of factory executives in modern methods of planning and controlling factory operations, and of maintaining industrial peace. There were many establishments in which these methods were applied with great effect; but there were a great many more in which the managers did not even know that such a technique exists. Some companies developed their own staff training courses, but this course was possible only in the largest. The need for communal training of factory executives was acute, but facilities for it did not exist.

These methods, at least as far as control of factory operations was concerned, have been brought to their highest development in American automobile factories. The establishment by American manufacturers of branches in Australia multiplied the number of trained men in this country, and led to the commencement of training in foremanship and industrial management. From a small commencement a few years before the war, such training is now carried on in technical schools in the largest industrial centres, whilst other localities are assisted by an extensive correspondence system. Facilities have also been provided for the training of industrial executives of higher ranks, and for research and exchange of experience in the various branches of industry.

The conditions hampering Australian industry in competition with the rest of the world are being overcome to a large extent by careful planning and control of operations. Production methods are being adapted to limited market conditions in such a way as to minimize these handicaps; Australian executives are learning the dangers of transplanting overseas manufacturing procedure without modification. The application of modern methods of control of finance, materials, and the flow of work is not proving difficult; and the principal opening for developmental work on methods seems to lie in the sphere of creating and maintaining satisfactory relations between factory employees and management. Whilst general principles enunciated in other countries can be followed in this work, their application demands closest attention to local conditions.

SCOPE FOR EXPANSION

Australia's pre-war importations included large quantities of natural products such as tea, tobacco, fibres and petroleum products that are not available in sufficient quantities from domestic sources. Nearly half were, however, classed as textiles, machines, automobiles, paper, and chemicals.

Large-scale projects for the production of tinplate, paper pulp, and paper were prevented or hindered by the war, but seem capable of development with little excess cost. The production of artificial fibres has not yet been attempted, but will receive considerable attention.

Machinery offers a difficult problem. A manufacturing economy cannot be secure unless it can provide a reasonable proportion and range of the machines needed. Several types are now being produced at little excess cost; and many others could be if it were possible to standardize them. Such a procedure would, however, handicap machine-using industry which requires the best and most up-to-date plant procurable anywhere. The Government has tried to steer a middle course in this matter.

The manufacture of luxury goods, and those in which fashion is important, is heavily handicapped by the small Australian market. A notable example is cotton piece-goods. Whereas it might be possible to produce a few patterns at reasonable cost, it would be extremely costly to make more than a very small fraction of the enormous range normally available through imports. If consumers' choice were too heavily restricted, the aggregate demand would probably shrink, and activity in the manufacturing of clothes would be reduced.

By the end of the war development had gone a long way into the production of intermediate materials, and it is likely to proceed still further when conditions make it possible; but development into the large fields of machinery and luxury goods will be hampered, though not prevented, by the difficulties described above.

In every industry there is scope for expansion of manufacture into individual branches and items not yet attempted, and though these may individually be small, in aggregate they will be important.

So far stress has been laid on the development of manufactures to replace imports. This is natural in a country of incomplete industrial development. Australia as a whole cannot, however, be charged with a desire to achieve autarchy regardless of results. The experience of the past has shown that increasing industrial development creates increasing demand for luxury imports, and the result is that imports change more in nature than in volume. There is no desire to shut out the rest of the world, but only to develop the country's natural and human resources to the full.

The expansion of manufactures to replace imports will, of course, in due time reach a limit. Thereafter, as far as her domestic market is concerned, Australia must look to increasing population, and to increasing demand by each unit of the population for her field of industrial expansion. Like all industrial countries, her main hopes lie in rising standards of comfort for her people which could open greatly extended markets.

As in the past, Australia's prosperity will depend, in considerable measure, on her exports of primary products, but considerable expansion of exports of the more highly fabricated goods may be expected, the urge to do this arising partly from desires to use plant that has been expanded for war purposes beyond peacetime needs. This will result in an interest in world trade among sections of the community that have not before looked beyond their national borders. Australia may thus be expected to show considerable interest in international measures designed to realize the objectives of the Atlantic Charter.

Chapter XIX

FEDERAL AND STATE POWERS

BY SIR ROBERT GARRAN, G.C.M.G., K.C.

Formerly Solicitor-General to the Commonwealth of Australia

THE Commonwealth of Australia is an example of that apparent contradiction in terms: a Dominion "under the Crown of the United Kingdom," and yet a self-governing nation, freely associated with the other members of the British Commonwealth of Nations, and equal in status with the United Kingdom itself. The key to the puzzle lies in the distinction between the legal position on the one hand, and the "constitutional" or conventional position on the other. In theory the Parliament of the United Kingdom is sovereign over the whole British Commonwealth; in practice it does not exercise legislative power with respect to a Dominion except at the request and with the consent of the Dominion. To do so would not be illegal, but would be "unconstitutional," and therefore unthinkable. This "Dominion status" has developed gradually out of the old colonial system over a long period, and in 1931 received statutory recognition in the Statute of Westminster, not as something enacted by that statute, but as a declaration of "the established constitutional position" existing apart from the statute.

A FEDERAL COMMONWEALTH

When in 1900 the peoples of the six Australian colonies contemplated union in an Australian Commonwealth, they wished to unite for national purposes, but to remain separate for local purposes. So they chose the federal form of government, of which the living patterns that they knew best were those of the United States and Canada.

The federal principle requires that the power of making laws be apportioned between the Federal and the State Parliaments. This raises the problem of how and where the line shall be drawn between them.

There is a choice between alternatives: either the central legislature may be given specific subject-matters, deemed to be of special national concern, the whole residue of legislative power being left with the local legislatures; or certain specific subject-matters may be given to the local legislatures, the general residue being left with the central legislature.

The United States chose the former method. The several American colonies were jealous of their new-won independence. and did not wish to pool more power than was absolutely necessary for security and common purposes. The "enumerated powers" were not given exclusively to Congress; so that the State legislatures had *concurrent* power to legislate in any way not inconsistent with laws passed by Congress.

When the Canadian Constitution of 1867 was framed the American Civil War was not yet over; and "State rights" were regarded as one of the causes of that war. So Canada wished to have a stronger national government, and deliberately chose the second method of apportionment: broadly, to give to the Provinces specific subject-matter of legislative power, and to the Dominion *exclusive* power as to everything else.

In Australia, the position closely resembled that of the American colonies. Indeed, the attachment to "State rights" was perhaps even stronger than in America. Each colony had a long tradition of independence, and there was nothing to bring them together but a dawning sense of a common nationality, and uneasiness about the growing interest of European powers in the Pacific area. So the American method of apportionment was followed; the powers of the Federal Parliament were limited to specific subject-matters, and never, in the Convention, in debate, or in the press, was it suggested that the Canadian precedent should be followed.

Where to draw the line between Commonwealth and State powers needed more consideration in Australia. For a start, the list of American subject-matters was adopted with some variations.[1] In one respect, the American precedent was followed too closely.

The power of the Commonwealth Parliament with respect to trade and commerce was limited to trade and commerce with other countries and among the States. This divides into two parts a subject-matter which is essentially one. Commerce is the same thing, whether it does or does not cross a State boundary; and the disadvantages of the division had become abundantly evident in America. The complexity of

---

[1] The following is a classified summary of the main heads of powers of the Federal Parliament:

Commercial: Trade and commerce, interstate and external (including navigation and shipping). Banking and insurance; trading and financial corporations, etc. Currency, coinage and legal tender. Bills of exchange and promissory notes. Weights and measures. Bankruptcy and insolvency.

Railways: Control of State railways for defence. Acquisition of State railways, with consent of State. Construction and extension of railways, with consent of State. Preferential and discriminating rates.

Defence

External Affairs

Social and Industrial: Arbitration in industrial disputes extending beyond one State. Invalid and old age pensions.

Administrative: Posts, telegraphs and telephones. Quarantine. Lighthouses, etc. Census and statistics. Meteorological observations. Commonwealth electoral law. Commonwealth public service.

Miscellaneous: Marriage and divorce. Immigration and emigration. Copyright, patents and trade marks. Naturalization. Matters referred to Commonwealth by State Parliaments.

Judiciary: Creation of federal courts. Investing State courts with federal jurisdiction. Procedure in federal courts.

States and Territories: Admission or establishment of new States. Alterations of limits of State, with consent.

Finance: Taxation. Customs and excise. Borrowing money. Appropriation of money for purposes of Commonwealth. Bounties on production or export of goods. Financial assistance to States. Taking over State public debts.

Amendment of Constitution: (with approval of electors).

modern commerce makes it impossible, without frequent recourse to the courts, to fix the exact boundary between commerce within a State and commerce between States. The same persons are often engaged in both classes of commerce at the same time; the same highways and vehicles are used in both; the same facilities and obstructions may affect both. In Australia, as in America, it has been difficult to determine which set of laws applies to each particular case.

Some deficiencies in the American list of federal powers were made good in the Australian Constitution. Federal trademark law is not limited in its application (as it is in America) to interstate and external trade. Telegraphs, telephones and other like services were added—and this has been held to include the important new service of radio broadcasting. Banking and insurance were added, and it was intended to give the Commonwealth power to enact uniform company laws; but, unfortunately, a High Court decision left this power with little substance. Bills of exchange and promissory notes are included. The subjects of marriage, divorce, and matrimonial causes were also included; but the subject is such a thorny one politically, owing to the clash of opinion between those who want divorce made easier and those who want it made harder, that no Government has yet ventured to touch the subject, except for a recent Act merely dealing with domicile and jurisdiction.

RAILWAYS

One of the Australian problems that called for special provision concerned railways. With trifling exceptions, the railways in Australia were State-owned and State-operated. They had been constructed mostly with borrowed money, were both a large asset and a large liability, and had been built and operated in each State for the development of that State, without any thought for national development as a whole, and with more care, perhaps, for the interests of the cities than for

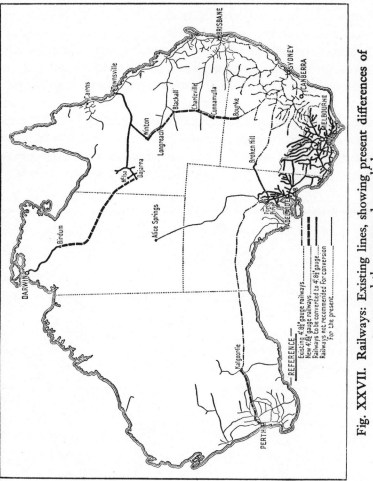

Fig. XXVII. Railways: Existing lines, showing present differences of gauge and the proposed new links.

the producing interests. New South Wales and Victoria, that is to say, Sydney and Melbourne, were competing by means of differential railway rates for the trade of the rich Riverina district—an Australian Mesopotamia. In Victoria, there were competitive rates to entice the trade to Melbourne. Both States were anxious to keep control, after federation, of their railway policy, upon which not only city commercial interests but also railway revenue depended; but the country interests in the competitive territory favoured some federal control, because the competition was of a kind that was more a bane than a blessing to them. The interstate commerce clause, if left to itself, would place the Commonwealth in control, which, from the State point of view, was unwelcome. The Convention decided, however, that limited federal control was necessary

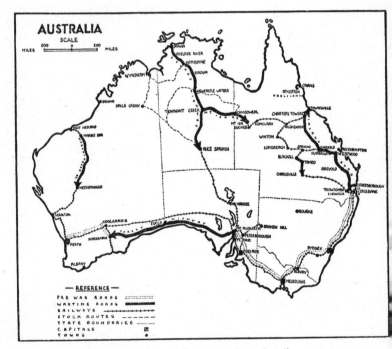

Fig. XXVIII. Defence roads and railways.

in the national interest. The compromise ultimately agreed on was to provide for the creation of an Interstate Commission, somewhat on the lines of the Interstate Commerce Commission constituted by the Congress of the United States, with such powers of adjudication and administration as the Federal Parliament might think necessary to enforce the interstate commerce laws of the Commonwealth. The Federal Parliament passed an Act constituting the Commission; but the High Court held that the proposed powers of the Commission trespassed on the judicial power. However, the power to reconstitute it on different lines remains, but its exercise has not been found necessary, as the causes of complaint have mostly been removed. The right of the Commonwealth to construct new railways or to acquire State lines was limited by writing into the power to construct the qualification "with the consent of that State." Defence powers, however, were recognised as paramount: the Federal Parliament was given power to make laws for the control of railways for defence purposes.

RIVERS

Another matter that caused much trouble was the right to use the waters of rivers. The Murray-Murrumbidgee-Darling system of rivers includes in its catchment area a large part of New South Wales, Victoria and Queensland, where the main interest was irrigation; and the lower Murray flows to the Southern Ocean through South Australia, where the main interest was then navigation. Here was a matter of national concern, and on the navigation side it was within the federal commerce power. The common law of England—a comparatively wet country—entitled lower riparian proprietors, against upper ones, to an undiminished flow; but there was uncertainty about the applicability of this law to a dry country like Australia, where the taking of water from rivers for conservation and irrigation might seriously affect navigation in the lower reaches. And, apart from common law, federal laws for preserving navigability might seriously affect the rights of users in New South Wales and Victoria, which claimed, with some reason, that "This is our rainfall, we have a right to keep it." The compromise in this case was a clause declaring that the Commonwealth shall not "abridge the right of a State or of the residents therein to the reasonable use of the waters of rivers for conservation or irrigation." What is "reasonable" can be decided, in case of dispute, by the courts.

In 1915 a River Murray Agreement was made between the Commonwealth, New South Wales, Victoria and South Australia. It set up a commission representing the parties, and provided for the construction of two large storage basins and twenty-six locks and weirs on the Murray, and nine locks and weirs on the Murrumbidgee or the Darling. Substantial progress has been made with this vast undertaking, though much still remains to be done. It is a statesmanlike scheme, and reconciles the claims of navigation with those of conservation and irrigation.

INDUSTRIAL ARBITRATION

The federal power to make laws with respect to industrial conciliation and arbitration was due to the persistent advocacy of Henry Bournes Higgins, of Victoria (afterwards President of the Commonwealth Court of Conciliation and Arbitration), and Charles Cameron Kingston, of South Australia. There had recently been a seamen's strike and a shearers' strike —both difficult of settlement by the tribunals of one colony, because the employees travelled from colony to colony. Eventually, the Convention agreed to the power, limited to the prevention and settlement of industrial disputes "extending beyond the limits of any one State."

The Commonwealth Court of Conciliation and Arbitration, established under this power, has done a vast amount of excellent work; but it has been much hampered by the terms of the power, which have involved it in a "Serbonian bog of technicalities."

The clause conferring the power is a classic example of how the limits of a subject-matter should not be defined. The essence of the matter is the prevention and settlement of industrial disputes. But it does not cover all industrial disputes —only those extending beyond a State. It is often difficult to ascertain the extent of a dispute; and for the purposes of prevention—at the stage where the dispute does not yet exist—it is hard to see in what sense it can have extent. Again, the power does not cover all means of prevention and settlement. There may often be other and perhaps better means than conciliation and arbitration, but they are not available to the Commonwealth. The defect of competing jurisdictions was aggravated because Labour, coming into power with ideas for social and industrial reforms, soon found that almost the only power concerning industrial conditions possessed by the Commonwealth was this one dealing with what we may call two-State disputes. With the organization of Federated Trade Unions, nothing was easier than to make a dispute so extend. The High Court made some attempts at first to distinguish between genuine and artificial disputes, but had inevitably to come to the conclusion that a dispute was a dispute, no matter how it had been brought about.

DEFENCE

The defence power covers the whole subject—the naval and military defence of the Commonwealth and the States— without limitation or qualification. Doubtless the draftsmen never dreamed how widely it might come to be applied, because they had no conception of total war; but the words they used made it possible to meet total war with total defence. The full scope of the defence power was first demonstrated, during the war of 1914–18, by the decision of the High Court of Australia in the Bread Case, when a war regulation fixing the price of bread was upheld. The ground of the decision was that modern war involved the marshalling of the whole resources of the country, material and moral, for defence; and the Court in effect said that, unless satisfied that a law could have no conceivable effect upon defence, they would not declare it beyond the scope of the power. That decision gave almost unlimited scope to the wartime legislation of the Commonwealth. In the second war, the High Court did not go quite so far. It now appears that the Commonwealth, to uphold a wartime regulation, must show affirmatively that it has some real relation to defence, or to some other specific power of the Commonwealth. However, the rule in this narrower form is still adequate to the needs of defence.

EXTERNAL AFFAIRS

External affairs covers relations with other British Dominions and dependencies, as well as with foreign countries. It includes the power to make and execute treaties and conventions with other countries. In the execution of such agreements, how far will the federal power of legislation extend into the field that is generally regarded as the "preserve" of the States? We get some guidance from a decision of the High Court upholding Commonwealth legislation for carrying out a treaty relating to aerial navigation. The treaty extends to aerial navigation within a State, and is therefore not covered by the federal commerce power; yet it was held that the Federal Parliament can implement the provisions of the convention in that sphere. Some members of the court expressed themselves guardedly as to the general application of the decision to *all* international arrangements. The subject of this convention was clearly proper for international arrangements under the head of external affairs; but it did not follow that all international arrangements, pledging the parties to domestic legislation, would be so classed. The future development of the rule cannot be foreseen, but it will be very difficult to distinguish between different kinds of conventions, so as to include some as "proper for international arrangements," and to exclude others.

EXPENDITURE FOR THE PURPOSES OF THE COMMONWEALTH

The Constitution gives the Federal Parliament power to appropriate money "for the purposes of the Commonwealth." How far this power extends is a moot point. There is no direct judicial decision on the question; but an imposing array of expert opinion holds that the "purposes of the Commonwealth" are limited to purposes with respect to which the Federal Parliament has power to make laws. The writer is strongly of opinion that the words go much further than this, and that the question whether a given appropriation is for a purpose of the Commonwealth is a political question, of which Parliament itself is the judge, and with which the courts will not interfere. The American Congress for more than a hundred and fifty years, and the Parliament of the Commonwealth for more than forty years, have consistently acted on the principle that there is no need to refer an appropriation of money to any specific power of the Federal Parliament; and it is significant that neither in the United States nor in Australia has any appropriation ever been set aside as unconstitutional.

INTERPRETATION

It will be clear that it is often hard to determine whether a given law is or is not within the scope of a particular subject-matter. This is inevitable. Matters overlap and interlock; and with the growing complexity of social, industrial and commercial relations the difficulty is increasing. Some matters, such as currency and coinage, or weights and measures, are self-contained and easy to define; but when we get into the regions of commerce, industry, and general welfare it is otherwise. An Australian Industries Preservation Act prohibited certain acts in restraint of trade. The Federal Parliament cannot regulate trade within a State; but it has power over another matter, "trading and financial corporations." So the prohibitions of the Act were directed, as to interstate and external trade, against everybody, but as to trade within a State, against trading and financial corporations only. Was this a law with respect to corporations, and therefore valid? Or a law with respect to trade within a State, and therefore invalid? The High Court held that the real subject-matter of the law was restraint of trade, and that the attempt to control the conduct of corporations, as distinct from natural persons, in relation to trade within a State, was an attempt to control trade within a State when conducted by corporations, and therefore was outside the power of the Federal Parliament.

A still more difficult question arose in what is known as the Harvester Case. The customs tariff protected manufacturers against undue competition from abroad. The Deakin Government, with its slogan "the New Protection," wished to protect employees against low wages; but the Federal Parliament had no power to regulate wages. So it imposed an excise duty on agricultural machinery, with a remission of duty to manufacturers who paid fair wages. The Commonwealth claimed that this was a lawful exercise of its taxing power, but the High Court held, by a majority, that the pith and substance of the Act was the regulation of wages, and that what purported to be a tax was really a penalty masquerading as a tax. The Harvester Case is an excellent example of the difficulty of "arbitrating" between Commonwealth and States as to the exercise of legislative power.

Another problem that has worried the High Court is: How far can federal laws be applied to State authorities and agencies? The High Court, at an early stage, laid down what is known as the rule of mutual non-interference, as between Commonwealth and States: namely, that it is an implied term of the Constitution; that any attempt by either Commonwealth or State to interfere with an agency of the other is invalid.

The application of this rule to a variety of cases soon got the court into great difficulties. The climax came when the State of Western Australia claimed immunity from the Commonwealth Arbitration law for certain trading concerns that the State had established: factories and engineering shops that were owned and worked by the State, but otherwise were ordinary trading ventures. The court was in a dilemma. The case could only be distinguished from that of the State railways by distinguishing between State governmental functions and State trading activities. That was how the Supreme Court of the United States had dealt with a claim for immunity by a State liquor saloon. But the court shrank from the task of bringing Herbert Spencer up to date and saying: "This is a proper governmental function, that is not." On the other hand, to grant the immunity would have invited the States to cut out the Commonwealth powers one by one, by simply making the subject-matter a Government agency. The court found its position untenable, and had the courage to retire from it. So it swept away the implied prohibition of interference, and came back to the text of the Constitution. In the particular case, it held that the words "industrial disputes," in their natural meaning, included disputes to which a State Government was a party, and therefore that the Commonwealth power extended to making awards binding on the State as employer. It held that each subject-matter of Commonwealth power must be read in its natural meaning, without any implied prohibition of interference with the States; and the States retained all their pre-federal powers not expressly denied them by the Constitution, subject only to the condition that their exercise must not conflict with any valid federal legislation.

CONCURRENT AND EXCLUSIVE POWERS

It does not follow, from the fact that the Federal Parliament has power to make laws with respect to a matter, that the State Parliaments have not. Only a few of the federal powers are exclusive. Except within the ambit of an exclusively federal matter, the States retain a concurrent power, subject to the condition mentioned above, that State laws inconsistent with a valid federal law are invalid to the extent of the inconsistency. Chief among the exclusive federal powers is the power to make laws for federal Territories, whether within the Commonwealth or outside the Commonwealth; control of the Commonwealth Public Service; customs and excise, and defence. As to all such Territories the Federal Parliament is not limited to specific matters, but has plenary and exclusive power. Other matters are exclusive in their nature—such as control of the Commonwealth Public Service. The Federal Parliament has exclusive power to impose duties of customs and excise, in accordance with the principle that trade among the States must be free; and its defence power is substantially exclusive, because the States are expressly prohibited from raising or maintaining any naval or military force without the consent of the Federal Parliament.

A fundamental distinction must be noted between the specific powers of the Federal Parliament and the residual power of the State Parliaments. The State jurisdiction may be compared with the occupation of a continuous field, in which are a number of separate enclosures (the subject matters of Commonwealth power) which *may* be occupied by the Commonwealth, but which, unless and until so occupied by the Commonwealth, remain in the occupation of the States.

Neglect of this distinction led, in the early days of the Commonwealth, to the frequent use of the phrase "reserved powers of the States." This phrase carried a suggestion that there were some whole *subject-matters* reserved to the States; but this is a fallacy. Some aspects of education, for example, might come under, say, the Commonwealth defence power, or the power with respect to persons of alien race. There is a reserved *power* of the States—the whole field outside the fences that mark the limits of the Commonwealth powers. But there are no fences enclosing State preserves. Such fences, if they were wholly outside the Commonwealth enclosures, would be superfluous, because they are in parts of the field that the Commonwealth cannot enter; whilst if they cut into the Commonwealth enclosures they would be a contradiction.

SPECIAL PROHIBITIONS

The Constitution contains little in the way of a "Bill of Rights," or guarantees of liberty. There is just one clause which forbids the Commonwealth to make any law establishing any religion, or imposing any religious observance, or prohibiting the free exercise of any religion, or to require any religious test as a qualification for any Commonwealth office. Other fundamental freedoms were thought to be so firmly established as to need no guarantee, and the convention did not think it its business to establish guarantees against the State Governments; that was left to the States themselves.

But there is one important clause which, as now interpreted, leaves an awkward "gap" in the legislative power which neither Commonwealth nor States can fill. Section 92 declares that "trade, commerce and intercourse among the States . . . shall be absolutely free." If there is one clause in the Constitution about whose meaning the draftsmen had no doubt, it is this; and yet it has given the High Court more trouble than any other. It was meant to guarantee interstate free trade, in the political sense, against both Commonwealth and States: the abolition of border duties and other restrictions on interstate trade. And for the first ten years no one seems to have thought it meant anything else. Then the High Court took a curious view of it: that it was a prohibition directed to the States only, excluding them from *regulating* interstate trade in any way whatever, whether restrictively or not, and practically making the power an exclusive one of the Commonwealth. The court reached this conclusion by assuming that freedom of trade, in Section 92, meant freedom from regulation of any kind; therefore the prohibition could not be directed to the Commonwealth, which was expressly empowered to regulate such trade.

That assumption, when examined, means that all law is an abridgment of freedom—a proposition that in any broad sense is clearly untenable. The court soon began to have misgivings about it; and with the aid of the Privy Council it is now established that the prohibition extends only to laws that are restrictive of interstate free trade, and, so interpreted, is directed to the Commonwealth as well as the States. It still, however, applies more widely than the political meaning of free trade that the draftsmen had in mind.

WAR LEGISLATION

The matters which were considered of national concern when the Constitution was framed comprised very little of the social, economic and industrial field that nowadays looms so large in the affairs of every country in the world. This is not surprising. In the first place, every written Constitution tends to lag somewhat behind the age—to reflect the times that are passing away, rather than the times that are coming. This is especially true of the Australian Constitution, because the chief models on which it was based were already several generations old. The advances in social legislation since the framing of the American and Canadian Constitutions—and even the Australian Constitution—are prodigious; and many things that are commonplaces to us today were not even dreamed of by the fathers of federation fifty years ago.

Twice since then—in 1914 and in 1939—the advent of total war has made it necessary to organise Australia for total defence. Each time, free use was made of the wide scope of legislation covered by the defence power. In 1939, the Federal Parliament promptly passed the National Security Act—based upon British legislation, and upon our own War Precautions Act of 1914—which empowered the Governor-General to make regulations for securing the public safety and defence of the Commonwealth and the Territories of the Commonwealth. Particular matters were enumerated as coming within the scope of this regulation-making power—the taking possession or control of any undertaking; prescribing the conditions of disposal or use of any property or goods, and requiring persons to place themselves and their property at the disposal of the Commonwealth for public safety, defence, or the efficient prosecution of the war. In pursuance of these powers, regulations were passed from time to time covering a wide range of subjects: among which may be mentioned regulations dealing comprehensively with economic organization, manpower, prices, rationing, and control of many industries.

A few of these regulations have been held invalid; but no provision of the National Security Act itself has been successfully challenged, and the principles laid down by the High Court, as described in an earlier part of this chapter, have enabled the war organization of the community to function to the full. It must be mentioned that these regulations, while proceeding from the authority of the Commonwealth, have made great use of State authorities and agencies for their administration, and the co-operation of the States has been a valuable contribution to the war effort.

POST-WAR POWERS

What will become of the war powers of the Commonwealth during the period of transition from a war economy to a peace economy? There is very little direct judicial authority to guide us, and therefore there must be much uncertainty. But there are a few beacon lights which may help us to get our bearings. We know that the power of the Commonwealth to carry on war extends to ending the war: not only to joining in a treaty of peace, but to making laws to give effect to the rights and obligations arising under a treaty of peace. But we do not know—and we have no reason to believe—that the power extends to all those matters which are summed up in the familiar but indefinite phrase "post-war reconstruction" —all the rebuilding of our way of life, in the direction of social welfare and justice, the opportunity for which is afforded by the reconstruction that must follow the destruction of war. The position has been picturesquely expressed by saying that the powers of the Commonwealth extend to unwinding the war effort, but not to winding up the peace effort. But the application of this metaphorical generality to particular practical problems is difficult: the problems, for instance, of getting a million of displaced men and women not only into the right employments, but into the right social adjustments—which must often be not the old adjustments, but readjustments with a difference; of getting the streams of commerce and industry to flow again—and not always in just the old channels; of gradually relaxing economic controls until they can be reduced to normal; of directing production, on a system of priorities, to the most urgent needs, under conditions in which there will be a serious initial shortage of many materials, and perhaps of some kinds of labour and directive skill, and a general scramble of producers to get ahead, in an unco-ordinated way, with the supply of demands of all sorts and all degrees of public importance. In these and many other matters the people of Australia, and the Governments and Parliaments, will be faced with the question: "What precisely are the respective powers of the Commonwealth and the State?"

For example, the Commonwealth power to control prices depends entirely on the wartime extension of the defence power. Will it continue into the peace to enable a gradual relaxation of control? Or will it cease abruptly on the conclusion of peace? Nobody knows; but there is nothing in the decisions of the High Court to suggest any such continuance into the transitional period; and the difficulty of setting any definite term to such continuance suggests that the logical answer is likely to be that of abrupt termination. Or take the reinstatement and advancement of service men and women, and war-workers. The defence power will presumably extend to their rehabilitation—to fitting them to *take their place* in the peace economy. But when it comes to *fitting them into a place* in the peace economy—housing and employment and general welfare—the peacetime limitations of the Commonwealth must be taken into account. The Commonwealth can, of course, make grants to the States for these purposes, and co-operate in various ways with the States; but how far can it exercise a directive oversight to secure a uniform policy?

AMENDMENT OF THE CONSTITUTION

For many years there has been a wide recognition of the need for greater Commonwealth powers—coupled with much difference of opinion as to the nature and extent of the needed powers. An amendment of the Constitution requires to be passed by an absolute majority of the members of each House of the Federal Parliament (or twice by one House), and approved at a referendum by a majority of all the electors voting, and by separate majorities in a majority of the States. Between 1906 and 1944, eighteen proposed laws for the amendment of the Constitution have been passed by the Parliament and submitted to the electors; but only three have passed the ordeal of the referendum, and of these only one had any significance: the States Debts amendment, authorising agreements with the States as to their public debts, the taking over of such debts by the Commonwealth, their conversion, etc., and the future borrowing of money by the Commonwealth and the States. This amendment was passed by over-whelming majorities in all the States in 1928, during the depression after the War of 1914–18, when there was a general conviction of the need for strengthening the credit of Commonwealth and States.

Experience has shown that the referendum is a conservative institution, heavily loaded against change, and that it is hard to get substantial amendments carried except on great occasions. The framers of the Constitution did not wish it to bend before each passing gust of public opinion. Amendment was to be "its medicine, not its daily food." So they made it difficult. Perhaps they made it too difficult. On "performances," the odds against a "Yes" vote look like six to one.

It may perhaps seem that the readiness of the Federal Parliament to ask for more powers, and the unreadiness of the electors to grant them, show a tendency on the part of members of Parliament to magnify their office, and a determination on the part of their constituents to keep them in check. But the figures of the voting at the different referendums do not bear this out. The "No" margin has often been small. Several substantial requests for power—for instance, as to trade and commerce, monopolies, industrial matters, and companies—have at one time or another been approved by four or even five States—but not at the same referendum. Again, Parliament has usually asked for too much at a time. When several separate amendments have been put to the electors at once, the answer has usually been "No" to all of them—an elector who has something against one votes against all. It is significant that two of the three amendments approved by the electors have been "singletons."

In 1927 the Commonwealth Government appointed a Royal Commission to enquire into and report upon the powers of the Commonwealth and the working of the Constitution, and to recommend changes thought to be desirable. The commission took voluminous evidence and presented a valuable report

Plate 23. Broken Hill Associated Smelters, Port Pirie, South Australia.

Plate 24. Electrolytic Zinc Works, Risdon, near Hobart, southern Tasmania.

Plate 25. Newsprint mills, Boyer, southern Tasmania.

Plate 26. Taraleah power station, Tasmania.

Plate 27. Captain Cook Graving Dock, Sydney, New South Wales, with the aircraft carrier H.M.S. *Illustrious*, first vessel to be docked.

Plate 28. The University, Perth, Western Australia.

making a number of recommendations; but no action was taken upon it.

In 1934 the Commonwealth Government invited the State Governments to a conference to discuss constitutional matters. At the conference a number of amendments were suggested both by the Commonwealth and by the States; but no agreement was reached upon any of them.

In October 1942 the Commonwealth Government introduced a proposed law to amend the Constitution, by adding to the powers of the Parliament a new power to make laws "for the purpose of carrying into effect the war aims and objects of Australia as one of the United Nations, including the attainment of economic security and social justice in the post-war world, and for the purpose of post-war reconstruction generally." It will be noticed that this was a novel way of defining legislative power, according to the *purpose* and not the *subject-matter* of the legislation. The proposed law proceeded to declare that the above words extended to all measures which in the declared opinion of the Parliament would tend to achieve economic security and social justice, including security of employment and the provision of useful occupation for all the people, and that the above powers included a number of *matters* that were set out.

There was much criticism, especially from the State Governments, of the sweeping nature of these proposals; and exception was also taken to the idea of a referendum during the war. The Commonwealth Government, however, urged the importance of an immediate decision as to post-war powers, to enable preparation of plans for post-war reconstruction to proceed; and invited the Premiers and the leaders of opposition in the States to a convention to discuss the matter.

The convention favoured, instead of wartime amendment, the alternative of using the power of the Commonwealth Parliament to make laws as to "matters referred to the Parliament of the Commonwealth by the Parliament or Parliaments of any State or States, but so that the law shall extend only to States by whose Parliaments the matter is referred, or which afterwards adopt the law." It adopted a draft bill, to be submitted to the State Parliaments, referring to the Commonwealth Parliament, for a period of five years after the termination of hostilities, a specified list of matters. The draft bill recited that at the convention it was unanimously resolved that adequate powers to make laws in relation to post-war reconstruction should be referred to the Parliament of the Commonwealth by the Parliaments of the States, and that the Premiers of the States had agreed to do their utmost to secure the passage through their Parliaments of a bill in that form.

The bill was accordingly passed in New South Wales and Queensland. It was passed in Victoria with a provision that it should not take effect until passed by all the States. It was passed in South Australia and Western Australia with substantial alterations and limitations of the powers referred. In Tasmania it was twice rejected by the Legislative Council, and not passed.

State unanimity not having ben achieved, the Commonwealth Government reverted to the plan of amending the Constitution, and passed through Parliament a proposed amendment giving the Commonwealth Parliament, almost verbatim, the powers set out in the Convention Bill, with the addition of constitutional guarantees of freedom of speech, expression, and religion. In the referendum campaign the Commonwealth opposition members, with few exceptions, opposed the amendment, which was defeated in the Commonwealth and in four States and so did not become law.

This need not be, and must not be, a final refusal to the Federal Parliament of that adequate power which is recognised as necessary. The door is still open for either amendment of the Constitution or reference of power by the States. The problem is, just what powers are necessary. In looking for a solution of the problem, it should be remembered that the Federal Parliament, like the State Parliaments, is an agent of the people, and that the question is: Which of two agents, the central or the local, is the more suited to the particular purpose? The elements of the solution of the problem would seem to be:

(1) Co-operation between the Commonwealth and the States. Post-war reconstruction is a job not for the Commonwealth alone, but for the States as well.

(2) There is need of uniform law to lay down the main principles of action, and this must be the function of the Federal Parliament. Experience has shown, more than once, that uniform laws are hardly attainable from six State Parliaments —even when the six Governments in conference have agreed on them.

(3) The States should have *concurrent* power over the whole field not occupied by Commonwealth legislation, so as to fill in the details of the scheme conformably with local conditions.

(4) The States should have the utmost freedom of administration consistent with uniformity of national policy. The ideal is central legislation, with as much decentralisation of administration as is practicable.

(5) Central legislative power is not inconsistent with decentralised administration. In the exercise of its war powers the Commonwealth has, by delegation and devolution, placed a large part of the administration in the hands of the States. It is impossible to lay down in the Constitution a hard and fast line between legislative and administrative functions—the two are so interlocked; but the system of devolution will naturally be followed in the future as in the past, as the most practical and efficient method.

(6) It is difficult to measure exactly the extent of Commonwealth power necessary; but the danger of giving more than necessary is insignificant compared with the danger of

giving less. In a democracy, weakness is more to be feared than strength.

(7) The characteristic of the British system of responsible government, under which Parliament is responsible to the people, and Government to Parliament, is to trust the Parliament to check abuses of power. Government and officials are the servants of the people, not its masters. With a vigilant people, and a vigilant Parliament, there can be no such thing, under our system of government, as "bureaucracy."

TAXATION

Left to the last, because it stands apart and distinct from other legislative powers, is the power of taxation, the power to raise money for public purposes. It is the most necessary of all powers for a national parliament. The Commonwealth power of taxation has no limits, and is subject to one condition only: that it must not discriminate between States and parts of States. As to duties of customs and excise, the Commonwealth power is exclusive. One of the leading principles of the Constitution is that the Commonwealth should be a single tariff area, without internal border duties or other protectionist devices between the States. As to all other kinds of taxation, the States retain all their previous taxing powers for State purposes. Their fond hope was that customs and excise revenue would suffice for the needs of the Commonwealth, and that the field of direct taxation would be left to them. And so it might perhaps have been, but for war. True, in 1910 a Labour Government imposed a tax upon unimproved land values, with an exemption of £5,000, but this was frankly with the object of "breaking up large estates," and not with an eye to revenue. But an estate duty came in 1914; and in 1916 the Commonwealth Government, in view of its huge war commitments, imposed an income tax. The States hoped that this would be a war measure only, and when peace came they suggested its discontinuance; but the Commonwealth's heavy obligations for war-loan interest, war gratuities, war pensions and repatriation made this impossible. Later, at a conference with State Ministers in 1934, the Commonwealth Government suggested that it should vacate the income-tax field, if the States would forgo the annual "per capita grant" mentioned in the next section of this chapter; but by that time the State Governments had become sensible of the political advantages of revenue which they did not have to raise themselves, and declined the offer. There was circulated at the time an unofficial paraphrase of their response:

> We thank you for your offer of the cow;
> But we can't milk, and so we answer now,
> We answer in a loud emphatic chorus:
> "Please keep the cow, and do the milking for us."

In 1942 the Commonwealth tried to convince the State Governments of the advantages that would accrue, in amount of revenue, in economy of collection, and in convenience to the taxpayers, if instead of double income taxes—Federal and State—the Commonwealth were to impose one aggregate income tax, and make compensatory grants to the States. But again the States declined. The Commonwealth, however, gave effect to the proposal by raising the rates of Commonwealth income tax, and making payable, to any State which in any year had not imposed an income tax, compensatory grants. The States were thus forced into line. There was an appeal to the High Court against the constitutionality of this legislation, but it was unsuccessful. The Commonwealth now, therefore, in the income-tax field, owns the only cow, and does all the milking.

To meet its obligations resulting from two world wars, the Commonwealth has from time to time resorted to other forms of direct taxation: e.g., estate duty, entertainment tax, sales tax, pay-roll tax, etc.

FINANCIAL RELATIONS OF COMMONWEALTH AND STATES

The financial relations of Commonwealth and States gave the framers of the Constitution much trouble. Customs and excise had been a large source of revenue of all the federating colonies, but in differing degrees. The revenue of the Commonwealth from this source would vastly exceed its initial needs, and it was clear that, for some years at least, the surplus must be returned to the States, which otherwise would be unable to balance their budgets except by an unthinkable amount of direct taxation. But the questions were: How much should be returned? How should it be apportioned among the States? How far could the convention, not endowed with the gift of prophecy, decide the matter for the distant future, and how far must it trust the Federal Parliament to deal with it from time to time in the light of experience? Those whose first aim was to leave the States in comfortable circumstances wanted a permanent endowment; those who were for founding a nation strong to meet all emergencies were loth to fasten upon the Commonwealth obligations which might cripple it in some future unforeseeable crisis.

For the early years, they all contemplated a "bookkeeping" system for Commonwealth revenue—a system of credit, debit, and payment of balances to the States. But there was difficulty in finding the basis for credit and debit. The population basis was thought the most federal, and probably, after some years of union, the fairest; but as, at the time, the several colonies, under widely differing fiscal systems, were contributing widely different per capita amounts through the customhouse, and as these differences would probably persist, in lessening degree, after the imposition of a uniform tariff, a basis according to contributions might be fairer to begin with.

Ultimately, the bookkeeping period was fixed by the Constitution for a period of five years from the imposition by the Federal Parliament of the first uniform tariff, and thereafter till the Parliament made other provision; and during that period the Commonwealth was to credit to each State the revenue contributed from that State, debit to each State the expenditure of departments transferred to the Commonwealth and its population share of other federal expenditure, and pay to each State monthly the balance in favour of the State. The Commonwealth never regarded this provision as requiring the Treasury to be emptied monthly of every penny actually unexpended. That would have condemned the Commonwealth to perpetual insolvency—inability to pay its debts out of its own money as they fell due. It regarded "surplus revenue" as meaning revenue above its needs and commitments, and treated money appropriated to specific purposes as being taken out of the category of surplus revenue, though not actually expended. Accordingly, it was the practice for Parliament annually to pass appropriations of amounts thought necessary to be retained for its commitments. This practice was given statutory authority in 1908. The State of New South Wales challenged it in the High Court, which upheld it as being in accordance with the Constitution.

Because of special circumstances in Western Australia, that State was allowed for five years to retain its customs duties, upon a diminishing scale, upon goods from the other States. And some elasticity was given to the mathematical basis of distribution by a clause empowering the Federal Parliament to grant, on such terms as it thinks fit, financial assistance to any State.

GUARANTEES TO THE STATES

The above provisions for allocation of the surplus revenue of the Commonwealth afforded no guarantee to the States of the *amount* of the surplus. The States were insistent on some such guarantee. They feared that the Commonwealth might be persuaded by Sir George Reid, the New South Wales

Premier, to "go free-trade" and raise too little customs revenue, or that it might be tempted by its overflowing revenue to be extravagant. Either contingency would diminish the dividends to the States. Out of many solutions, the one chosen was the "Braddon clause"—called by its detractors the "Braddon blot"—which required that the Commonwealth should not spend more than one-fourth of the net revenue from customs and excise, and should pay the balance to the States. As passed by the convention, this clause was permanent; but it raised such opposition in free-trade New South Wales, where it was feared that it would commit the Commonwealth for ever to a high tariff policy, that the other States were forced to agree to its being limited to ten years from the establishment of the Commonwealth, and thereafter till the Federal Parliament should make other provision.

It is fortunate that no ironclad system of limiting its expenditure was fastened permanently on the Commonwealth, because all the elaborate calculations of the financial prophets have been made to look foolish by events—especially by the huge obligations that the Commonwealth has had to incur in two world wars.

PER CAPITA GRANTS

The Federal Parliament allowed the bookkeeping period to continue until the expiration of the ten-year period, when it became able to put an end to the Braddon clause. On the eve of that event, the States begged for the continuance of the clause. The Commonwealth Government refused this, but offered instead a "per capita grant"—the yearly payment of an amount per head of the population of each State. After some haggling, the amount was agreed at twenty-five shillings, and the Commonwealth Government rashly undertook to try to get the grant made perpetual by an amendment of the Constitution. Against strenuous opposition, a proposed law for the amendment was passed by the Parliament, but at the referendum it was defeated by a narrow margin. Again, therefore, the Commonwealth was saved from a serious limitation of its financial power.

The general election, on the same day as the referendum, gave the Deakin Government its congé, and placed Mr. Fisher's Labour administration in power. The Labour Party had strongly opposed a permanent per capita grant; but it passed legislation giving effect to it for the next ten years, at the same time terminating the Braddon clause. The bookkeeping provision for paying surplus revenue to the States remained nominally in force; but by this time Commonwealth expenditure (with the help of invalid and old-age pensions, inaugurated in 1908) had about overtaken available revenue, and "surplus revenue" ceased to exist.

FINANCIAL AGREEMENT

Then came the war of 1914–18, and the subsequent depression. Both Commonwealth and States badly wanted loan money, and the independent recourse of both to the loan market had created serious difficulties. The time had come for the long-deferred project of the transfer of the State public debts to the Commonwealth, and concerted action as to future borrowing. This involved adjustment of the financial arrangements between Commonwealth and States on an entirely new basis. The per capita payments were terminated, and Commonwealth and States concluded the Financial Agreement of 1927, validated by the Constitution Alteration (State Debts) 1927.

The Financial Agreement provides for the Commonwealth taking over the public debts of the States as at 1 July, 1929, and assuming liability therefor to the bondholders; some £7,-500,000 per annum for fifty-eight years being contributed by the Commonwealth towards interest, and the excess of interest being paid by the States to the Commonwealth. It also established a sinking fund, to which the Commonwealth contributes one-third and the States two-thirds, and an Australian Loan Council, consisting now of the Prime Minister of the Commonwealth and the Premiers of the States, or their nominees. The Loan Council deals with future borrowings by Commonwealth and States and settles the borrowing programme for each financial year.

FINANCIAL EMERGENCY AND DEBT CONVERSION

The financial emergency of 1931 led to a conference between Commonwealth and State Ministers, at which a plan was agreed on for stabilising Commonwealth and State finances and restoring prosperity. The means included reductions in Commonwealth and State expenditure, and conversion of the internal public debts of Commonwealth and States at reduced rates of interest. There was further provision designed to secure, as far as possible, equal sharing by all of the sacrifices entailed, e.g., reduction of interest on mortgages and private securities generally, and all-round reduction of wages. Commonwealth and States confirmed these agreements by Financial Agreement Acts and Debt Conversion Acts, and the conversion was arranged for by the Commonwealth and duly completed.

Chapter XX

AUSTRALIA'S INTERESTS IN THE ADJACENT ISLANDS

BY G. L. WOOD

Professor of Commerce, University of Melbourne

IT IS HARD to find a name which will cover that great array of islands which stretches from the Philippines to New Caledonia and from Sumatra to the Solomons. None of the familiar terms—Indonesia, East Indies, Malay Archipelago—is wide enough to cover all the islands to the north and north-east of Australia, or limited enough to denote those that are more significant for the present purposes. In this discussion "the islands" will embrace the Dutch East Indies, New Guinea, the Solomons, New Hebrides, and New Caledonia. Such an arbitrary and general term flouts orthodox description; but it will avoid tedious definition.

It is even harder to describe the variety of area and surface which these units of the world's largest archipelago present. Thousands are but islets, so tiny as to appear only on large-scale Admiralty charts; many are great clusters of untouched resources, from rich volcanic soils to mineral deposits of great value. Some are barren; most are covered with such dense jungle that development or even exploration is a feat of sustained endurance and skill. Some, like Java, are of enormous fertility, and sustain a native population as large as that of the United Kingdom, with a highly developed civilization. Others, like Borneo, are largely unexplored, developed only on the maritime fringes, and hide in the jungles and mountains of the interior scattered tribes of the world's most primitive peoples.

These islands stretch in depth across the whole northern front of Australia and continue round the north-east of the continent like a partly submerged mountain system fifteen hundred miles in length and a thousand miles from the mainland. Just as Japan regarded the whole island system from Sumatra to the Solomons as the southern palisade of her political and economic "co-prosperity sphere," Australians see it as the northern bastion of their own defence system. Unless the islands are strongly held by friendly powers, they are a constant threat to Australia's security, and Australian foreign policy must be largely dominated by considerations of their future control. This island arc forms Australia's most vulnerable frontier.

Australia's interest, however, is not confined to strategic problems which are the natural result of geography. The islands are, in sober fact, as essential to the development as they are to the defence of Australia. This does not mean that the Commonwealth must acquire more territory in the islands; but rather that her development will require access to their resources and unrestricted opportunities for trade throughout the Archipelago, as well as full recognition of the part that the islands must play in the military and economic defence of the Commonwealth. For both reasons Australians must be concerned about the kind of control to be exercised over them, whether it be a reversion to the old form of remote imperial control, a new form of co-operative international supervision, or a compromise between them.

Three circumstances have scorched the significance of the islands upon the minds of Australians: first, the speed and efficiency with which Japan effected total occupation; secondly, the inadequacy of military knowledge about the islands and of power to defend them; and lastly, the part played by naval forces and by air-power in moving Japan's frontier two thousand miles to the south in a few months and in pushing it back again with rather less speed. Protection by distance abruptly became a myth, and organized industrial resources for the essentials of modern war became the new form of defence in depth. Immediately the Philippines, Malaya, and the Dutch East Indies had fallen, Australia became the area most directly threatened by conquest; and the new realities of global war were bitten into the consciousness of the two isolated democracies in the South Pacific. Australia and New Zealand were inescapably involved in the effort to recover the islands, and committed to new and heavy responsibilities for maintaining a friendly and powerful administration there.

Not to put too delicate an edge upon statement, the whole area has become too important, strategically, to permit ownership that is not backed by military power to defend and financial resources to develop it. Whatever the protective system which finally emerges from international agreements, Australia's interests in shaping and sharing in its defence are clear, and it is imperative that her position should be understood by the United Nations. Delicate questions have already arisen, whether colonial structures, however efficient their contribution to the economy of imperialist groups, can be regarded as the basis of the post-war administrative system. The islands are economically too tempting and strategically too significant to permit mere reversion to the *status quo* without qualification. Geography and economics have combined to place them in a position of world importance almost without parallel in modern history.

The problems related to the future status of Japan and China, the complex problems represented by south-east Asia, and the scarcely less complex problems of co-ordinating the foreign policies of the Allied Nations have thrust the western Pacific into the forefront of world politics. The control and development of Malaysia, Melanesia, and Micronesia will inevitably assume new importance, and those areas will be steadily drawn into a more closely integrated world economy. Pre-war complacency and nonchalant attitudes towards control of the islands, and incidentally towards the welfare of native peoples, are now outmoded. Those attitudes, despite much platitude concerning the "white man's burden," had become anachronisms even before the war. But it required the war to bring home to the world the fact that the production of the islands became one of the pillars of modern industry. In an age of almost unlimited demand for tropical products such as rubber, sugar, coffee, tobacco, quinine, to name only a few, the islands have become the richest source of supply in the world. For this reason alone they would exercise a magnetic attraction for investment which would gear their exports more and more closely into the world economy. What has been accomplished in developing these areas is a mere token of what is possible. Millions of acres of rich virgin lands lie unused. Even more important in this age of mechanisation, the islands have great undeveloped mineral resources. They have the only important reserves of oil in eastern Asia. Their deposits of iron are probably larger than those of either China or Japan. They produce nearly a quarter—with Malaya more than half—of the world's supply of tin. Many other minerals occur, but the extent and quality of the deposits are known only imperfectly.

That this region can, with the help of modern science and industrial technique, become fabulously productive is proved by the case of Java. With improved methods production in Java was increased so greatly that the population grew from four million to forty million in a century. Even with its great fertility, however, the food resources of Java are scarcely sufficient to maintain a population which increases by half a million each year. Here is a great reservoir of labour for developing the unused resources of the islands. In a million square miles of the most varied and difficult terrain, there is much land which merely awaits trained labour, capital, and enterprise to enable it to contribute greatly to the world's supply of raw materials. Borneo is larger than France, Sumatra is larger than California, New Guinea is as large as the States of California, Oregon and Washington together, Celebes alone is as large as Wisconsin, Iowa and Illinois combined. By contrast, the whole area of the Dutch Islands with about seventy millions natives has been administered by less than 250,000 Europeans. Seldom has such temptation been spread in the sight of ambitious or necessitous nations. Instability and insecurity must persist as long as control over this tropical treasure is weak or hesitant.

It is in those terms that Australia views her Near North. Yet not in those terms alone. The islands of the Archipelago and the continent of Australia are not merely geographic neighbours, they are economic complements as well. Many foodstuffs and materials which Australia requires for her expanding industrialization are here within easy reach, and some in great plenty. Nearly all the industrial products, from agricultural machinery to the equipment needed for the development of the islands, are already produced in Australian factories. China, Indo-China, Thailand, as well as the islands, will require capital and production goods in vast supply for the development which will become a central feature of economic expansion in the twentieth century; and it is only to the highly industrialized countries, the United States, Britain, Australia, that these countries can look for their capital equipment, from harbours and irrigation works to railways and aerodromes. They, like Soviet Russia under the decade of reconstruction, will also need to import the engineers and technicians to start and staff their new industrial programmes.

That there is a community of white interests in the political and economic future of the islands may be taken as axiomatic. Australia and New Zealand form a mere spearhead of European civilization now thrust into closest contact with Asia and its teeming peoples. They form "outliers" which depend for their safety upon the guardianship of the United States and Great Britain. The Dutch East Indies and the Dutch colonial system form an economic and political parallel to the Indian Empire; and the future administration of both India and the Indies must acquire increasing significance to Australia. Co-operation for economic development and defensive alliance will tax the statesmanship and vision of all Governments interested in this complex area. Enlightened trusteeship on the part of the United Nations, freer access for all countries to the resources of the South-west Pacific, and "open door" policies in general must take account both of old traditions and of new realities. For Australians there is an obvious conflict between the desire for peaceful development and the need for a strong defensive system which will provide a reasonable measure of security. They see no way of reconciling these objectives save by close co-ordination of Australian policy with the policies of the other United Nations, co-operative insurance with safeguards.

Other dangers derive from economic privilege exercised by the powers administering Malayan and Indonesian areas. Price control of strategic raw materials, restriction schemes affecting important commodities such as rubber and tin, and virtual monopolies in the production of important materials such as quinine, were doubtless attempts to stabilize certain industries in the interests of producers; but they are apt to appear as provocative anomalies so far as consuming interests are concerned. Political control of this sort in one of the world's most productive and populated areas bore some resemblance to a "closed door," so far as manufacturers and traders in North America were concerned. When the principles of co-operation now expressed in international agreements are applied to the Pacific, it would seem that wide and deep changes will become inevitable. In the reconstruction, Australia will wish to have an influence comparable with her immediate interests and vulnerable position.

Australians generally would endorse a policy of promoting "good neighbour" trade relations with the Dutch East Indies. The development of the British and Dutch colonial systems has been marked by export of capital from the mother countries, for the purpose of stimulating exports of foodstuffs and raw materials from the colonies which could minister to the expanding industrialization and world trade of the homeland. The British and Dutch colonial systems have thus tended to canalize investment, and to maintain trade in parallel lines which seldom met except after careful agreement. Informed Australian opinion is convinced that the wartime expansion of Australian secondary industry can only be maintained by enlarged export of every type of manufacture to available markets of the Western Pacific. For such an expansion Australia has many trading advantages. But some Australians, considering that existing preferences are the substance, and prospective free competition in trade the shadow of economic advantage, would be reluctant to yield any preferred position in the markets of the United Kingdom without adequate compensations elsewhere.

This must seem to observers remarkably like wanting the best of both worlds; but "giving too little and asking too much" is a technique well understood in most countries. Mr. Curtin's speech in September 1943 clearly marks the evolution in Australian thought. "The place Australia will occupy in the Pacific postwar period," he said, "can never be the same as it was up to 1939. . . . Australia cannot allow her economic position to be misunderstood with the Pacific studded by bases occupied by a half dozen nations shut out behind tariff walls." That statement implies a desire on Australia's part for enlarged trade in the Pacific which would result from the partial removal of trade restrictions by all countries simultaneously, the fear that the old imperialism will die hard, and concern about the future control of the islands.

Australians realize too the difficulties of administering this vast and varied region with fairness to the native peoples and to the world at large. The dangers to stability are inherent in the ethnology as much as in the geography of the area. The dangers stem from conditions that must be studied as intensively as those of Central and South-east Europe before economic and political reconstruction is attempted. They may here be sketched only as a mass of resistances to reconstruction which are of great importance. These resistances will be misunderstood unless the distinction is kept in mind between the masses of peasants cultivating their lands by intensive labour, and the foreign groups interested in plantations, mechanization, large-scale secondary industries, trade and finance.

Owing partly to this economic dichotomy and partly to the inertia of custom and tradition which accompanies it, there prevails a complete lack of political sense among the native peoples. This amounts to an equally complete lack of any unity of interest among the "countries" of the region from Thailand to New Caledonia, and from the Philippines to Java. Lennox Mills merely stated facts when he said that these countries "have little in common save that all are weak, largely undeveloped, and politically and economically under foreign control. There is a broad similarity of problems, but this is outweighed by differences that mark off the peoples from one another. They are divided by long-established customs and ideas, hostilities that are generations old, religion, and divergent historical development. The recent appearance of separate nationalisms has added a new and growing element of disunity."

The economic future of the whole area is bound to take the form, not of self-sufficiency, but of greater interdependence upon the world economy. A transition from the broadly triangular trade relations with Europe and the United States to a new multi-angular trade in which nearer and industrially younger countries such as Australia, India and China will share, is likely to develop. In the rebuilding of the Pacific system the needs of nearer industrial countries than those of Europe must be taken into account. They, too, will need tropical foodstuffs and raw materials, as well as markets for their expanding industrial output. In these circumstances old patterns of trade agreements, tariffs, and financial connections can scarcely be expected to persist.

A mere beginning of incorporating this rich under-developed area into the world economy had been made by 1939. In relation to the developmental needs, or in comparison with investment in other areas, this investment was almost insignificant. H. G. Callis has estimated that in South-east Asia and the islands the total capital invested was of the order of 4,000 million U.S. dollars just before the outbreak of war. Half of this, approximately, had been applied in the Dutch East Indies, while British Malaya, Indo-China and the Philippines came next in order of importance. Even more significant is the origin of these investments which, for the main areas, is shown below as deduced from the estimates of Callis:

DISTRIBUTION OF FOREIGN CAPITAL IN S. E. ASIA
(In millions of American dollars)

Country of Receipt	U.S.A.	U.K.	Dutch	French	Chinese
Philippines	200	45	...	...	100
Dutch East Indies.	100	200	1,400	...	150
Burma	...	200	...	...	14
British Malaya	30	320	30	...	200
Thailand	...	100	...	...	100
Indo-China	...	...	...	350	80
Total	330	865	1,430	350	644

In the Dutch East Indies, out of a total population of about seventy million, only about 850,000 persons or a little more than one per cent were engaged in domestic or factory manufactures. The remainder were mainly employed, directly or indirectly, in rural industry. The percentage of world exports from these islands for certain commodities was as follows: cinchona 91, kapok 72, rubber 37, copra 19, palm oil 27, tea 24, sugar 11. In 1937 the Dutch East Indies imported goods to the value of about $267m. and exported to the value of about $383m. The total production came, however, from only about one-tenth of the area of the Dutch holdings, and at the outbreak of war the Government was engaged energetically in stimulating migration from Java to the outer Provinces. At the same time, it was vigorously promoting the expansion of factory industries in Java and Sumatra. In Borneo, Celebes, Dutch New Guinea and many other of the Dutch possessions very little more than the beginnings of development in a few coastal areas had been attempted.

If the developments in some of the richer islands of the group have been so spectacular, it needs little imagination to foresee the possibilities throughout the whole area. In New Guinea little more than mining and planting had been begun. In New Britain, in the New Hebrides, in the Solomons, in New Caledonia, it is impossible in our present state of knowledge to do more than guess at the resources or to estimate broadly the fields for investment and development which they represent. From petroleum to nickel, from gold to water power, from copra and rubber to sugar and coffee there are almost unlimited opportunities for expansion of production.

That Australia can import and use much larger quantities of many materials in which her own economy is deficient cannot be doubted. The chief difficulty will arise from the low purchasing power of the native peoples. Even in rich, developed Java the income per head is very low. Amry Vanderbosch estimates that the average annual income of the peasant family in Java was about twenty United States dollars in 1937. The average annual income for the native worker was about eight dollars. Only 32,000 Indonesians had, in 1939, an annual income of 360 United States dollars. For the other countries of South-east Asia the figures of average income are probably much lower. The crux of the problem is obviously to be found in raising the purchasing power, i.e., in raising the prices of native products in relation to the prices of imports. Before any great expansion of trade is possible, and before any great development of these unused tropical lands can take place, a firm long-term policy of raising standards of living will be needed. Land reform, cheap capital, extension of education and especially technical education, wage regulation, international economic collaboration—all are involved in this greatest of Pacific problems.

Chapter XXI

AUSTRALIA IN THE PACIFIC

BY DR. JOHN ANDREWS

Lecturer in Geography, University of Sydney

In the minds of most people Australia and Asia are widely separated and unrelated land masses. This mental attitude is largely a legacy of the trading habits that have been developed around both areas in the last three centuries. Actually, through the eyes of the political geographer, Australasia is a south-eastern projection of Asia in much the same sense that Africa is a southward projcetion of the Eurasian landmass. Aviation has almost reduced the gap between Singapore and Darwin to unimportance; but a much more powerful influence separating the two areas is the general aridity of the savannah across northern Australia, which can be compared for its effect to the Sahara and Sudan in separating the Mediterranean from southern Africa. Even this influence will be much weakened when the economic problems connected with the production and transport of savannah-bred meat have been solved. The Air Revolution has upset all the economic assumptions of the past; the hurtling speed with which the Japanese "leap-frogged" along the Austral-Asiatic chain of peninsulas and islands to Australia's northern shores, and the still more re-markable three-pronged thrust by the U.S.A.A.F. against Japan have shown how intimately Australia is concerned in the affairs of the Far East, and how remote in military emer-gency were London and Washington. These are the two cen-tral facts which now dominate thought in Australia about affairs in the Pacific.

308

Strategically Australia is part of the Western Pacific, both because of Australia's entanglement in the net of Asiatic affairs, and because of Australia's value as a base from which an Asiatic aggressor can be opposed. American strategy has proved that the vast spaces of sea between Australia and North America are no longer the barriers they were in the past, and in the future may not be even formidable. In the recent conflict Australia survived as the sole bastion of "Western" interests after all bases in the enormous area north of Moresby, east of India, and west of Midway had been lost, and Australians feel that they must never be unprepared for the recurrence of such a situation. For the time they have lost faith in the protection afforded by isolated though strongly fortified bases against a powerful and resourceful enemy. The defence of Malta and Gibraltar are not an effective reply to the failure to hold Singapore and Pearl Harbor.

Beyond these strategic considerations, however, are the dynamics of political geography in the Western Pacific. In eastern and southern Asia there are some thousand million people, mostly with depressed standards of living but with a growing section which is becoming ever more conscious of the standards that can be attained by progressive, technically equipped nations. Australians see these teeming millions of people as a great dam threatening to break and flood the islands and sparsely occupied Australia and New Zealand. The question ever present in their minds is whether Australia will still be "white" and independent at the end of the century, or whether our occupancy here is merely a short-lived colonial experiment. While some may think this attitude is unduly fearful, the imminence of invasion by Japan in this war and the probable consequences of such invasion are hard to forget.

In the second place, immediately to the north lie great potential resources of tropical produce. Malaya and Indonesia are, by climate, soil, labour supply, and agricultural experi-

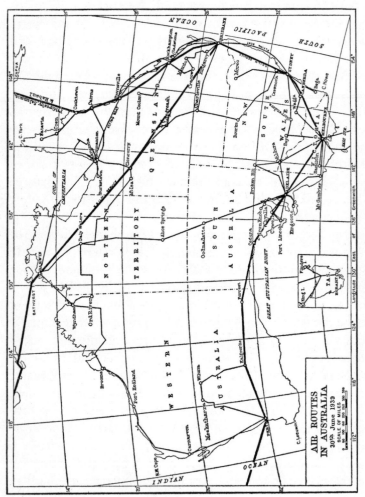

Fig. XXIX. Air routes, 1939.

ence ideally suited to become a great region of varied tropical production, and they also contain very important mineral resources. The value of these resources for world industry, the subordinate status of the native peoples, and the complexity of interests involved, have made this one of the main areas of political tension in the world, as the San Francisco discussions concerning colonial trusteeship revealed. Five great Powers have economic and territorial interests in an area where Australian security is vitally involved.

The third problem concerns the great differences in social and economic status of the Austral-Asiatic peoples. At the northern end of the Western Pacific coast, the Japanese, and at the southern end, the Australians, were two industrialized, politically conscious and nationally integrated peoples. In 1938 the one was armed and aggressive with a martial tradition, the other by temperament, resources, and geography conditioned to the defensive. Between the two were the colonial and quasi-colonial peoples of the northern sub-tropics and of the tropics, all sharing the characteristics of little or no industrialization or mechanization and more or less subjection to external Powers. These differences in development made for stresses and strains between the indigenous peoples, as well as providing the opportunity for intervention by outsiders, as well as a fertile breeding-ground for friction between the native peoples themselves. The lack of unity among the native peoples, added to lack of international control in the area, is the cause of Australia's concern for the future.

The power position in south-eastern Asia was therefore complicated. There was the ambition of Japan, the strong Asiatic Power, to carve itself an empire and oust competitors; there were the external colonial Powers in whose interest it was to unite against Japan. Unfortunately, the interests of these Powers were constantly at variance; and, until the southward move of Japan, their defence systems were not co-ordinated. Moreover, the economic and political awakening of the indigenous peoples brought them into conflict with the "white" Powers, and made them fit subjects for Japanese political warfare. The explosive possibilities of this situation remain now that the Japanese system has been shattered, and Australia is therefore vitally interested in the establishment of an international authority that will yet allow for the development of self-protecting native societies.

The geography of Indonesia inevitably makes the control and defence of this area of first-rate importance to Australian security. The Japanese irrupted into the Java Sea through the water-passages of Karimata Strait (between Sumatra and Borneo), Macassar Strait and Molucca Passage; they followed an "airfield-hopping" strategy in which the capture of one airfield led to combined operations against the next. Air control of these water-passages from the airfields along their coasts allowed the invasion fleets to be brought up for the final blow against Java. If sufficient aircraft had been available these passages could have been sealed against the Japanese and the conflict kept away from the main bases. But only a co-ordinated defence plan could have held these passages, since the capture of one outflanked the others—and the difficulty of defence co-ordination is that of collaboration between the different Powers which controlled the relevant airfields in the Philippines, French Indo-China, Malaya, and Netherlands Indies.

Once the Singapore-Surabaya-Amboina line was breached, the defence of Australia became a question of holding her last insular rampart—the screen of islands which forms an arc from Timor through New Guinea to the Solomons, New Hebrides, and New Caledonia. As well as being attacked from the Indonesian bases, this arc was also attacked at the other end from the Marshall and Caroline bases. It was breached at Timor, and the results were seen in the heavy attacks on Darwin, and the fall of Rabaul. Port Moresby—and probably thereby the Australian mainland itself—was saved by the

American capture of the Solomons, by Allied sea-air action in the Coral Sea, by the remarkable campaign by Australian troops across the Owen Stanley Range, and finally by the American offensive after Buna. The lessons of the whole war in the Western Pacific are that Indonesian defence is a single problem which can only be solved by one co-ordinated plan; that Australia's outermost defence line runs from Manila eastwards through the Marshalls and Carolines; that the Timor-New Caledonia island screen is Australia's last rampart and an integral part of the Australian defence system; that any defence system of the "Western" Powers against an Asiatic aggressor would finally be based on Australia, with a fortress area around the shores of the Java Sea and outer defences running north from that sea to Manila and guarding the water passages giving access to the fortress area.

All of this points to the vital necessity for some adjustments in south-eastern Asia and Indonesia. The pre-war power pattern was the result of a historical process in which the distribution of power was conditioned first by the search for spices, and later by the search for markets for industrial products and for sources of tropical raw materials. During the time the pattern was being developed the "Western" Powers had little to fear from any Asiatic Power, so that their own conflicts were their chief preoccupation. Now, however, even if Japan is finished as an industrial Power, at least two Powers on the mainland are growing rapidly in strength, and in strength based on that industrialism which formerly was the unique possession and source of strength of the Occident and which later gave Japan dominance in the Western Pacific. "Western" interests can no longer be safeguarded merely by a Singapore or a Corregidor. In the new power pattern which has been uncovered by the present conflict, these are hostages to fortune just as surely as would be the British Isles in the Atlantic sphere if they were not made an impregnable fortress against a hostile Europe and secured by a firm base across the Atlantic.

The lines of communication from Plymouth to Singapore are too long and those from Pearl Harbor too vulnerable to meet the needs of the new situation, and both Holland and France are in worse case as they have fewer transferable forces and small Indonesian bases.

There are other elements in the general situation which are not so apparent, because the course of the war emphasised operations in the Pacific. Australia is not only a Pacific Power looking eastwards, she also faces the Indian Ocean and is concerned with her western approaches. History has not made this plain. Until the outbreak of war with Japan, the Indian Ocean had been for more than a century a British lake with the gateways into the region sealed by the naval bases of Capetown, Aden, and Singapore, and by the land frontier of the North-west Provinces. The only threat to the Indian Ocean system between 1798 and 1941 came from Russia or Germany. Australians have twice fought in the Middle East when the German threat to the Indian Ocean became actual aggression. During the intervals of peace the "accidents" of Australian geography, which have concentrated the greater part of our resources and population in the eastern third of the continent, obscured our real interests in the Indian Ocean; we looked at it as through a back window, or merely as something to be traversed quickly while en route to England.

A new situation developed in 1942. The Japanese breached and occupied the north-eastern gateway to the Indian Ocean; the Germans and Italians were gravely threatening the north-western gateway; raiders from both ends of the Axis were operating in Indian Ocean waters; India was in ferment. The occupation of Madagascar emphasized the danger. If the forces of the eastern and western Axis partners were to meet in the Indian Ocean, the main aim of their global strategy would have been achieved; they would have control of practically all ports in the Euro-Asiatic landmass, Russia and China would have been sealed off from the other United Nations except for the one breathing-hole of Murmansk, and Britain and the United States would have been where the German geopoliticians wanted them—waging a war as maritime Powers against the continental Powers. Australia, at the end of the island bridge from Asia, could have been reduced at leisure between pincers from the Indian and from the Pacific Oceans.

The peoples living around the Indian Ocean have been well served by the *Pax Britannica* of the past. But it may be doubted whether in the future Britain will be able to carry such a high proportion of the burden of maintaining peace in the region; and, in any case as industrialisation proceeds, the United States, Australia, New Zealand and the Powers and peoples interested will be expected to play a greater part. India and Australia have well-developed industrial resources. There is abundant manpower in India, and there is a variety of raw materials in both India and Australia. In the peculiar geographic circumstances of the region, co-operation between the local peoples offers a good chance of security. At the same time the external Powers, particularly Britain and the United States, must retain an interest in the Indian Ocean. The Middle East, the Indian Ocean and Indonesia are all part of one strategic realm; and dominance of it by an anti-"Western" Power would have far-reaching effects on the world balance of power and general security. Collaboration between the local peoples, and the development of their bases for use in time of need by the friendly maritime Powers, are essential for sealing off the northern gateways. India and Australia, because of their existing industrial resources, will be the two bastions of the system.

Australia is, first, part of the rampart between the Indian and Pacific Oceans; and, secondly, a member of both the Indian and Pacific Ocean regional groups. Australia and New Zealand are the only countries peopled by European stock in the Indian sphere or in the Western Pacific. Their importance in regional security systems and in general "Western" strategy is determined by these facts. Australia, and to a less extent New Zealand, have considerable coal and iron and other metallic resources; a high level of technical skill and experience; great food-producing capacity; a well-sheltered position behind the island screen, provided that this be prepared for defence; and lines of communication to Britain and North America which enjoy fairly high protection because of the vast spaces of the oceans through which they run. There can be no better proof of Australia's significance in the new power pattern than the importance which she has had in the recent conflict.

Australia's economic future and her place in Pacific economy will depend very largely on the post-war settlements. On the face of it, she does not fit very well into the Western-Pacific pattern, because most of the goods she has to offer are food products or primary raw materials of such type and quality that they are beyond the purchasing power of most of the native peoples of southeastern Asia and China. At the same time her manufacturing industries are being increasingly organized for export production since her capacity to supply war needs has been demonstrated. Only with Japan has her trade been considerable in the past, the main articles of trade being exports of wool and minerals and imports of textiles, china and crockery. Australia's most important customers and suppliers have been in Europe and North America, and her overseas trade position has been generally that of a raw-material exporter and an importer of manufactured goods. That position is likely to change rapidly. It is often forgotten, however, by outside observers that the manufacturing industries are now more important than the primary in the Australian economy; they have a value of production greater than that of the primary industries, but this is overlooked because their produce is almost wholly consumed within the country. Outsiders still think most Australians are raisers of sheep and growers of wheat.

It has been difficult in the past to stimulate further trade with the East because of lack of demand for the things Australia has had to offer. But now there is pressure to do so from two directions, first by the desire to enter more fully into the Western Pacific pattern and to share some of the commercial advantages that exist there, and secondly because it is agreed by practically all Australians that there is an urgent need for increasing Australia's population, and the obvious way to do that is to create a demand for exports of the type that Australia can supply. The main difficulties will be two: first, the problem of the low purchasing power of most Eastern peoples, and second, competition with other nations, particularly those which already have large trade interests in the region. The first of these factors operates not only through the inability of the native peoples to purchase Western goods; most of them are small farmers or farm workers, and any increase in their purchasing power will come, in the first instance, through increased productivity per head in the agricultural industries. Only at a later stage, and gradually as capital is invested, will the establishment of factory industries alter the position. There are probably, however, opportunities for the export of Australian animal produce—meat and dairy goods—since south-eastern Asia and China are primarily crop-producing and not animal-producing regions, and are likely to remain so because of climatic characters and population density. The second of these factors (competition with other trading Powers) will have to be discussed at the peace settlements, and Australians are of the opinion that the questions of trade opportunities and participation in the Western Pacific must be considered by the concert of Powers not from a narrow economic but from a very much wider strategic angle. The improvement of living standards and the industrialisation of Asia are likely to be achieved only by international collaboration; but they will result in a greatly increased volume of trade and in many new trade opportunities. Collaboration in sharing these opportunities may be just as desirable as their creation.

If Australia is to be a base of "Western" power, then it will need to be provided with the defence installations and the constructional and repair industries which will enable it to function as such. This does not mean necessarily that battle-ships should be built in the country, but it is vital that there should be facilities and technical skill for servicing and repairing them. These services can be rendered nowhere else in the Western Pacific, for the area north of the Java Sea is too exposed to potential enemy action, and the south-eastern Asian region has not the necessary resources for industrialization on the scale that will be required for the fighting of any future wars. On the other hand, the necessary capacity of such industries cannot be achieved in a country of such small population unless they have access to external markets to support themselves during peace. Australians therefore feel that their existence as a people is bound up with the strategic-economic planning that will form the basis of the peace settlements; and it is perhaps somewhat difficult for the people of other countries to understand Australian persistence on these issues at San Francisco.

The power pattern of the Pacific has usually been one whereby a Power or group of Powers has had such overwhelming preponderance of strength that little resistance to it was possible. In the new conditions that obtain today, stability will not be achieved without a more equitable balancing of strengths. This point of view does not rest exclusively on a continuance of power politics; indeed, it is not likely that there will be lasting peace in the Indo-Pacific region if any Power or group of Powers attempts to establish dominance. There is ample scope for the wisest international co-operation in eliminating those wide disparities in living conditions and national opportunities which are such fruitful sources of conflict; collaboration between all interested Powers will be needed for the rehabilitation of the devastated areas and the peaceful and orderly economic development of the Asiatic nations. But it would be foolish for Australians, in the light of their recent experiences, to exclude from their national planning all strategic considerations. Australia is a member of the Indo-Pacific group of nations and must be prepared to collaborate with the other members for the improvement of economic conditions and relations, and for the maintenance of peace; she is a member of the "Western" group of nations which also have economic and strategic interests in the area and in the maintenance of Australian security. Stability in both oceans depends, in the last analysis, on equilibrium of strengths; Australia has a very definite part to play in the achievement of that equilibrium. The playing of the part and the discharge of her commitments to both the above groups depend on Australia's own strength, and that strength will reach a significant level only if full development of her economic potential is possible.

HISTORICAL AND GEOGRAPHICAL SUMMARY—AUSTRALIA

STATISTICAL SUMMARY—AUSTRALIA

From Official Statistics Published by Commonwealth Bur. of Census and Statistics

	1901	1921	1931	1941	1943	1944
Population—Total ...	3,824,913	5,510,994	6,552,606	7,137,222	7,266,441	7,341,715
	1901–02	1921–22	1931–32	1941–42	1942–43	1943–44
Agriculture ...						
Wheat—						
Area, mlln. acres ...	5.12	9.72	14.74	12.00	9.28	7.88
Yield, mlln. bushels ...	38.56	129.09	190.61	166.71	155.73	109.72
Av. yield bushels per acre ...	7.54	13.28	12.93	13.89	16.78	13.93
Sugar Cane—						
Area, productive acre ...	86,950	128,356	241,576	254,564	240,988	*227,000
Yield, mlln. tons ...	1.37	2.44	4.21	5.15	4.69	3.69
Av. yield tons per acre ...	15.73	18.99	17.44	20.25	19.47	16.09
Total gross value of all agric. production, £mlln. (a) ...	23.84	81.89	74.49	94.45	110.08	113.50

* Estimated.

STATISTICAL SUMMARY—AUSTRALIA (Cont'd)

From Official Statistics Published by Commonwealth Bur. of Census and Statistics (*Cont'd*)

	1901–02	1921–22	1931–32	1941–42	1942–43	1943–44
Pastoral, Dairying, etc.						
Live-stock—						
Sheep, mlln.	72.04	82.22	110.62	125.19	124.62	123.17
Cattle, mlln.	8.49	14.44	12.26	13.56	14.01	14.18
Horses, mlln.	1.62	2.44	1.78	1.61	1.52	1.45
Pigs, mlln.	.93	.96	1.17	1.48	1.56	1.75
Wool production (b), mlln. lb.	539.4	723.1	1007.5	1167.2	1151.2	1169.
Butter production, mlln. lb.	103.75(c)	267.07(c)	390.65	375.69	383.57	350.2
Cheese production, mlln. lb.	11.85(c)	32.65(c)	31.42	67.52	80.94	80.25
Total gross value of all pastoral and dairying production, £mlln.	36.89	119.47	103.02	184.86	205.44	202.32

	1901	1921	1931	1941	1942	1943
Mineral Production						
Gold, £mlln.	14.02	4.02	3.56	15.99	†	†
Silver and lead, £mlln.	2.25	1.54	1.44	6.26	†	†
Copper, £mlln.	2.22	.80	.57	1.51	†	†
Zinc, £mlln.	.004	.28	.51	1.59	†	†
Coal, £mlln.	2.60	11.02	6.36	10.87	†	†
Total value of all mineral production, £mlln.	21.82	20.00	13.35	41.26	†	†

† Production abnormal owing to war.

STATISTICAL SUMMARY—AUSTRALIA (Cont'd)

From Official Statistics Published by Commonwealth Bur. of Census and Statistics (Cont'd)

	1901	1921–22	1931–32	1941–42	1942–43	1943–44
Factories—						
Hands employed, Number		378,540	336,658	725,342	759,045	766,498
Value of production, £mlln. (a)		121.67	110.98	316.44	352.00	366.335
Commerce—						
Imports—Oversea, £mlln. (a)	42.434	103.07	56.98	186.70(d)	265.13(d)	263.06(d)
Exports—Oversea, £mlln. (a)	49.70	127.85	107.98	159.33(d)	125.55(d)	146.68(d)
Principal Oversea Exports—						
Wool—						
Quantity, mlln. lb.	518.04	927.83	893.64	1142.	1152.	1164.
Value, £mlln.	15.24	47.98	32.10	58.04	44.32	45.77
Wheat—Value, £mlln.	2.78	28.64	19.22	4.65	4.88	8.26
Flour—Value, £mlln.	.59	5.52	3.83	4.19	3.49	6.70
Butter—						
Quantity, mlln. lb.	34.61	127.35	201.64	130.35	124.32	104.23
Value, £mlln.	1.45	7.97	9.81	8.13	8.09	6.87
Meats—Value, £mlln.	2.61	5.54	6.37	14.09	10.90	11.20
Government Railways—						
Length of line open, miles.	12,579	23,502	26,959	27,241	27,223	27,213
Capital cost, £mlln.	124.00	244.00	323.4	322.00	324.00	325.00
Gross revenue, £mlln.	11.04	38.20	37.58	66.48	84.75	82.31
Working expenses of earnings, per cent	64.63	73.64	74.88	76.78	75.55	80.89

STATISTICAL SUMMARY—AUSTRALIA (Cont'd)

From Official Statistics Published by Commonwealth Bur. of Census and Statistics (Cont'd)

	1901	1921–22	1931–32	1941–42	1942–43	1943–44
Trading Banks—						
Advances, £mlln.	86.35	182.24	260.92	323.85	291.68	270.86
Deposits, £mlln.	91.49	273.87	319.24	482.72	616.43	694.49
Savings Banks—						
Total deposits, £mlln.	30.88	154.40(e)	197.97(e)	274.28(e)	358.00(e)	471.53(e)
Average per head, £ (a)	8.15	28.0	30.01	38.23	49.5	64.59

Wheat: Averages 1930–31 to 1939–40

Area sown, acres	14,176,000
Production, bushels	177,758,000
Proportion of world production, per cent	3
Exports, bushels	102,500,000
Yield per acre, bushels	12.54
Australian proportion of world exports, per cent	18.4
Average price	3s. 4½d.

Wool: Averages 1934–35 to 1939–40

Number of sheep	114,250,000
Weight of clip, greasy, mlln. lbs.	1,030
Proportion of world production, per cent	27
Value	£56,700,000
Greasy wool, av. price per lb.	
Australian, pence	12.66
Sterling, pence	10.19
Gold price, pence	5.97

(a) Australian currency throughout.
(b) Greasy.
(c) Years ended December.

(d) Merchandise only.
(e) Includes Commonwealth Savings Bank deposits.

HISTORICAL AND GEOGRAPHICAL SUMMARY—
AUSTRALIA

COMMONWEALTH OF AUSTRALIA

West and North-west discovered by Dutch 1606–16
Discovery of East Coast by Captain Cook 1770
First Settlement by Governor Phillip 1788
Commonwealth founded 1901

THE FACTS IN FIGURES

AREA—2,975,000 sq. mi. (approx.)

AREA OF STATES AND TERRITORIES

State	Area—sq. mi.	Percentage of total
New South Wales	309,433	10.40
Victoria	87,884	2.96
Queensland	670,500	22.54
South Australia	380,070	12.78
Western Australia	975,920	32.81
Tasmania	26,215	.88
Northern Territory	523,620	17.60
Australian Capital Territory...........	939	.03
Total	2,974,581	100.00

Within tropical zone—1,150,000 sq. miles; 38.6 per cent

NOTE

The Australian pound (£A.) contains 20 Shillings (s.) or 240 pence (d.). Its present value is approximately 3.25 U. S. dollars. A ton equals 2240 lbs.

INDEX

325